Glencoe Science **New York Regents Review Series**

CHEMISTRY
THE PHYSICAL SETTING

New York Reviewers
Jebb • McCaffery • Tucker
Veyvoda • Wiener

Glencoe

29
70
C4H8

Glencoe

The *McGraw-Hill* Companies

Send all inquiries to:
Glencoe/McGraw-Hill
8787 Orion Place
Columbus, OH 43240-4027

ISBN 0-07-868204-5

Printed in the United States of America.

5 6 7 8 9 10   024   10 09

NEW YORK REVIEWERS

Paul Jebb

Chemistry Teacher

Ticonderoga High School

Ticonderoga, NY

- Member of Foundation for Excellent Schools
- Chemistry/Biology Mentor Network of NYS
- Chemistry Mentor with Teacher/Leader Quality Partnership (TLQP) Grant from University of Rochester
- Analysis of Regents scores for TLQP project item analysis

Colleen McCaffery

Chemistry Teacher

Guilderland High School

Guilderland Center, NY

- Consultant for NYS Chemistry Core curriculum development

Charles Tucker

Chemistry Teacher

Mount Vernon High School

Mount Vernon, NY

- Member of development team for the Yonkers and the Mount Vernon district curriculum revisions

Alice Veyvoda

Former Chemistry Teacher

Half Hollow Hills High School West

Dix Hills, NY

- Member of the development committee for the NYS Chemistry Core Curriculum
- Member of the development committee for the NYS Chemistry Reference Tables
- Test item writer for the NYS Regents Examination in Chemistry

Harvey Wiener

Former Chemistry Teacher

JFK High School

Belmore, NY

- Former Coordinating Mentor in the NYS Chemistry Mentor Network
- Past President of STANYS
- Member of the development committee for the NYS Chemistry Core Curriculum
- Test item writer for the NYS Regents Examination in Chemistry
- Awarded Middle Atlantic Regional Award and Nichols Award for Outstanding Teaching from the ACS

CONTENTS

CONTENTS

Introduction

This review handbook has been designed to help you prepare for the **Regents Examination—Physical Setting: Chemistry**. Before you begin reading this handbook, take a minute to flip through the pages, scan the sections, and examine how information is organized.

The first part of this handbook explains what you can expect on the Regents Exam and offers test-taking strategies. Read these pages before you begin reviewing and again a few days before you take the exam. Use this information to create your own plan of action.

The content sections contain chemistry review material. They include major topics such as "Atomic Concepts" and "Nuclear Chemistry." Each major topic is divided into subtopics that provide in-depth concept coverage and explanations. "Carbon Compounds" is a subtopic of "Organic Chemistry."

Each section includes a list of vocabulary words. Scan the list and write down terms that are unfamiliar to you. Check the glossary at the end of this book for their definitions and write them in your review notebook. As you read this handbook, you will see the vocabulary words in boldface type. In your notebook, add supporting details and related facts after the words' definitions.

Graphs, charts, and illustrations reinforce the content of each section. If a concept is difficult for you, copy the graph, chart, or illustration in your notebook. Drawing ideas may help you remember them.

Within each section, you will find a Regents Exam question with explanations of the answer choices. This feature is to help you practice analyzing multiple-choice answers. In addition, there are periodic questions in the text for you to check your understanding of content. The questions after a subtopic called "Quick Review" also help you check your understanding of content. Each section ends with Content Questions for Regents Exam Practice.

What to Expect on the Regents Exam

The **Regents Exam— Physical Setting: Chemistry** consists of a three-hour written test in three parts: A, B, and C. There are no optional sections; you must answer all questions.

Part A consists of content-based multiple-choice questions that assess your ability to apply, analyze, synthesize, and evaluate your knowledge of the chemistry core curriculum. Part A is about 30–40% of the exam's raw score.

Part B includes content-based and skills-based questions that are approximately 25–35% of the exam's score. There are multiple-choice and simple constructed-response items that test skills and understanding of the chemistry core curriculum.

Part C contains extended constructed-response questions that assess your ability to apply science knowledge and skills to real-world situations. These questions require detailed answers written in complete sentences. Answers must include examples and applications that support your response. These questions are about 20–30% of the exam's raw score. Test scorers use a table to convert raw scores to final scores.

Test Strategies for Success

Multiple-Choice Questions

Have you ever thought about what you do when you take a multiple-choice test? Do you read the question and then look for the right answer among the choices? Do you read the choices first, and then the question? No single strategy works for everyone, but the following suggestions might give you more confidence with multiple-choice questions.

- Read the entire question before reading answer choices.
- Carefully study any photo, diagram, or other graphic associated with the question. Be sure you understand what is shown, then reread the question.
- When you read a question, circle or underline key words or phrases. Consider key words when thinking of an answer to the question. When you are certain of the answer, read the choices. Select the answer that most closely matches yours.
- If no answer is similar to the one you thought of, eliminate those answers that you know are incorrect. Select an answer from the remaining choices.
- If you cannot decide on an answer after eliminating one or two choices, read the question again. If you still cannot choose an answer, make a mark beside the question, then go on the next question. Sometimes, there is information in other exam questions that can help you with an answer. When you reach the end of the exam, return to unanswered questions. Reread each unanswered question and its answer choices. Again, eliminate answers that you know are wrong. Make an educated guess from among the remaining choices. On the Regents Exam, there is no penalty for guessing, so do not leave any blanks.

Constructed-Response Questions

Some of the questions in Part B and all of the questions in Part C of the **Regents Examination—Physical Setting: Chemistry** require you to construct a response. For some questions, you may need to write only a sentence or two. Others will require you to write a unified, coherent paragraph. Again, no single strategy works for everyone, but the following suggestions may help you with constructed-response questions.

- Carefully read the entire exam question.
- Underline or circle key words and phrases. Constructed-response questions contain words that instruct you on how to answer the question, such as *compare, contrast, explain, define, describe,* and *analyze.*
- Once you understand the question, write down what information you will include in your answer. You may create an outline and/or a concept map, chart, or other graphic tool to help you organize your thoughts.
- Be specific. Remember that you are not writing an essay. Use key terms and thoroughly explain any processes. Include relevant details, such as the names of processes.
- Make it easy to find your answers. For example, if a question consists of two parts, respond in two paragraphs. Be sure that the first paragraph answers part one of the question and the second paragraph answers part two.
- Write clearly and concisely. You will not lose points for incorrect grammar or mechanics, but poor handwriting can make it difficult for the scorer to read and understand your answers.

Using the Reference Tables

- Take time to become familiar with the Chemistry Reference Tables that will be provided when you take the exam. These Reference Tables are printed at the end of this handbook.
- The Reference Tables include the Periodic Table, Properties of Selected Elements, and important formulas. This information can help you answer questions during the Regents Exam, even when the question does not refer you to the Reference Tables. For example, you can use the information on properties of elements to help you answer a question about periodic trends in electronegativity.
- Use the Reference Tables when you take the Practice Tests for each section in this book. This will help you use them efficiently during the Regents Exam.

Preparing for the Exam

- Before you take the exam, review your class notes and the information in this book. If there are concepts you do not understand, reread the corresponding chapters in your textbook. Ask a teacher or a classmate to clarify confusing concepts.
- Set aside a notebook just for test preparation. Write down key terms and their definitions. Illustrate important concepts and processes.
- Study with friends and be tutors for each other. Quiz each other on content and skills. Take previous exams together and compare your answers.
- The night before the exam, get a good night's sleep. On the morning of the test, eat a good breakfast.

Taking the Exam

- Be on time and be prepared. Have several sharpened, number 2 pencils.
- Read through the directions carefully.
- Periodically during the exam, check to be sure that the question number you are currently answering matches the number on the answer sheet that you are filling in. This is especially important if you have skipped a question.
- Pace yourself. Do not rush through the exam, but do not linger on difficult questions either. First answer the questions you know, and then return to those you are not sure about.
- If there is time remaining, look over your answers, but do not change them without a reason. Often, your first choice is the correct one.

accuracy
conclusion
control
dependent variable
experiment

hypothesis
independent variable
measurement
precision
qualitative data

quantitative data
scientific method
scientific notation
significant digits
theory

Have you ever wondered why on a cool, dry day your clothes cling together when they come out of the dryer? Why copper turns green over time? Why water evaporates quickly on a hot, sunny day? Scientists explore these and other questions so that we have a greater understanding about our world. In this section, we will explore the methods that scientists use to discover and develop these explanations.

What Is Science?

Science is both a body of knowledge and a way of understanding how the world works. Science involves the application of human intelligence and creativity to explore, discover, and explain how the natural and physical worlds work.

Scientific explanations are developed when people make observations and then describe them based on what they already know about the world. An observation is a careful inspection of an object or an event in which the observer uses his or her senses. This leads to asking questions, which can lead to experimenting, collecting and organizing data, and drawing valid conclusions.

Scientific explanations are subject to change whenever new observations challenge existing explanations. By exploring the historical development of scientific concepts and the individuals who contributed to scientific knowledge, you can better understand scientific inquiry and the relationship between science and society.

Early Science

For thousands of years people had asked what all the different objects they saw around them were made of. Based on their own experiences, many scholars in ancient Greece, called philosophers, had pondered the question and came to different conclusions. Some, such as Empedocles, developed an idea that everything in the universe is composed of combinations of four elements. These elements were identified as fire, water, earth, and air.

Another group of scholars, led by Democritus and his students, had claimed that matter was composed of small indivisible parts. Democritus, or possibly his teacher, Leucippus, coined the term *atoms*, which means indivisible, to describe these parts. This term eventually evolved to the modern term *atom*.

Another influential philosopher, named Aristotle, rejected Democritus' idea. Aristotle believed that matter could be divided into smaller parts indefinitely because matter was a continuum. Aristotle expanded and refined Empedocles' idea to explain how just a few elements could combine in various proportions to account for the great diversity of matter.

Over time, Aristotle's influence won out over Democritus' ideas about atoms. Aristotle's views dominated in science for hundreds of years. One reason why Aristotle's ideas were so popular was because he was the first person in recorded history to have approached scientific problems by using evidence. In every case, he would examine what people had previously thought about the problem, consider what the general consensus of opinion was about the nature of the problem, and consider a multitude of subjects that were related to the subject he was studying. Aristotle's methods of observing natural phenomena and analyzing the results of these observations laid the foundation for modern science.

Although some scientists disagreed with Aristotle's ideas, Aristotle's concept of how matter was formed remain dominant until the seventeenth century. By then, scientists had realized that a scientific theory must be tested through experiments aimed to verify specific conclusions of the theory. A **theory** is an explanation of natural phenomena supported by a large body of scientific evidence obtained from many different investigations and observations. Aristotle did not to conduct experiments to test his theories. In the modern view, a scientific explanation is accepted when it is consistent with experimental and observational evidence and when it leads to accurate conclusions.

 CHECK FOR UNDERSTANDING How are scientific theories tested?

Scientific Inquiry

Scientific investigations use scientific methods to explain how things operate in the natural and physical worlds. A **scientific method** is a systematic approach used in scientific study. A scientific method typically involves one or more of the following:

- Observing
- Developing questions based on observations
- Developing a **hypothesis**—a tentative, testable prediction or statement about what has been observed
- Developing an **experiment**—a set of controlled observations that test the hypothesis
- Collecting and organizing data from the experiment
- Developing **conclusions**—explanations based on the observable results of an experiment
- Publishing results for peer review

The Scientific View of the World

The scientific view is founded upon direct observation of the world around us. To think scientifically, one must critically examine events and explanations and attempt to avoid all sources of bias. Keep in mind that scientific explanations are subject to change. No matter how well one explains a set of observations, it is possible that another explanation will fit just as well or better. In science, this testing and improving of explanations occurs continually.

The scientific view involves many individuals doing many different kinds of work, such as those in Figure 1.1. These people include scientists, engineers, mathematicians, physicians, technicians, computer programmers, librarians, and others. They contribute to the scientific view with data gathering, the building of scientific tools and instruments, and/or communicating. It is appropriate in science to turn to knowledgeable sources of information by seeking people

Figure 1.1 The scientific view of the world involves a variety of individuals who support scientists in their work.

who specialize in different disciplines. Well-accepted scientific explanations have been supported by the process of scientific testing and involve the contributions of many different individuals.

 CHECK FOR UNDERSTANDING Why does a scientific discovery involve the assistance of many people in addition to scientists?

Testing Proposed Explanations

Suppose your teacher brought in several brands of paper towels and asked the class the following question: *Which brand of paper towel is most absorbent?* This is the beginning of a scientific inquiry. Your teacher then instructs the class to think about ways to answer this question. The teacher also brought in magnifiers, rulers, beakers, cylinders, plastic tubs, eyedroppers, and balances. You would apply your thinking skills to design a plan to test the absorbencies of the different brands of paper towels.

Scientific Inquiry and Testing

Inquiry involves asking questions. These questions should lead to forming a tentative plan or plans to test the paper towel samples. Among the questions you might consider before developing a testing plan are:

- What is absorbency?
- What aspects of paper towel absorbency can be investigated using the available materials?
- What factors need to be controlled in order to compare testing results?
- Will you buy the most absorbent brand of paper towel after you complete your tests?

Inquiry involves examining the questions used to formulate a good experimental design. The class might consider testing the various brands of paper towels to determine which paper towel absorbs the greatest volume of water, which absorbs the most water in a given period of time, or which has the greatest change in mass when immersed in a specific amount of water. Solutions to each of these investigative possibilities can be explored through the development of a research plan and of a hypothesis to test methods being considered.

Figure 1.2 Using the Internet allows scientists to research topics quickly and from worldwide sources.

Developing a Research Plan

When a scientist defines a problem for investigation, such as exploring the absorbency of several brands of paper towels, he or she usually follows it with a search for information about the topic to be investigated. It is important to know what other people have learned about the topic before beginning research. This involves the development of a tentative research plan in which background information can be obtained that will assist in developing a hypothesis and devising an experimental design. Most research plans begin with a thorough library search that can include a review of the literature contained in scientific journals and a search of library databases and the Internet, as shown in Figure 1.2.

Classroom research on the topic of paper towel absorbency can even include contacting the manufacturers of each brand being tested. In addition, it may include a careful review of the tests and results that each company has conducted on its brand of paper towel. Familiarity with the existing research on a topic allows a scientist to avoid repeating investigations already done and to plan the best approach for investigating the problem. In the course of their research, scientists must make judgments about the reliability and relevance of the information they uncover.

 CHECK FOR UNDERSTANDING Why is it important to develop a research plan before fully investigating a problem?

Developing a Hypothesis

Next, a scientist formulates an explanation for the question or problem that can be tested. This explanation is known as a hypothesis. In a cause-and-effect relationship, such as the paper towel absorbency problem, the hypothesis is an educated guess about the outcome of the investigation of which paper towel absorbs the most liquid. Experiments that follow either will or will not support the hypothesis. A hypothesis cannot be proven or confirmed with absolute certainty.

In formulating a hypothesis, a scientist should know what is involved in solving the problem based on his or her previous observations and research. The hypothesis often is written as an "if–then" statement or as a statement where you can add, "I think that" to the beginning. If you are investigating the problem of paper towel absorbency based on the amount or volume of water that a paper towel sample can absorb, a possible hypothesis might be: *The thickest paper towel is the most absorbent.* This statement is testable and can lead to designing an experiment that will either support or fail to support the hypothesis.

CHECK FOR UNDERSTANDING Why is the statement of a hypothesis so critical to the experiment that will follow?

For the paper towel problem, the proposed hypothesis does not prove which paper towel is the most absorbent. Additional hypotheses based on surface area absorption and rate of absorption could lead to other experiments, which might indicate another brand of paper towel as being the most absorbent. A hypothesis sets the groundwork for designing an experiment to support or to contradict it. The following are examples of hypotheses.

- If two balls of the same size roll down the same ramp, they will get to the bottom of the ramp at the same time, no matter what they are made of.

- If two different balls are thrown in the air, the heavier one will fall to the ground faster.

- A cloth wrap keeps a bottle of water cold longer than a foil wrap.

- Dense objects sink in water.

Experimenting

Once a scientist has completed background research on a problem and has developed a hypothesis, he or she designs an experiment to test the hypothesis. An experiment is an investigation consisting of procedures that test a hypothesis by collecting information under controlled conditions.

Controls and Variables

Science experiments usually have a control component. In an experiment, a **control** is the standard that is used for comparison. This is in contrast to an experimental, or test, group. For the experimental group, all conditions are kept the same as the control except the condition being tested. For example, in an experiment that tests the effect of new medication, the control is usually a placebo, which is a substance that is similar in appearance to the experimental medication, but contains no medication of any kind. Common placebos include water and calcium carbonate tablets.

The condition that is tested or manipulated in an experiment is known as the **independent variable** because it is the only variable that affects the outcome of the experiment. When changing the independent variable, the scientist observes or measures a second condition that responds to the change in the dependent variable.

This condition is known as the **dependent variable** because it depends on the changes made to the independent variable. In complex experiments, there may be more than one independent variable and more than one dependent variable.

If you continue your paper towel exploration to determine which of several brands soaks up the greatest volume of water, you also would have to control several factors in designing an experiment. Variables to control include:

- testing each brand with the same volume of water and in the same size beaker or tub,

- testing the same area of toweling,

- soaking each towel for the same amount of time,

- allowing each soaked towel to drip water back into the beaker for the same amount of time.

The brand of towel that leaves the least amount of water remaining in the beaker or tub would be rated the most absorbent. In this case, the independent variable would be the various brands used, while the dependent variable would be how much water each towel absorbed.

In 1697, German physicist and chemist Georg Ernst Stahl postulated a theory of combustion that involved a substance called phlogiston. At the time, what are now known to be oxidized or corroded metals were called calxes. Stahl claimed that metals are composed of their calxes and phlogiston and that all matter contains different quantities of phlogiston. Carbon, because of its combustion properties, was thought to be rich in phlogiston. The phlogiston theory was used successfully to explain many chemical reactions.

The phlogiston theory, however, was not without its problems. Some metals, when oxidized, gained mass, which was contradictory to the phlogiston theory. In order to maintain a more universal principle of conservation of mass, modifications had to be made. Antoine-Laurent Lavoisier, pictured in Figure 1.3, performed carefully controlled experiments demonstrating that the calx of a metal always gains mass rather than losing it. The gain is accomplished by absorbing something from air during combustion. Lavoisier named the substance absorbed from air oxygen.

In 1783, Lavoisier published the results of his experiments that identified many inconsistencies in the phlogiston theory. Many predictions of the phlogiston theory proved to be false. Rather than attempting to fix a theory that he demonstrated to be erroneous, Lavoisier developed an alternative theory of combustion that soon became accepted by other chemists. The success of Lavoisier's demonstrations depended strongly on the fact that he carefully controlled variables in his experiments.

Among Lavoisier's many accomplishments in chemistry was the development of the precursor of modern chemical notation. This innovation was responsible, in part, for the rapid development of chemistry in the years that followed.

✔ **CHECK FOR UNDERSTANDING** What is the independent variable in the phlogiston experiment?

Figure 1.3 In 1775, Lavoisier experimented to determine that a metal gains mass when it burns because it combines with oxygen in the air.

Carrying Out an Investigation

When carrying out an investigation, scientists need tools that enable them to record information as accurately as possible. Selecting scientific equipment, considering safety precautions, and planning how to maintain the accuracy of the results are important parts of carrying out an investigation.

The safe and proper use of scientific tools is a key factor in determining accurate results in any investigation. In addition, the number of samples and trials conducted also helps to determine the accuracy of an investigation. Consider Lavoisier's investigation of combustion. Suppose he burned one piece of wood in a sealed container and then burned one piece of wood in the open air. Would such an experiment provide accurate results?

Proper testing would include multiple trials. You would burn several pieces of wood of equal size and composition. The reason for conducting multiple trials is to prevent an accidental error from invalidating the results of the experiment. You also would include several samples in the control group and in the experimental group to make sure that the results are consistent and not peculiar to a particular sample.

Table 1.1 • Water Absorbency in Different Brands of Paper Towels			
Brand	Amount of Water in Container Before Soaking	Amount of Water in Container After Soaking (60 s)	Amount of Water Absorbed by the Paper Towel
A	150 mL	126 mL	24 mL
B	150 mL	118 mL	32 mL
C	150 mL	132 mL	18 mL

The same factors should be considered in the paper towel experiment. Multiple trials and multiple samples involving each brand of towel would have to be tested to see if the results of the testing were consistent. Repeated trials with large sample sizes provide information that is more accurate and reduce the probability of introducing an error.

Observing, Analyzing, and Concluding

During experiments, scientists collect data based on the observations they make. Data are all of the information obtained from an experiment and sometimes are referred to as experimental results. Data is divided into two types: qualitative and quantitative. **Qualitative data** is information that describes color, odor, shape or some other physical characteristic. **Quantitative data** is numerical information describing how much, how little, how big, how tall, how fast, etc.

✓ CHECK FOR UNDERSTANDING What is the difference between qualitative data and quantitative data?

Gathering and Organizing Data

Scientists organize and analyze data. Scientists make decisions based on their analyses of data. Data can be organized into diagrams, charts, graphs, equations, matrices, and tables. Sometimes data are expressed in verbal or written form that describe observations. Often, data are expressed in numerical form based on measurements. A **measurement** is a comparison between an unknown quantity and a standard. Common measurements include those of time, mass, length, area, volume, and temperature.

To collect the quantitative data from a combustion experiment, a scientist would have to measure the change in mass of each sample in the control group and the experimental group.

These measurements are taken each time the experiment is performed. Then the results can be recorded in a data table.

A data table, such as Table 1.1, is one way to record and organize the results of testing the volume of water absorbed by several different brands of paper toweling. In general, data tables can help scientists examine information collected while doing an experiment.

One way that scientists examine data is by constructing a graph. A graph allows a scientist to represent data visually, often making it easier to make comparisons using the data collected. Graphing also allows scientists to see patterns in data, such as those shown in Figure 1.4. You will read more about graphing later in this section.

Often scientists organize data with computers. Spreadsheet software is used to analyze data, generate graphs, and answer what-if questions. Computerizing the data-collection process allows scientists to see graphed data instantly, and thus discern patterns more readily.

✓ CHECK FOR UNDERSTANDING Describe three ways in which a scientist can collect and organize data.

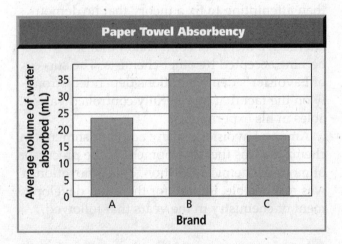

Figure 1.4 Data from the paper towel experiment is represented in this bar graph. Which of the three brands absorbed the most water in the experiment?

Construct a data table for the following experiment: A 335-gram potato is cut in two and allowed to dry in the sun. The mass of the potato is measured as the days pass. After 1 day, the mass of the potato is 330 grams; after 7 days, 300 grams; 12 days, 180 grams; 14 days, 150 grams; 21 days, 160 grams; 26 days, 120 grams.

1 Analyze the Problem

- Determine which is the dependent variable and which is the independent variable. Often, time is an independent variable.

    independent variable: time

    dependent variable: mass

- Make an empty table with the dependent variable in the first column and the independent variable in the second column.

Day of Measurement	Mass of Potato (g)

2 Solve for the Unknown

Enter numbers in the table by putting the values of the independent variable in sequence in column 1 and then writing in the matching values of the dependent variable.

Time of Measurement (d)	Mass of Potato (g)
0	335
1	330
7	300
12	180
14	150
21	160
26	120

3 Evaluate the Answer

- **Does the answer make sense?** The independent variable is the number of days and the dependent variable is the mass. The data table is easier to understand at a glance.

Developing Valid Conclusions

Careful analysis of data collected in an experiment allows a scientist to make decisions about the outcome of the experiment. Those decisions often are referred to collectively as conclusions.

A scientist will need to determine if the stated hypothesis was supported by the actual results of the experiment. Scientists usually consider data from an experiment valid after that experiment has been repeated several times and yielded similar results. Statistical analysis techniques often are used by scientists to determine if their results were affected by errors in measurement, differences among test samples, or by chance. Once a pattern or relationship can be supported through repeated testing, a scientist then tries to explain these results.

Reporting Results

Because of the nature of science, it should be possible for individuals who conduct similar experiments to arrive at similar conclusions. With few exceptions, experiments that cannot be repeated cannot be considered valid. Research among scientists must be reported clearly and in detail so that other scientists can repeat the investigation and duplicate the results. If a careful attempt to replicate the results of an experiment fails, the validity of the experiment may come into question.

The results of investigations are reported in scientific journals or are shared with colleagues during professional meetings. A report describes the hypothesis, including a literature review of previous studies and how the experiment was performed. It also describes data and states the scientists' conclusions. Public discussion and review of an experiment may result in a scientist revising his or her explanation and thinking about additional research.

Peer Review

Peer review is a process in which scientists evaluate the results of scientific investigations and the explanations proposed by other scientists. A peer review can be a presentation. It generally includes analysis of experimental procedures, careful examination of evidence, identification of faulty reasoning and statements that go beyond the evidence, and suggestions for alternative explanations for the same observations. Peer review serves as a system of checks and balances for scientific research.

Evidence is a collection of facts offered to support or refute the validity of an idea. In modern science, claims must be supported by a large collection of evidence before they are considered valid. Although scientific claims are always subject to peer review, experiments that use questionable procedures usually receive further scrutiny. These questionable procedures include using small sample sizes, biased or inadequately controlled conditions, or misleading graphs.

In science, a hypothesis that is supported by many separate observations and investigations over a long period of time becomes a theory. A theory results from a continuing process of verification and refinement of many related hypotheses. A valid theory often raises more questions. Theories can change or be refuted as new information and data are derived from experimentation. The theory of motion began with the observations of philosophers. Over the years, many scientists and others have researched the many aspects of motion to form one general theory.

✓ CHECK FOR UNDERSTANDING Why is it so difficult for the results of an experiment to become a theory?

Measuring

What do we mean when we say that an object is 20 cm long? We use a tool, such as a meterstick or a tape measure, and compare the length of the object to the markings on the tool. The marked distances on the tool tell us how long the object is. The expression "20 cm" represents a quantity because we are saying how much of something there is—in this case, the quantity is length. A quantity always is described by a number and a unit of measurement.

In chemistry, three fundamental quantities are distance, time, and mass, and the standard units of measurement of these quantities are the meter (m), the second (s), and the kilogram (kg). These units are defined with respect to international standards of measurement. At one time, the 1-m and 1-kg standards were defined as the length and the mass, respectively, of special objects maintained at constant temperature in a sealed vault at the International Bureau of Weights and Measures at Sevrès, France. One second was defined as $\frac{1}{86,400}$ of a mean solar day. Later, scientists developed more accurate ways to define the meter, kilogram, and second.

SI Units

SI is an abbreviation for Système Internationale d'Unités. This is the standard for units used in science around the world. SI units are based on seven fundamental units, shown in Table 1.2. From these seven units, dozens of derived units have been created. A derived unit is a unit that combines one or more of the SI base units. One example is the lux, which is defined as candelas per square meter.

Table 1.3 shows the prefixes that are used with many derived SI units. Learning these prefixes will help you to understand derived units and use them correctly. For example, the prefix "kilo" means one thousand. So, a kilometer is a unit of distance equal to 1000 meters.

There are other units outside the realm of SI units that are easily defined and used with SI units. One such unit is the liter. A liter (L) is defined as one cubic decimeter and is a common unit of measurement for liquids.

Scientific Notation

Scientists write numbers that are very large or very small in an abbreviated form that simplifies comparisons and computations. This form is called **scientific notation**. A number in scientific notation is written as a multiple of two factors: a number between 1 and 10, and 10 raised to a power, or *exponent*. The power of 10 gives the relative size, or *order of magnitude*, of the quantity. Suppose a car has a mass of 1736 kg. In scientific notation, you can write this as 1.736×10^3 kg. Numbers less than 1 have a negative exponent when expressed in scientific

Table 1.2 • SI Base Units	
Quantity	Base Unit
Time	second (s)
Length	meter (m)
Mass	kilogram (kg)
Temperature	kelvin (K)
Amount of a substance	mole (mol)
Electric current	Ampere (A)
Luminous intensity	candela (cd)

		Table 1.3 • Prefixes Used with SI Units		
Prefix	Symbol	Factor	Scientific Notation	Example
giga	G	1,000,000,000	10^9	gigameter (Gm)
mega	M	1,000,000	10^6	megagram (Mg)
kilo	k	1000	10^3	kilometer (km)
deci	d	1/10	10^{-1}	deciliter (dL)
centi	c	1/100	10^{-2}	centimeter (cm)
milli	m	1/1000	10^{-3}	milligram (mg)
micro	μ	1/1,000,000	10^{-6}	microgram (μg)
nano	n	1/1,000,000,000	10^{-9}	nanometer (nm)
pico	p	1/1,000,000,000,000	10^{-12}	picometer (pm)

notation. The mass of a paper clip, for example, is 0.93 g. In scientific notation, this quantity is written as 9.3×10^{-1} g.

To convert a number into scientific notation, first you need to identify the multiplier, which is a number that is no less than 1 and less than 10. The number has all the same digits as the original number, but the decimal point must be moved to get the right magnitude. The number of spaces the decimal point moves gives you the exponent in the scientific notation. If the decimal point moves to the left, the exponent is positive. If the decimal point moves to the right, the exponent is negative.

For example, the United States Census Bureau estimates the population of New York state to be about 19,190,000. First, you need to write down the number and move the decimal point.

$$19,190,000$$

The decimal point moves seven spaces to the left, so the exponent of 10 is +7. The remaining number is 1.919. The population of New York state in scientific notation is 1.919×10^7.

Mitochondria are small parts of a cell that convert energy in living organisms. In human muscle cells, the average size of mitochondria is 0.000000036 m. To convert this number to scientific notation, write the number and count the number of spaces that the decimal point needs to be moved.

$$0.000000036$$

The decimal point moves eight spaces to the right, so the exponent of 10 is −8. The size of mitochondria can be written as 3.6×10^{-8} m.

Example Problem 2

Convert the following to scientific notation.
a 75,000 kilograms
b 0.0081 meters

1 Analyze the Problem
- Determine the component between 1 and 10.
- Determine the component of 10 raised to an exponent.

2 Solve for the Unknown
Move the decimal point to find the component between 1 and 10. Count the number of places and direction you move the decimal point to determine the power and sign of the exponent. Moving the decimal point to the left results in a positive exponent and moving it to the right results in a negative exponent. After moving the decimal, remove any extra zeros at the beginning or at the end.

a Move the decimal point four places to the left.
The 1 through 10 component = 7.5
The number of places moved = +4
Scientific notation 7.5×10^4 kg

b Move the decimal point three places to the right.
The 1 through 10 component = 8.1
The number of places moved = −3
Scientific notation = 8.1×10^{-3} m

3 Evaluate the Answer
- **Do the answers make sense?** If the decimal point moved to the left, is the exponent positive? If the decimal point moved to the right, is the exponent negative? Is the first factor of the answer between 1 and 10? Do the digits of the first factor match the digits in the original number?

Multiplying in Scientific Notation

The process for multiplying numbers written in scientific notation is somewhat different from standard multiplication and division. Suppose you need to multiply 2.36×10^8 and 3.1×10^3.

First, multiply the multipliers, 2.36 and 3.1.

$(2.36)(3.1) = 7.316$

Then multiply the powers of 10 by adding the two exponents.

$10^8 \times 10^3 = 10^{8+3} = 10^{11}$

Finally, combine the results to get the product.

7.316×10^{11}

Occasionally, the process may be more complicated. For example, if you multiply 3.11×10^{-3} and 9.07×10^{-6}, the product of 3.11 and 9.07 is greater than 10.

$(3.11)(9.07) = 28.2077$

You can write the product of the two numbers as 28.2077×10^{-9}, but this is not a number written in scientific notation, because the multiplier must be a number between 1 and 10. You must move the decimal point and adjust the exponent accordingly. In this case, the decimal point moves to the left, so the exponent must increase by 1. Therefore, the product in scientific notation is 2.82077×10^{-8}.

Dividing in Scientific Notation

Division is similar to multiplication. To divide two numbers in scientific notation, first divide the two multipliers. Then subtract the exponent of the second number from the exponent of the first. Finally, move the decimal point in the multiplier and adjust the exponent to make sure that the multiplier is between 1 and 10.

For example, to divide 1.3×10^4 by 8.77×10^4, first divide the multipliers.

$1.3/8.77 = 0.148$

Then, subtract the second exponent from the first.

$10^4/10^4 = 10^{4-4} = 10^0$

Finally, move the decimal point and adjust the exponent.

$0.148 \times 10^0 = 1.48 \times 10^{-1}$

When multiplying and dividing numbers in scientific notation, you must take care that the exponents are added or subtracted correctly.

For example, when you multiply two numbers with exponents $+2$ and -3, respectively, the exponent of the product, before adjusting the decimal point, is -1. When dividing two numbers with exponents $+3$ and $+5$, respectively, the exponent of the product before the adjustment is -2.

Adding and subtracting numbers in scientific notation requires converting them to the same order of magnitude. This means that the numbers first must be written with the same power of 10. For example, 3.1×10^3 and 4.5×10^3 can be added directly because the exponent is the same.

$$(3.1 \times 10^3) + (4.5 \times 10^3) = (3.1 + 4.5) \times 10^3$$
$$= 8.6 \times 10^3$$

However, if you want to add numbers that do not have the same order of magnitude, such as 3.1×10^3 and 4.5×10^4, then the process is more complicated. First, convert the exponent of one of the numbers so it matches the exponent of the other number. Then add the numbers.

$$3.1 \times 10^3 = 0.31 \times 10^4$$
$$(0.31 \times 10^4) + (4.5 \times 10^4) = 4.81 \times 10^4$$

The procedure for subtraction is the same as that for addition.

Significant Digits

It is a general principle in chemistry that the result of any measurement is an approximation of the exact amount. An example of this principle is the process of measuring the length of an object with a typical metric ruler. A metric ruler usually is labeled in centimeters (cm), and millimeters (mm).

The length of the object in Figure 1.5 is between 9 and 10 cm. Using the lower ruler, the measurement can be estimated to the nearest tenth of a centimeter. The millimeter markings on the upper ruler allow for a more precise measurement. The length is between 9.5 and 9.6 cm (or between 95 and 96 mm).

When you measure a quantity, not all the digits in the number that represents your measurement are equally reliable. For example, if you use the bottom ruler in Figure 1.5, you may write the result of the measurement as 9.5 or 9.6 cm. You also can estimate the result to be 9.55, but this estimate would be unreasonable given the precision of the ruler. Looking at the top ruler, you can confirm with certainty that the length is 9.5 cm and you can estimate the third digit to be 0 or 1. The valid digits of a measure-

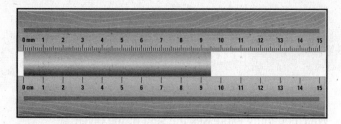

Figure 1.5 The top ruler can be used to measure the rod with three significant digits, while the bottom ruler allows only two significant digits.

ment, which include all known digits and one reliably estimated digit, are called **significant digits**. In the case of the rod in Figure 1.5, both 9.50 or 9.51 have three significant digits.

Each nonzero digit in a number is a significant digit. A zero may be a significant digit, depending where it appears in the number. A zero that appears between two significant digits, such as 607.1 m, is always a significant digit. All final zeros of a number that appear to the right of the decimal point and to the right of a nonzero digit, such as 0.110 m/s and 21.00 kg, also are significant. On the other hand, zeros that simply act as placeholders in a number are not significant digits. For example, if you estimate the mass of an insect to be 0.0012 kg, the three zeros are not significant digits. If you estimate the population of a town to be 25,000 people, the three zeros are not significant digits. However, in the term 25,000. with a period, the zeros are significant and the term has five significant digits.

There is a close relationship between significant digits and scientific notation. All the digits in the multiplier of a number written in scientific notation are considered to be significant digits. For example, if you write the mass of Venus as 4.8685×10^{24} kg, all five digits—4, 8, 6, 8 and 5—are significant digits. If you write the same mass as 4.9×10^{24} kg, there are only two significant digits—4 and 9.

Math and Significant Digits

When you perform multiple arithmetic operations with quantities, the measurements may not have the same number of significant digits. By convention, when you add or subtract quantities, the number of digits to the right of the decimal in sum or difference should not exceed the least number of digits to the right of the decimal in the terms. For example, if you add the

mass of a proton with five significant digits, 1.6726×10^{-27} kg, and the mass of a neutron with four significant digits, 1.675×10^{-27} kg, the result has five significant digits.

$$(1.6726 \times 10^{-27} \text{ kg}) + (1.675 \times 10^{-27} \text{ kg}) = 3.3476 \times 10^{-27} \text{ kg}$$

However, by the standard convention, the result should be rounded to three digits to the right of the decimal, or 3.348×10^{-27} kg. If both masses were given to five significant digits, the sum could be left with five significant digits.

$$(1.6726 \times 10^{-27} \text{ kg}) + (1.6749 \times 10^{-27} \text{ kg}) = 3.3475 \times 10^{-27} \text{ kg}$$

By standard convention, when you multiply and divide the numbers, you need to round the result to the number of significant digits that is equal to the least number of significant digits among the quantities involved.

✓ **CHECK FOR UNDERSTANDING** Which zeros in a number are significant digits?

Precision and Accuracy

When you perform a calculation, the significant digits of the answer show its precision. Precision should not be confused with accuracy. **Precision** is the degree of exactness of a measurement. Precision depends on the tools and methods used to make the measurement.

Accuracy describes how well two descriptions of a quantity agree with each other. **Accuracy** is the degree of agreement of a measurement with an accepted value obtained through computations or other competent measurement.

Figure 1.6 on page 12 represents the results of experimental measurements of three students. Each measurement involved placing an object on a spring and measuring the length of the stretched spring. Each student repeated the experiment several times, starting with springs of the same length. The students obtained different averages for their experiments. Student 1 reported his results as (14.6 ± 0.2) cm. student 2 reported (14.8 ± 0.3) cm and student 3 reported (14.0 ± 0.1) cm. The measurements taken by students 1 and 2 are in agreement, but they do not agree with the results reported by student 3.

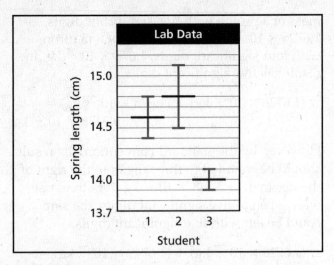

Figure 1.6 Measurements taken by students 1 and 2 likely are more accurate than measurements taken by student 3.

Student 3 appears to have obtained the most precise results because the data vary by the least amount. However, these results do not appear to be accurate because they are significantly different from the results of students 1 and 2, which are in agreement.

One way to measure accuracy is to determine the percent error of a measurement. Percent error is the ratio of the difference between the measured and accepted value to an accepted value.

Percent Error
$\text{Percent Error} = \dfrac{|\text{accepted} - \text{measured}|}{\text{accepted}} \times 100$

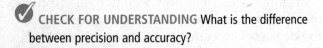 CHECK FOR UNDERSTANDING What is the difference between precision and accuracy?

Graphing and Mathematical Analysis

In mathematics, a variable is a quantity that changes. A constant is a quantity that does not change, like the number of things in a dozen and the number of centimeters in an inch. In chemistry, we frequently experiment by manipulating one variable (the independent variable) and observing what happens to a responding variable (the dependent variable). Recording our observations generates a set of data points. The data points can be arranged in a table with the independent variable arranged from the smallest number to the largest number.

STEP 1 READ the Regents Question . . .
Which quantity expresses the sum of the given masses to the correct number of significant digits?

$$\begin{array}{ll} 22.1 & \text{grams} \\ 375.66 & \text{grams} \\ +\ 5400.132 & \text{grams} \end{array}$$

(1) 5800 g   (3) 5797.9 g

(2) 5798 g   (4) 5797.892 g

STEP 2 ANALYZE each choice . . .

(1) 5800 g is the least precise of the choices; it is known only to the nearest 100 g.

(2) 5798 g is known to the nearest 1 g.

(3) 5797.9 g is known to the nearest 0.1 g.

(4) 5797.892 g is the most precise of the choices; it is known to the nearest 0.001 g.

STEP 3 CHOOSE the best answer . . .
The answer is only as accurate as the least precise of the masses that are being added. The least precisely known of the added masses is 22.1 g, which is known to the nearest 0.1 g. After considering all of the options, the correct choice is (3) because only this choice is precise to 0.1 g.

Graphing

There are many different ways to represent data collected in an experiment. An important tool is the graph. To represent raw data, it is common to use a scatterplot. Each point in the scatterplot represents one measurement. To find the relationship between the independent and the dependent variable, it is common to approximate the results of an experiment with a simple curve that fits the data closely. Linear, quadratic, and inverse relationships are some of the relationships commonly modeled by curve fitting.

Sometimes it is beneficial to group data before displaying the information. Most such displays involve statistical analysis. There are three basic forms of graphs for statistical display: circle graphs, bar graphs, and line graphs. A scientist must decide which type of graph is the most effective means of presenting data. The primary purpose of a circle graph is to represent part-whole relationships. Such graphs are less common in chemistry than scatterplots, bar graphs, and line graphs. There are several rules that should be followed when constructing a bar or a line graph, or a scatterplot.

1 Create a title for your graph.

2 The independent variable is plotted on the horizontal or *x*-axis. This is the factor you alter or vary.

3 The dependent variable is plotted on the vertical or *y*-axis. This is the variable that you observe or measure because of the experiment.

4 Create a scale on each axis by marking off equal spaces on each axis. Make sure that each scale covers the range of data collected for each variable.

5 Make sure your *x*-axis and *y*-axis are titled and units are labeled, if necessary.

6 When constructing a line graph, you can connect the successive data points with line segments. Line graphs are a common display when the independent variable is time.

7 When constructing a bar graph, you can represent each group of data by a vertical bar or a short horizontal line. Bar graphs are a common display when the independent variable is not numeric.

8 When displaying data in a scatterplot, never connect the datapoints. The line in the graph is an approximation of the data that corresponds to a model for the data.

✓ **CHECK FOR UNDERSTANDING** Which types of graphs are commonly used in chemistry? Which types of graphs are infrequently used in chemistry?

Example Problem 3

Graph the data table from Example Problem 1.

1 Analyze the Problem
- Determine which variable will be on the *x*-axis and which will be on the *y*-axis.
- Determine an appropriate scale for the graph.

2 Solve for the Unknown
The independent variable is time, so it is placed on the horizontal axis. The dependent variable is the mass, so it is placed on the vertical axis. Label the axes.

Choose a scale for each axis. The time scale ranges from 1 to about 30 days, and the mass scale ranges from 0 to about 350 grams.

Subdivide the scale for each axis and plot the data points from the table of values.

3 Evaluate the Answer
- **Does the answer make sense?** The graph makes it easier to see if there is a trend in the data.

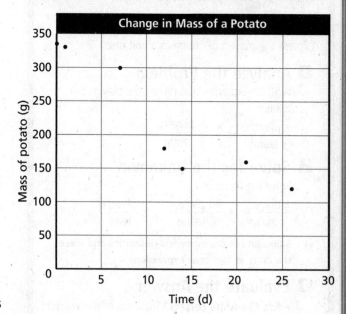

Dimensional Analysis

Often we want to convert a measurement from one unit into a different unit. This can be done by the use of a conversion factor. A conversion factor is a ratio of the relationship of one set of units to another. For instance, if you want to convert 0.021 kg to grams you use a conversion factor, based on the equality 1000 g = 1 kg. So 0.021 kg multiplied by 1000 g/kg equals 21 g.

A rate is a relation that uses division to compare two quantities with different units of measurement. Rates are used frequently in chemistry. For example, if a reaction rate is 50 L in 2 h, the rate is $\frac{50\ L}{2\ h}$. A unit rate compares one quantity to a single unit of another quantity. For example, if every box contains 12 pencils, the rate is $\frac{12\ pencils}{1\ box}$ or 12 pencils/box. A unit rate is a rate that has been simplified so that the denominator becomes 1.

$$\frac{50\ L}{2\ h} = \left(\frac{50}{2}\right)\left(\frac{L}{h}\right)$$
$$= \frac{25\ L}{h}$$

We also can write the unit rate as 25 L/h or 25 liters per hour.

Mathematical Analysis

Plots of data take many different shapes and reflect different relationships. When the line representing the data is a straight line, the dependent variable varies linearly with the independent variable. The relationship between the two variables is known as a linear relationship. The following equation describes the relationship.

| Linear Relationship $y = mx + b$ |

The y-intercept, b, is the point where the graph crosses the y-axis. The slope of the line, m, is defined as the ratio of vertical change to the horizontal change, also referred to as rise over run, as shown in Figure 1.7.

| Slope $m = \dfrac{rise}{run} = \dfrac{\Delta y}{\Delta x}$ |

The slope of a line is very useful for interpreting data. The slope tells you how rapidly one variable changes with respect to another variable. If the slope is large, then a small change in the independent variable causes a large change in the dependent variable.

In Figure 1.7, the slope is

$$m = \frac{\Delta y}{\Delta x}$$
$$= \frac{(16.0\ L - 14.5\ L)}{(30.\ s - 10.\ s)}$$
$$= 0.075\ L/s$$

Example Problem 4

There are 48 players on six teams in a soccer league. Express the players per team as a unit rate.

1 Analyze the Problem

Write an equation that relates the players per team.

$$\frac{x\ players}{y\ teams} = \frac{x}{y} = \frac{players}{team}$$

2 Solve for the Unknown

Solve the equation

$$\frac{x\ players}{y\ teams} = \frac{48\ players}{6\ teams} = 8\frac{players}{team}$$

Substitute in the numerical quantities and leave the units as algebraic expressions.

3 Evaluate the Answer

- **Are the units correct?** The units of the answer are a rate, as expected.
- **Does the answer make sense?** Yes, the average number of players is the total number of players divided by the number of teams.

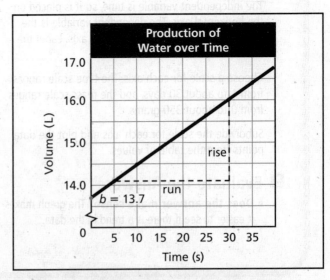

Figure 1.7 Slope of a line is the ratio of rise over run.

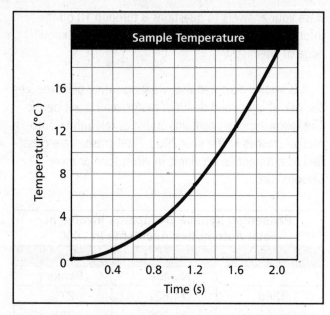

Figure 1.8 In a quadratic relationship, one variable depends on the square of the other.

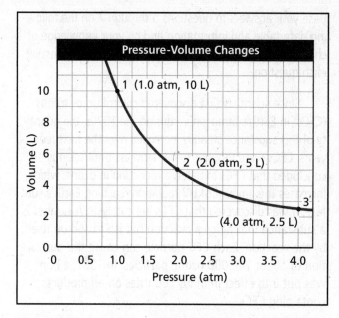

Figure 1.9 In an inverse relationship, the change in one variable depends on the reciprocal of the change in the other.

Because this value of the slope is a small number, it tells you that a it takes a long time to produce a significant change in the amount of water produced.

The line shown in Figure 1.8 shows the change in temperature in a reaction over time. By recognizing that the graph is not a straight line, you can see that the relationship is not linear. Two of the most common nonlinear relationships in science are quadratic and inverse. Figure 1.8 represents a quadratic relationship that can be described by the following equation.

Quadratic Relationship $y = ax^2 + bx + c$

✔ **CHECK FOR UNDERSTANDING** What equation represents a linear relationship? What does each variable in the equation represent?

Figure 1.9 shows the inverse relationship between pressure and volume of gas at constant temperature. As pressure increases, volume decreases. This relationship is represented by the following equation.

Inverse Relationship $y = \dfrac{a}{x}$

In chemistry, the linear, the quadratic, and the inverse relationships often are used to model simple processes.

Quick Review

1 Mike read in a health book that he should drink eight glasses of water (1.9 liters) each day. He has decided that he will try it. How many liters of water will he drink each week?
(1) 0.27 L   (3) 13 L
(2) 1.9 L   (4) 130 L

2 A furlong is an old English measure of length that is equal to 220 yards. How many yards are in 11 furlongs?
(1) 20
(2) 200
(3) 1200
(4) 2400

3 Which of the following is a unit rate?
(1) 5 km/1 h
(2) 3 T-shirts/$8.00
(3) 4 pack/30 matches
(4) 75 pills/5 bottles

4 On a hiking trip, how far does Jim travel in five days if he averages 60. kilometers per day?
(1) 300. km/d   (3) 12 km/d
(2) 12 km   (4) 300. km

Base your answers to questions 5 through 7 on the following data table and information and on your knowledge of chemistry. Use one or more complete sentences to answer each question.

Since scientists first discovered chlorofluorocarbons (CFCs) in Earth's atmosphere during the 1970s, the quantity of this substance steadily increased over the next few years. CFCs were thought to be harmless until scientists concluded that CFCs initiated a reduction in ozone, which increases the amount of UV radiation reaching Earth's surface. It was discovered that CFCs are catalysts. A catalyst is a substance that helps a reaction but isn't used up itself by the reaction. Each CFC particle can cause the destruction of about 100,000 ozone particles. In 1987, a ban was put into effect in many countries on all products containing CFCs.

Concentration of CFCs in the Atmosphere	
Year	CFC-11 Concentration (ppt)
1977	128
1979	154
1981	171
1983	188
1985	207
1987	229
1989	250
1991	268
1993	272
1995	273

5 In which time span did the level of CFCs increase the fastest?
   (1) 1977–1979
   (2) 1983–1985
   (3) 1985–1987
   (4) 1987–1989

6 If the ban reduced the amount of CFCs released into the atmosphere, why didn't the amount of CFCs in the atmosphere diminish?

7 Is there still a danger to Earth?

Base your answers to questions 8 through 10 on the information and data table below and on your knowledge of chemistry.

It is widely accepted that wearing safety belts reduces the risk of injury and death in motor vehicle accidents. The following chart contains statistics relating to automotive crashes in the year 2000. Fatal crashes are classified as automotive accidents in which one or more persons died.

Passenger Vehicle Occupants Involve in Fatal Automotive Accidents in 2000		
Safety Belt Used		
	Number	Percent
Died	11,622	27%
Survived	31,328	73%
Safety Belts Not Used		
	Number	Percent
Died	17,672	56%
Survived	13,985	44%
Safety Belt Use Unknown		
	Number	Percent
Died	2616	36%
Survived	4742	64%

Source: 2000 Annual Assessment of Motor Vehicle Crashes (Revised November 2001), **National Center for Statistics & Analysis**

8 Does the data in the table scientifically support the notion that safety belts in automobiles save lives?

9 What additional data would be needed in order to better support this conclusion?

10 Explain why wearing safety belts is a less risky behavior than not wearing safety belts.

11 The following graph shows how solubility is affected by temperature.

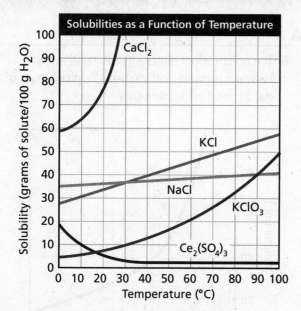

Which of the curves has a negative slope?
(1) KCl
(2) NaCl
(3) $KClO_3$
(4) $Ce_2(SO_4)_3$

12 Determine the thickness of a page of one of your books using your knowledge of rates. Use a ruler to measure the thickness of 30, 55, and 70 pages. Reduce each of these rates to the equivalent unit rate. Average all three of the rates to obtain the answer.

13 Which graph best represents the inverse relationship between pressure, *P*, and volume, *V*, for a fixed mass of an ideal gas at constant temperature?

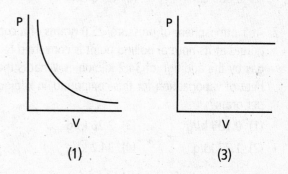

(1)   (3)

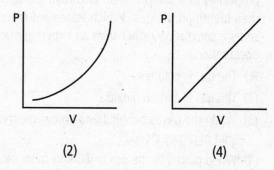

(2)   (4)

Part A

1 Which measurement contains three significant digits?

(1) 0.08 cm   (3) 800 cm

(2) 0.080 cm   (4) 8.08 cm

2 At 1 atmosphere of pressure, 25.0 grams of a compound at its normal boiling point is converted to a gas by the addition of 34.2 kilojoules. What is the heat of vaporization for this compound, in kilojoules per gram?

(1) 0.105 kJ/g   (3) 2.26 kJ/g

(2) 1.37 kJ/g   (4) 34.2 kJ/g

3 A student investigated the physical and chemical properties of a sample of an unknown gas and then identified the gas. Which statement represents a conclusion rather than an experimental observation?

(1) The gas is colorless.

(2) The gas is carbon dioxide.

(3) When the gas is bubbled into limewater, the liquid becomes cloudy.

(4) When placed in the gas, a flaming splint stops burning.

4 If 11 grams of a gas occupies 5.6 liters what is its approximate density?

(1) 2.0 g/L   (3) 60 g/L

(2) 1.5 g/L   (4) 0.50 g/L

5 The volume of a gas sample is 22.4 liters. The density of the gas is 1.34 grams per liter. What is the mass of the gas sample, expressed to the correct number of significant digits?

(1) 16.7 g   (3) 30 g

(2) 17g   (4) 30.0 g

6 The graph below represents the relationship between pressure and volume of a given mass of a gas at constant temperature.

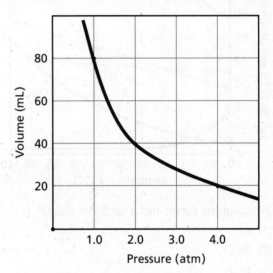

The product of pressure and volume is constant. According to the graph, what is this product in atm•mL?

(1) 20 atm•mL   (3) 60 atm•mL

(2) 40 atm•mL   (4) 80 atm•mL

7 A student calculated the percent by mass of water in a sample of $BaCl_2 \cdot 2H_2O$ to be 16.4 percent, but the accepted value is 14.8 percent. What was the student's percent error?

(1) $14.8/16.4 \times 100\%$

(2) $16.4/14.8 \times 100\%$

(3) $1.6/14.8 \times 100\%$

(4) $14.8/1.6 \times 100\%$

8 Which equilibrium constant indicates the highest concentration of the product?

(1) $K_{eq} = 1 \times 10^{-1}$ (3) $K_{eq} = 3 \times 10^{-3}$

(2) $K_{eq} = 2 \times 10^{-2}$ (4) $K_{eq} = 4 \times 10^{-4}$

9 During a laboratory activity, a student combined two solutions. In the laboratory report, the student wrote "A yellow color appeared." The statement represents the student's recorded

(1) conclusion   (3) hypothesis

(2) observation   (4) theory

10 A 2.00-liter sample of a gas has a mass of 1.80 grams. What is the density, in grams per liter?

(1) 0.900   (3) 11.2

(2) 1.80   (4) 22.4

11 Which quantity is equivalent to 50 kilojoules?

(1) 5000 J   (3) 5×10^3 J

(2) 0.05 J   (4) 5×10^4 J

12 Expressed to the correct number of significant digits, the sum of two masses is 445.2 grams. Which two masses produce this answer?

(1) 210.10 g + 235.100 g

(2) 210.100 g + 235.10 g

(3) 210.1 g + 235.1 g

(4) 210.10 g + 235.10 g

Part B–1

13 What is the product of (2.324 centimeters)(1.11 centimeters) expressed to the correct number of significant digits?

(1) 2.58 cm²   (3) 2.5796 cm²

(2) 2.5780 cm²   (4) 2.57964 cm²

14 A solution contains 12.55 grams of a solid dissolved in 50.0 milliliters of water. What is the number of grams of solid dissolved per milliliter of water, rounded to the correct number of significant digits?

(1) 0.25 g/mL   (3) 0.3 g/mL

(2) 0.251 g/mL   (4) 0.2510 g/mL

15 A student obtained the following data to determine the percent-by-mass of water in a hydrate.

Mass of empty crucible + cover...	11.70 g
Mass of crucible + cover + hydrated salt before heating................................	14.90 g
Mass of crucible + cover + anhydrous salt after thorough heating....................	14.53 g

What is the approximate percent by mass of the water in the hydrated salt?

(1) 2.5%   (3) 88%

(2) 12%   (4) 98%

16 A sample of water is being heated from 20°C to 30°C, and the temperature is recorded every 2 minutes. Which table would be most appropriate for recording the data?

Time (min)	Temp (°C)
0	
2	
4	
6	
8	
10	

(1)

Time (min)	Temp (°C)
20	
22	
24	
26	
28	
30	

(2)

Temp (°C)	Time (min)
0	
2	
4	
6	
8	
10	

(3)

Temp (°C)	Time (min)
20	
22	
24	
26	
28	
30	

(4)

Part C

Base your answers to questions 17 through 19 on the following table and information.

A student used a balance and a graduated cylinder to collect the following data:

Sample mass	10.23 g
Volume of water	20.0 mL
Volume of water and sample	21.5 mL

17 Calculate the density of the element. Show your work. Include the appropriate number of significant digits and proper units.

18 If the accepted value is 6.93 grams per milliliter, calculate the percent error.

19 What error is introduced if the volume of the sample is determined first?

The concept of the atom began as a model for the smallest, invisible parts of matter. As a model, it was used successfully to explain the behavior of matter at many different levels. We now know that the atom is made up of even smaller particles, called *electrons, protons,* and *neutrons*. Scientists have even captured images of individual atoms, so perhaps the atom should no longer be considered a model. In this section you will see how our understanding of the atom has changed from the earliest models to the current quantum theory.

Early Models of the Atom

An **atom** is the smallest part of an element that retains all the properties of that element. An **element** is a substance that cannot be broken down into simpler substances by chemical means. Diamond is made of the element carbon. Suppose that you could grind up a pure diamond into smaller and smaller pieces. The smallest possible piece you could produce that would still be carbon would be a single atom. Based on experiments done during the eighteenth century, as well as his own work, the English schoolteacher John Dalton formulated a new theory of atoms in the early nineteenth century.

Dalton's Theory

Dalton's atomic theory stated that atoms are small, indivisible particles that cannot be created or destroyed. Look at the reaction in Figure 2.1.

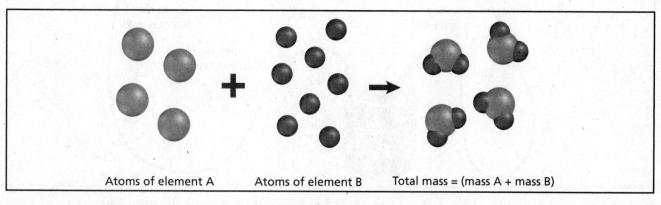

Atoms of element A   Atoms of element B   Total mass = (mass A + mass B)

Figure 2.1 The number of each type of atom is the same before and after a reaction occurs.

There are four atoms of element A on both the left and right sides. Likewise, there are eight atoms of element B on the left and right sides. Because the atoms are neither created nor destroyed, the total mass on the left side equals the mass on the right side.

Dalton's atomic theory could explain why mass is conserved when a chemical reaction occurs. Until the eighteenth century, scientists did not understand that some substances were elements and that others were **compounds**, which are chemical combinations of two or more elements. When substances react, atoms are rearranged and regrouped to form new substances, but the total mass does not change.

Dalton's theory further stated that atoms of a given element are identical in size, mass, and chemical properties. When atoms combine, they do so in whole-number ratios. Dalton's theory was able to explain this as well. As a result of Dalton's work, the idea of an atom as a tiny, indivisible particle finally was accepted.

✔ CHECK FOR UNDERSTANDING According to Dalton, what happens to the atoms when a substance reacts?

Discovering the Electron

By the mid 1800s, scientists were making discoveries about electricity that seemed to indicate that maybe an atom was not indivisible after all. One observation involved a device called a cathode-ray tube. This is a glass tube with metal plates at either end that can be connected to a source of electric voltage. The plate attached to the negative side of the voltage source is called the *cathode* and the plate attached to the positive side is called the *anode*. The tube has most of the air pumped out. When the connections are made to the cathode and anode, a stream of tiny, negatively charged particles are emitted by the cathode, as shown in Figure 2.2.

When the material used for the cathode was altered, the stream of particles was still observed. The stream also was observed when the gas in the tube was changed. Scientists concluded from these observations that the particles must be present in all matter. J.J. Thomson did carefully controlled experiments and was able to determine the charge-to-mass ratio of these particles. To his astonishment, the particles appeared to have a mass that was much smaller than a single hydrogen atom. This was a surprise because a hydrogen atom was thought to be the smallest possible particle. Thomson realized he had discovered a smaller particle in what had been thought to be an indivisible atom. Today, these particles are called electrons. An **electron** is a fast-moving particle that moves through empty space surrounding an atom's nucleus. In 1909, Robert Millikan was able to directly measure the charge on the electron. From this value and Thomson's charge-to-mass ratio, the mass of the electron was calculated. It turned out to be $\frac{1}{1840}$ the mass of a hydrogen atom.

✔ CHECK FOR UNDERSTANDING What ratio helped Thomson discover the electron?

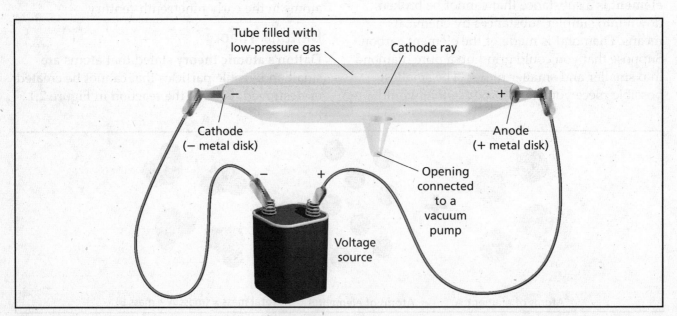

Figure 2.2 In a cathode-ray tube, negatively charged electrons are attracted to the positively charged anode.

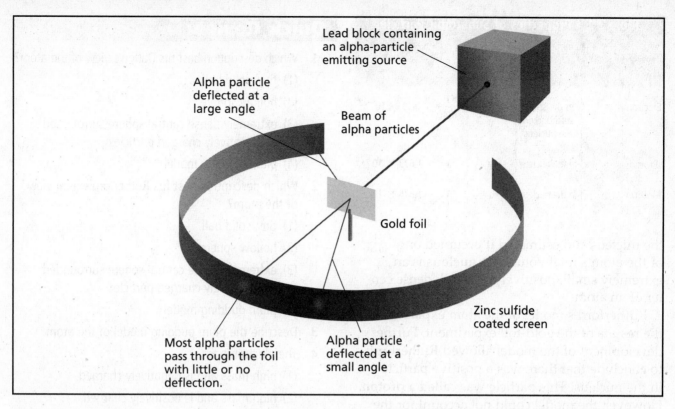

Figure 2.3 In Rutherford's experiment, most alpha particles passed through the gold foil, but some were deflected at a large angle.

Discovering the Nucleus

Because matter does not normally have a net electric charge and all matter contains electrons, there must be a positive charge that exactly cancels the negative charge of the electron. It is the nature of this positive charge that scientists turned to next.

In what he called the plum pudding model, Thomson imagined the electrons as embedded in a background of uniformly distributed positive charges similar to the way bits of plums are distributed in old-fashioned plum pudding. According to this model, there were no parts of the atom that were more dense or massive than any other part. Ernest Rutherford investigated the nature of atoms by firing relatively massive alpha particles at a piece of extremely thin gold foil, as shown in Figure 2.3. An **alpha particle** is made up of two protons and two neutrons and has a 2+ charge. Alpha particles have a high mass—about 8000 times the mass of an electron.

If the plum pudding model was correct, there should be little or no deflection of the alpha particles because the mass of the gold atom would be uniformly spread out. Rutherford's results were surprising. Most of the alpha particles did, indeed, go straight through the foil. But some were deflected at a large angle. Some were even deflected straight backwards.

Rutherford eventually realized that the plum pudding model could not account for the results of the experiment. A new model of the atom had to be devised, as shown in Figure 2.4. The model had to have a dense region that was massive enough to deflect the alpha particles. If the region was not dense, then there would be few deflected alpha particles. This region also needed to be positively charged. Because the alpha particles were only occasionally deflected, Rutherford was able to estimate the size of the dense region at the center of the atom. He called this region

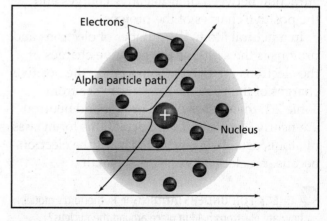

Figure 2.4 In Rutherford's model of the atom, large deflections occur because the nucleus is small and contains all of the atom's positive charge.

Table 2.1 • Properties of Subatomic Particles

Particle	Symbol	Location	Relative Electric Charge	Relative Mass	Actual Mass (g)
Electron	e^-	In the space surrounding the nucleus	1^-	$\frac{1}{1840}$	9.11×10^{-28}
Proton	p^+	In the nucleus	1^+	1	1.673×10^{-24}
Neutron	n^0	In the nucleus	0	1	1.675×10^{-24}

the nucleus and estimated it occupied only $\frac{1}{10,000}$ of the atom's total volume. A **nucleus** is an extremely small, positively charged, dense center of an atom.

Rutherford's model of the atom explained the results of the gold-foil experiment. Further development of the model allowed Rutherford to conclude that there was a positive particle in the nucleus. This particle was called a **proton.** However, the model could not account for the total mass of the atom. It wasn't until 1932 that James Chadwick discovered another particle in the nucleus that had no electric charge. This particle was called a **neutron,** which has a mass nearly equal to that of a proton, as shown in Table 2.1.

Atomic Mass

The model of the atom, as pictured by scientists in the early twentieth century, has a positive nucleus containing positive protons and neutral neutrons. The nucleus accounts for 99.97 percent of an atom's mass. Negative electrons orbit the nucleus and are held in place by the electric attraction between their negative charges and the positive charges of the protons.

In a neutral atom, the number of electrons and protons is the same, so the negative charges of the electrons are exactly balanced by the positive charges of the protons. As you can see from Table 2.1, the masses of the proton and neutron are nearly identical. Basic calculations for masses of atoms usually ignore the mass of the electron because an electron's mass is so small.

✓ **CHECK FOR UNDERSTANDING** In Rutherford's model, how are electrons held in place around the nucleus?

Quick Review

1 Which description best fits Dalton's view of the atom?
   (1) tiny, solid ball
   (2) hollow sphere
   (3) extremely dense central sphere surrounded by negatively charged particles
   (4) plum pudding model

2 Which description best fits Rutherford's final view of the atom?
   (1) tiny, solid ball
   (2) hollow sphere
   (3) extremely dense central sphere surrounded by negatively charged particles
   (4) plum pudding model

3 Describe the plum pudding model of the atom.

4 The electron has
   (1) high mass and is negatively charged
   (2) high mass and is positively charged
   (3) low mass and is positively charged
   (4) low mass and is negatively charged

5 The proton has
   (1) high mass and is negatively charged
   (2) high mass and is positively charged
   (3) low mass and is positively charged
   (4) low mass and is negatively charged

6 The neutron has
   (1) about the same mass as a proton
   (2) much more mass than a proton
   (3) the same charge as an electron
   (4) about the same mass as an electron

7 Compare and contrast the three particles found in the atom in terms of their charges and locations.

8 Most of the mass of an atom is
   (1) in the electrons   (3) in the neutrons
   (2) in the protons   (4) in the nucleus

9 In what order were the subatomic particles discovered?
   (1) electron, neutron, proton
   (2) proton, electron, neutron
   (3) electron, proton, neutron
   (4) neutron, electron, proton

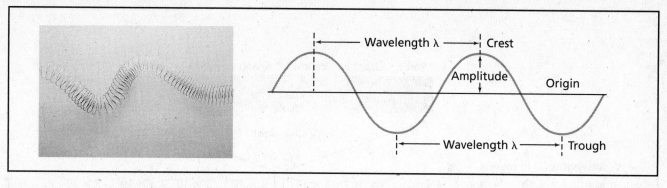

Figure 2.5 A wave is described by its wavelength and amplitude. The high points of the wave are crests and the low points are troughs. The wavelength equals the distance between one crest and the next. The amplitude equals the height of a crest.

Light and Quanta

While many questions had been answered about the structure of atoms, other questions arose. For example, why don't the negative electrons collapse in toward the positive nucleus? How are the electrons arranged in the space around the nucleus? How does the atomic model help explain the varying properties of different elements?

Scientists did know that when certain elements were heated until they glowed, characteristic colors of light were given off. This was a clue that led scientists to answers of more in-depth questions. In order to understand how scientists resolved the questions about atomic structure, first you must understand the nature of light.

✓ CHECK FOR UNDERSTANDING What was one clue scientists used to help understand the structure of the atom?

Wave Nature of Light

Visible light is a kind of electromagnetic radiation. **Electromagnetic radiation** is a form of energy exhibiting wavelike behavior as it travels through space. Electromagnetic waves, like all waves, have certain properties that can be measured. **Wavelength** is the shortest distance between equivalent points on a continuous wave, as shown in Figure 2.5. Wavelength is measured in units such as meters, centimeters, or nanometers. **Frequency,** which is the number of wave crests or troughs that pass a point per second, is measured in a unit called a hertz (Hz). One Hz equals one wave per second. Dimensionally, the hertz is equivalent to 1/s.

As the frequency of a wave increases, its wavelength decreases, and vice versa, as shown in Figure 2.6. Therefore, a high-frequency wave

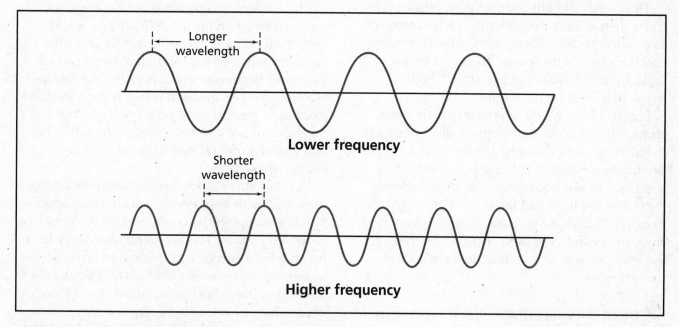

Figure 2.6 For waves moving at the same speed, as frequency increases, wavelength decreases.

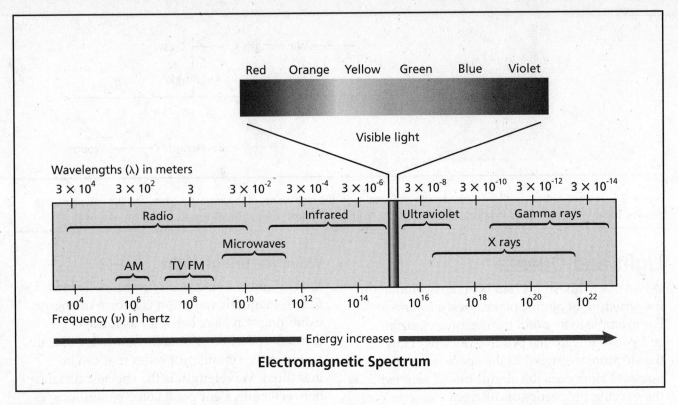

Red Orange Yellow Green Blue Violet

Visible light

Wavelengths (λ) in meters

3×10^4 3×10^2 3 3×10^{-2} 3×10^{-4} 3×10^{-6} 3×10^{-8} 3×10^{-10} 3×10^{-12} 3×10^{-14}

Radio   Infrared   Ultraviolet   Gamma rays

Microwaves   X rays

AM   TV FM

10^4 10^6 10^8 10^{10} 10^{12} 10^{14} 10^{16} 10^{18} 10^{20} 10^{22}

Frequency (ν) in hertz

Energy increases

Electromagnetic Spectrum

Figure 2.7 In order of increasing frequency, the electromagnetic spectrum includes radio waves, microwaves, infrared rays, visible light, ultraviolet light, X rays, and gamma rays.

has a small wavelength. This relationship is called an inverse relationship. The product of frequency and wavelength for any wave is its speed. Notice that using dimensional analysis, the units for wavelength and frequency multiply to give a unit for speed. The speed of light in a vacuum is always 3.00×10^8 m/s.

The energy of light is directly proportional to its frequency. Each frequency of light is perceived as a different color. Red is the lowest frequency and therefore, is the lowest energy of visible light. Blue and violet have relatively high frequencies and high energies.

Figure 2.7 shows the **electromagnetic spectrum**, which includes all forms of electromagnetic radiation, with the only difference in the types of radiation being their frequencies and wavelengths. The electromagnetic spectrum extends far below red light and far above violet light. For example, X rays are invisible rays with very high frequencies and very high energies. Microwaves are invisible waves with low frequencies and low energies.

✓ **CHECK FOR UNDERSTANDING** What happens to the wavelength and energy of light as the frequency increases?

Particle Nature of Light

There were two particular behaviors of matter that could not easily be explained using the wave model of light. It was well-known that heated objects of different compositions emit different frequencies (colors) of light. Sodium emits yellowish light, while copper emits greenish light. In other words, matter does not emit light of all frequencies when heated. Why not? Look at Figure 2.8 on page 27. Some metals give off electrons when struck by light above a certain threshold frequency, which is called the **photoelectric effect.** If the light is below the threshold frequency, regardless of how bright the light is, no electrons are emitted. Again, why not? The wave model of light had to be modified to explain these facts.

In 1900, Max Planck found that by assuming matter gains or loses energy only in small specific bundles of energy, he could explain the behavior of heated objects. This was a revolutionary idea because light energy was thought to exist only as a continuous, uninterrupted wave. Planck called these energy bundles *quanta*. According to Planck's assumption, a heated object can emit only certain quanta; others are not allowed. In terms of light

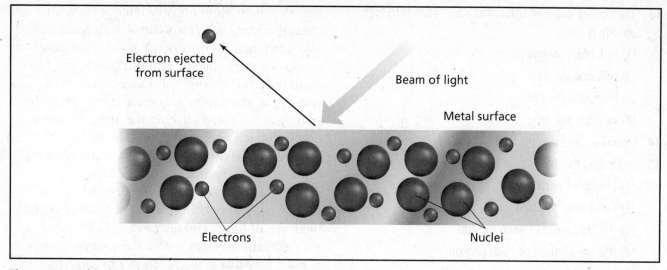

Figure 2.8 In the photoelectric effect, when light strikes a surface, electrons may be ejected only if the incident photons have frequencies higher than the threshold frequency.

emitted, this means only very specific frequencies can be emitted by each particular atom.

A **quantum** is the minimum amount of energy that can be gained or lost by an atom. The energy of the quantum is in a direct relationship with its frequency, ν. To calculate the energy of a quantum, multiply its frequency by a small number, known as **Planck's constant**, h, which is equal to 6.626×10^{-34} J•s.

Quantum Energy $E_{quantum} = h\nu$

The photoelectric effect also can be understood using the quantum theory. Quanta of light are called photons. A **photon** is a particle of electromagnetic energy with no mass that carries a quantum of energy. Photons can only free electrons from a metal's surface if the quanta are carrying a certain minimum energy that will be used to overcome the attraction of the electron to the metal surface. Unless the photons have this minimum energy (frequency), they will be unable to free electrons from the metal's surface. Increasing the intensity of the light only increases the number of photons, not their frequencies, as shown in Figure 2.8. Therefore, no matter how bright the light, if it has a frequency lower than the minimum threshold frequency, no electrons will be emitted.

✔ CHECK FOR UNDERSTANDING How did Planck describe the particle nature of light?

Light has a dual nature. In some ways it is like a wave. It has a wavelength and a frequency that can be measured. It also has other wavelike properties, such as refraction. On the other hand, light also has some particle properties. Albert Einstein proposed that light and, in fact, all electromagnetic radiation, has both wavelike and particlelike properties. This is the currently accepted view of the nature of light.

Quick Review

10 When light strikes a metal surface, electrons are ejected. This behavior is called
   (1) the photoelectric effect
   (2) quantum theory
   (3) the electromagnetic principle
   (4) Planck's theory

11 Which of the following electromagnetic waves has the highest-energy photons?
   (1) visible light
   (2) radio waves
   (3) microwaves
   (4) infrared rays

12 What force keeps electrons in orbit around the nucleus of the atom?
   (1) electrostatic force
   (2) magnetic force
   (3) force of gravity
   (4) force of friction

13 The correct order of colors from low energy to high energy is

(1) red, blue, orange

(2) red, orange, blue

(3) blue, orange, red

(4) orange, red, blue

14 Describe the main principle of the quantum theory.

15 Increasing the intensity of a light source increases the

(1) energy of each photon

(2) number of photons

(3) the frequency of each photon

(4) the wavelength of each photon

16 Light is a form of

(1) heat

(2) electromagnetism

(3) matter

(4) specialized gas

17 The person credited with first devising the quantum theory is

(1) Einstein   (3) Rutherford

(2) Bohr   (4) Planck

18 What is the speed of a wave with a wavelength of 3 meters and a frequency of 10 hertz?

19 Name one way energy behaves as a particle and one way it behaves as a wave.

Twentieth-Century Atomic Models

At the beginning of the twentieth century, the early planetary model of the atom faced challenges in explaining a variety of newly discovered phenomena. These phenomena included the recent understanding of the relationships among atomic structure, electrons, and atomic emission.

Bohr's Model and Energy Levels

In 1913, Niels Bohr incorporated the new ideas about the nature of light to explain in a more fundamental way why light emitted by heated objects is restricted to certain frequencies.

In Bohr's model, electrons orbit the nucleus at varying distances that correspond to varying amounts of energy. In most cases, the farther an electron is from the nucleus, the more energy it

has. When an atom absorbs energy from an outside source, electrons can absorb the energy and jump to a higher energy level. That jump requires a very specific amount of energy. The atom only can absorb particular amounts of energy; in other words, quanta of energy. If the energy of a photon striking the atom does not exactly match one of the possible energy changes of the atom, the energy of the photon cannot be absorbed. Conversely, when an electron drops to a lower energy level, it can release a very specific amount of extra energy in the form of light. The released light energy is a very specific amount with a definite frequency.

Bohr was able to use his theory to correctly predict the frequency of light emitted by a hydrogen atom as its electron went through various transitions. However, he was unable to predict the spectrum of elements with more than one electron. For this reason, his ideas were not fully accepted by most scientists.

✓ **CHECK FOR UNDERSTANDING** What has to happen in order for an electron to give off light?

Electron Waves

In 1924, Louis de Broglie proposed that particles, such as electrons, could have some wave properties. In particular, electrons moving around the nucleus could have a wavelength associated with their motion. De Broglie realized that if the electrons did have a wavelength, the distance the electron traveled around the nucleus (the circumference of the atom) would have to be a whole-number multiple of the wavelength. In this way, de Broglie was able to account for the fact that electrons can only orbit at certain specific distances. These distances correspond to circumferences of one, two, three, or more wavelengths. Experiments have been done that bear out the wave nature of electrons.

Heisenberg Uncertainty Principle

Meanwhile, Werner Heisenberg showed that it is impossible to know the exact position and velocity of an electron, regardless of the precision of the measuring equipment. When an electron is observed, the very act of making the observation changes the position and energy of the electron in an unpredictable way. The more precisely the

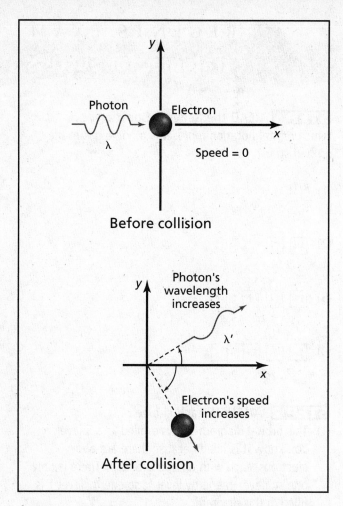

Before collision

After collision

Figure 2.9 Measuring an electron's position with a photon changes both the electron's position and its velocity. Therefore, the position and velocity cannot be determined exactly.

position is known, the less precisely the energy is known, as shown in Figure 2.9. The phenomenon is called the **Heisenberg uncertainty principle.** When this principle first was proposed, many scientists questioned it, but as more experiments were done it became clear that Heinsenberg was right.

When Erwin Schrödinger devised an equation for describing the electron as a wave, he incorporated the Heisenberg uncertainty principle by stating the solution in the form of a wave function that gave the probability of finding an electron at a given position. Electrons no longer could be visualized as tiny solid spheres. The modern view of electrons is that they exist as probabilities at a given position.

✅ **CHECK FOR UNDERSTANDING** How does the Heisenberg uncertainty principle apply to electrons?

Atomic Orbitals

Because it is impossible to define the exact position of an electron, the shape of an atom is somewhat hard to define. By convention, the shape of an atom is the shape that encloses a 90 percent probability of finding the electron. In the simplest case, hydrogen, the shape is a sphere, as shown in Figure 2.10.

An **atomic orbital,** also called a *shell,* is a three-dimensional region around the nucleus of an atom that describes an electron's probable location. Depending on the distance from the nucleus, orbitals can have a variety of shapes and may have a number of sublevels. The first energy level ($n = 1$) is closest to the nucleus and consists of a single spherical orbital (1s). The second

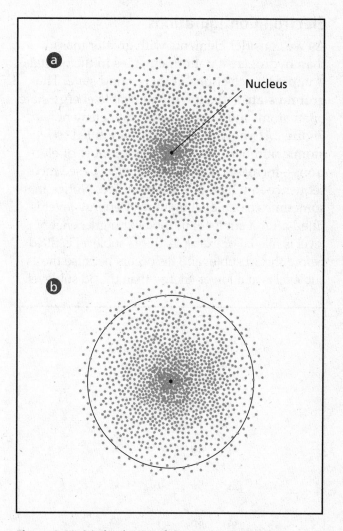

Figure 2.10 (a) The density of dots in this model of the hydrogen atom shows the probability of finding an electron at each point in the atom. **(b)** The boundary of the atom is defined as the volume within which there is a 90 percent probability of finding the electron.

energy level ($n = 2$) consists of two sublevels. One sublevel has spherical orbitals (2s). The other sublevel consists of three dumbbell-shaped orbitals (2p). The second energy level can hold a total of eight electrons: two in the 2s sublevel and six in the 2p sublevel. The third energy level consists of one spherical-shaped orbital (3s), a set of three dumbbell-shaped orbitals (3p), and a set of five double-dumbbell shaped orbitals (3d).

Principal energy levels are the major energy levels of an atom. Table 2.2 shows the first four principal energy levels for hydrogen.

✓ CHECK FOR UNDERSTANDING What is the probability of finding an electron in a hydrogen atom?

Electron Configurations

As we consider elements with greater mass than hydrogen, a pattern emerges in the orbitals occupied by electrons in the ground state. The **ground state** is the lowest allowable energy state of an atom, and is unique for each element. Figure 2.11 shows how orbitals are filled as atomic number—and therefore number of electrons—increases. Follow the arrows to see the sequence in which orbitals are filled. Notice that sometimes a sublevel in a lower energy level is filled after a sublevel in the next higher energy level is filled. For example, the 4s sublevel is filled before the 3d sublevel. This occurs because the 4s sublevel is at a lower energy than the 3d sublevel.

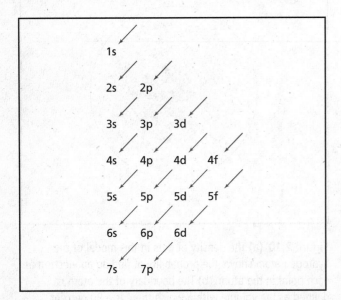

Figure 2.11 This diagram shows the order in which orbitals usually are filled: 1s, 2s, 2p, 3s, 3p, 4s, and 3d, etc. Which is filled first, the 5s or the 4p orbital?

STEP 1 READ the Regents Question . . .
Which orbital notation represents a noble gas in the ground state?

(1) ↑↓
   $1s^2$

(2) ↑↓ ↑↓
   $1s^2$ $2s^2$

(3) ↑↓ ↑↓ ↑ ↑ ↑
   $1s^2$ $2s^2$ $2p^3$

(4) ↑↓ ↑ ↑↓ ↑↓ ↑↓
   $1s^2$ $2s^1$ $2p^6$

STEP 2 ANALYZE each choice . . .
(1) This orbital diagram shows a filled 1s sublevel. You know it is filled because there are two electrons, each with an opposite spin. There is only one sublevel in energy level 1, so energy level 1 is filled in this diagram.

(2) This orbital diagram shows a filled 1s sublevel and a filled 2s sublevel. But the second energy level is not completely filled because the 2p sublevels, which are not shown, could each hold two additional electrons.

(3) This orbital diagram shows filled 1s and 2s sublevels, but the 2p sublevels are only half filled. The second energy level could hold three additional electrons (one more electron in each of the 2p sublevels).

(4) This orbital diagram shows filled 1s and 2p sublevels, but the 2s sublevel is not filled. This represents an atom with an excited electron (the atom is not in the ground state).

STEP 3 CHOOSE the best answer . . .
After considering all of the options, the correct answer must be number 1 because it is the only orbital diagram that has a completely filled outermost energy level. This orbital diagram shows the noble gas helium in the ground state.

Table 2.2 • Hydrogen's First Four Principal Energy Levels			
Principal Quantum Number (n)	Sublevels (Types of Orbitals Present)	Number of Orbitals Related to Sublevel	Total Number of Orbitals Related to Principal Energy Level (n^2)
1	s	1	1
2	s	1	4
	p	3	
3	s	1	9
	p	3	
	d	9	
4	s	1	16
	p	3	
	d	5	
	f	7	

There are a few simple rules for determining where ground state electrons will be in an atom.

Rule 1: Each electron occupies the lowest energy orbital available. This is known as the **aufbau principle.**

Rule 2: A maximum of two electrons can occupy a single atomic orbital, but only if the electrons have opposite spins. This is called the **Pauli exclusion principle.**

Rule 3: Single electrons with the same spin must occupy each equal-energy orbital before additional electrons with opposite spins can occupy the same orbitals. This is called **Hund's rule.**

The electron configurations of the first ten elements are listed in Table 2.3. An **electron configuration** is the arrangement of electrons in an atom, which is prescribed by the three rules mentioned above: the aufbau principle, the Pauli exclusion principle, and Hund's rule. Electron configurations can be represented by an orbital diagram, as shown in the table. An orbital diagram shows the electrons in each sublevel and also shows their spins. The electron configuration notation only shows the number of electrons in each sublevel.

✓ CHECK FOR UNDERSTANDING Which rule determines how many electrons can occupy a single orbital?

Table 2.3 • Orbital Diagrams and Electron Configurations for Elements in the First Two Periods							
Element	Atomic Number	Orbital Diagram					Electron Configuration
		1s	2s	$2p_x$	$2p_y$	$2p_z$	
Hydrogen	1	↑					$1s^1$
Helium	2	↑↓					$1s^2$
Lithium	3	↑↓	↑				$1s^2 2s^1$
Beryllium	4	↑↓	↑↓				$1s^2 2s^2$
Boron	5	↑↓	↑↓	↑			$1s^2 2s^2 2p^1$
Carbon	6	↑↓	↑↓	↑	↑		$1s^2 2s^2 2p^2$
Nitrogen	7	↑↓	↑↓	↑	↑	↑	$1s^2 2s^2 2p^3$
Oxygen	8	↑↓	↑↓	↑↓	↑	↑	$1s^2 2s^2 2p^4$
Fluorine	9	↑↓	↑↓	↑↓	↑↓	↑	$1s^2 2s^2 2p^5$
Neon	10	↑↓	↑↓	↑↓	↑↓	↑↓	$1s^2 2s^2 2p^6$

Table 2.4 • Electron Configurations for Elements in Period 3

Element	Atomic Number	Complete Electron Configuration	Abbreviated Electron Configuration
Sodium	11	$1s^2 2s^2 2p^6 3s^1$	[Ne]$3s^1$
Magnesium	12	$1s^2 2s^2 2p^6 3s^2$	[Ne]$3s^2$
Aluminum	13	$1s^2 2s^2 2p^6 3s^2 3p^1$	[Ne]$3s^2 3p^1$
Silicon	14	$1s^2 2s^2 2p^6 3s^2 3p^2$	[Ne]$3s^2 3p^2$
Phosphorus	15	$1s^2 2s^2 2p^6 3s^2 3p^3$	[Ne]$3s^2 3p^3$
Sulfur	16	$1s^2 2s^2 2p^6 3s^2 3p^4$	[Ne]$3s^2 3p^4$
Chlorine	17	$1s^2 2s^2 2p^6 3s^2 3p^5$	[Ne]$3s^2 3p^5$
Argon	18	$1s^2 2s^2 2p^6 3s^2 3p^6$	[Ne]$3s^2 3p^6$ or [Ar]

Valence Electrons

The electrons in an atom's highest energy level are called the **valence electrons** of that element. Because they lie on the outer edge of the atom, valence electrons determine the chemical properties of the element. Table 2.4 shows abbreviated electron configurations that utilize the noble-gas configurations. The noble gases have completely filled energy levels, so this method makes it easy to see the valence electrons of an atom. You can see in the table, for example, that sulfur has six valence electrons and chlorine has seven valence electrons.

✔ CHECK FOR UNDERSTANDING Why are abbreviated electron configurations useful?

Isotopes

The **atomic number** of an element is equal to the number of protons in the nucleus of an atom of that element. The atomic number uniquely identifies each element. For example, all carbon atoms have six protons in their nuclei and thus carbon's atomic number is 6. All oxygen atoms have eight protons and all uranium atoms have 92 protons. Not all atoms of an element are the same, however. It is possible for atoms to have the same number of protons but a different number of neutrons.

The different forms of an element are called **isotopes.** For example, carbon exists in three different forms (isotopes). The most common isotope of carbon accounts for 98.89 percent of all the carbon in the universe. This form has six protons (as all carbon does) and six neutrons. It is designated carbon-12, or C-12. The 12 represents the sum of the protons and neutrons in the nucleus. This number is called the **mass number.** Another isotope of carbon has six protons and eight neutrons. It is called carbon-14, or C-14. Another notation often used for isotopes is $^{14}_{6}C$. In this notation, the superscript (14) is the mass number and the subscript (6) is the atomic number. **Atomic mass** is the weighted average mass of all of the isotopes of an element. Figure 2.12 shows how to calculate chlorine's atomic mass, given the abundance of each isotope. The mass is given in atomic mass units (amu). An **atomic mass unit** is defined as one-twelfth the mass of a carbon-12 atom.

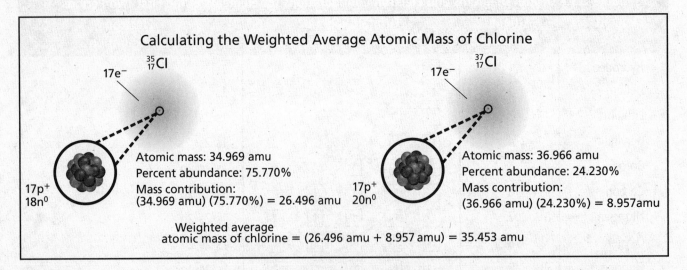

Calculating the Weighted Average Atomic Mass of Chlorine

$^{35}_{17}Cl$

17e⁻

17p⁺
18n⁰

Atomic mass: 34.969 amu
Percent abundance: 75.770%
Mass contribution:
(34.969 amu) (75.770%) = 26.496 amu

$^{37}_{17}Cl$

17e⁻

17p⁺
20n⁰

Atomic mass: 36.966 amu
Percent abundance: 24.230%
Mass contribution:
(36.966 amu) (24.230%) = 8.957 amu

Weighted average
atomic mass of chlorine = (26.496 amu + 8.957 amu) = 35.453 amu

Figure 2.12 This diagram shows the process for calculating the atomic mass of chlorine, given the abundances of the two chlorine isotopes. How would the procedure differ if there were more than two isotopes?

Example Problem 1

Given the data in the table below, calculate the average atomic mass for unknown element *X*. Assume that these are the only two isotopes of the element.

1 Analyze the Problem

Known:

^{80}X: $m = 191.57$ amu

   % abundance = 18.75%

^{79}X: $m = 198.21$ amu

   % abundance = 81.25%

Unknown:

atomic mass = ?

identity of element

Isotope	Mass (amu)	Percent Abundance
^{80}X	191.57	18.75%
^{79}X	198.21	81.25%

2 Solve for the Unknown

atomic mass = $(\text{mass}_{X\text{-}80})(\text{\% abundance}_{X\text{-}80}) + (\text{mass}_{X\text{-}79})(\text{\% abundance}_{X\text{-}79})$

= (191.57 amu)(0.1875) + (198.21 amu)(0.8125)   **Substitute** $m = 191.57$ amu; % abundance = 18.75%

= 35.92 amu + 161.05 amu = 196.97 amu $m = 198.21$ amu; % abundance = 81.25%

3 Evaluate the Answer

• **Are the units correct?** The units of the answer are in amu, as expected.

• **Does the answer make sense?** Yes, 196.97 amu is close to the more abundant isotope's mass.

Quick Review

20 Bohr's ideas were not fully accepted by other scientists because

(1) he was unable to describe the behavior of atoms with more than one electron

(2) his work had math errors in it

(3) his ideas were too strange to believe

(4) he claimed the farther an electron is from the nucleus, the more energy it has

21 According to Heisenberg, it is impossible to know precisely which of the following about an electron?

(1) its position and charge

(2) its energy and charge

(3) its position and energy

(4) its position, charge, and energy

22 Atomic orbitals are

(1) all spherical in shape

(2) only able to hold one electron

(3) areas in the nucleus of an atom

(4) regions where electrons exist

23 The aufbau principle states that

(1) electrons in the same orbital must have opposite spins

(2) electrons occupy the lowest energy level available

(3) electrons do not double up in a sublevel until there is no other space available

(4) two electrons fill an orbital

24 Electrons in the outermost energy level are called

(1) valence electrons

(2) neutral electrons

(3) positive electrons

(4) negative electrons

25 In oxygen-17 there are

(1) eight protons and nine neutrons

(2) nine protons and eight neutrons

(3) eight protons and eight neutrons

(4) eight protons and nine electrons

26 Which of the following has an atomic number of 10?

(1) $^{20}_{11}\text{Na}$ (3) $^{19}_{9}\text{F}$

(2) $^{11}_{10}\text{Ne}$ (4) $^{10}_{5}\text{B}$

Part A

1 An experiment in which alpha particles were used to bombard thin sheets of gold foil led to the conclusion that an atom is composed mostly of

(1) empty space, and has a small, negatively charged nucleus

(2) empty space, and has a small, positively charged nucleus

(3) a large, dense, positively charged nucleus

(4) a large, dense, negatively charged nucleus

2 The mass of a proton is approximately equal to the total mass of 1840

(1) electrons   (3) helium nuclei

(2) neutrons   (4) alpha particles

3 The modern model of the atom shows that electrons are

(1) orbiting the nucleus in fixed paths

(2) found in regions called orbitals

(3) combined with neutrons in the nucleus

(4) located in a solid sphere covering the nucleus

4 What is the maximum number of electrons that can occupy the fourth principal energy level of an atom?

(1) 6   (3) 18

(2) 8   (4) 32

5 Which electron configuration does *not* represent an atom in the ground state?

(1) $1s^2 2s^2 2p^5 3s^1$

(2) $1s^2 2s^2 2p^6 3s^1$

(3) $1s^2 2s^2 2p^6 3s^2$

(4) $1s^2 2s^2 2p^6 3s^2 3p^1$

6 All the isotopes of a given atom have

(1) the same mass number and the same atomic number

(2) the same mass number but different atomic numbers

(3) different mass numbers but the same atomic number

(4) different mass numbers and different atomic numbers

7 Compared to a sodium atom in the ground state, a sodium atom in the excited state must have

(1) a greater number of electrons

(2) a smaller number of electrons

(3) an electron with greater energy

(4) an electron with less energy

Part B–1

8 What is the structure of a krypton-85 atom?

(1) 49 electrons, 49 protons, and 85 neutrons

(2) 49 electrons, 49 protons, and 49 neutrons

(3) 36 electrons, 36 protons, and 85 neutrons

(4) 36 electrons, 36 protons, and 49 neutrons

9 The atomic mass unit is defined as exactly $\frac{1}{12}$ the mass of an atom of

(1) $^{12}_{6}C$ (3) $^{24}_{12}Mg$

(2) $^{14}_{6}C$ (4) $^{26}_{12}Mg$

10 The light produced by signs using neon gas results from electrons that are

(1) moving from a higher to a lower principal energy level

(2) moving from a lower to a higher principal energy level

(3) being lost by the neon atoms

(4) being gained by the neon atoms

11 In which principal energy level are the valence electrons of the elements in Period 2 found?

(1) 1   (3) 3

(2) 2   (4) 4

12 What is the total number of valence electrons in an atom of boron in the ground state?

(1) 1 (3) 3

(2) 7 (4) 5

13 Which particles are isotopes of each other?

(1) ^2_1X and ^3_1X (3) $_1X$ and ^4_2X

(2) ^2_1X and ^3_2X (4) ^3_1X and ^3_2X

14 The elements calcium and strontium have similar chemical properties because they both have the same

(1) atomic number

(2) mass number

(3) number of valence electrons

(4) number of completely filled sublevels

15 Hydrogen has three isotopes with mass numbers of 1, 2, and 3 and has an average atomic mass of 1.00794 atomic mass units. This information indicates that

(1) equal numbers of each isotope are present

(2) more isotopes have a mass number of 2 or 3 than of 1

(3) more isotopes have a mass number of 1 than of 2 or 3

(4) isotopes have only a mass number of 1

16 What is the maximum number of electrons in an orbital of any atom?

(1) 1 (3) 6

(2) 2 (4) 10

Part B–2

Base your answers to questions 17 through 19 on the information and diagram below.

One model of the atom states that atoms are tiny particles composed of a uniform mixture of positive and negative charges. Scientists conducted an experiment where alpha particles were aimed at a thin layer of gold atoms. Most of the alpha particles passed directly through the gold atoms. A few alpha particles were deflected from their straight-line paths. An illustration of the experiment is shown below.

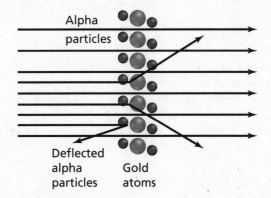

17 Most of the alpha particles passed directly through the gold atoms undisturbed. What does this evidence suggest about the structure of the gold atoms?

18 A few of the alpha particles were deflected. What does this evidence suggest about the structure of the gold atoms?

19 How should the original model be revised based on the results of this experiment?

Base your answers to questions 20 and 21 on the information and diagram below.

In the modern model of the atom, each atom is composed of three major subatomic (or fundamental) particles.

20 Name the subatomic particles contained in the nucleus of the atom.

21 State the charge associated with each type of subatomic particle contained in the nucleus of the atom.

Base your answers to the questions 22 through 24 on the information and data table below.

Electron affinity is defined as the energy released when an atom and an electron react to form a negative ion. The data for Group 1 elements are presented below.

Element	Atomic Number	Electron Affinity in kJ/mol
Cs	55	45.5
H	1	72.8
K	19	46.4
Li	3	59.8
Na	11	52.9
Rb	37	?

22 Label the y-axis *Electron Affinity* and choose an appropriate scale. Label the x-axis *Atomic Number* and choose an appropriate scale.

23 Plot the data from the data table and connect the points with straight lines.

24 Using your graph, estimate the electron affinity of rubidium, in kilojoules/mole.

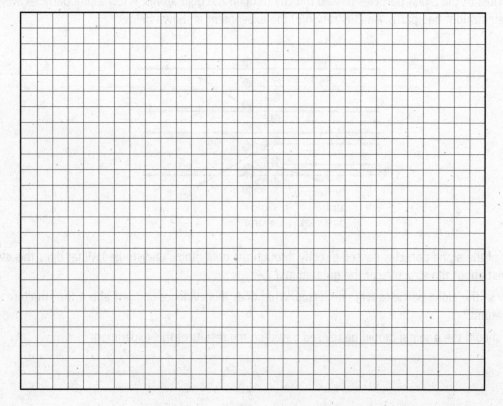

VOCABULARY

alkali metals	halogen	nonmetals
alkaline earth metals	ion	period
allotropes	ionization energy	periodic law
chemical property	metal	physical property
electronegativity	metalloid	transition metal
group	noble gas	

When you first look at the periodic table of elements, it may appear confusing. There are columns and rows like you find in many tables, but they are not all the same size. There is even a double row that appears below the main body of the table. How did the table come to be shaped like this?

Mendeleev and the Periodic Law

In the mid 1800s, a Russian scientist named Dmitri Mendeleev recognized that certain properties of elements repeat when elements are arranged by increasing atomic mass.

Properties of Elements

Physical properties can be used to identify an element. A **physical property** is a characteristic that can be observed or measured without changing a sample's composition. Copper, for example, has a characteristic color and electric conductivity that are different from those of any other element. Other examples of physical properties include density, hardness, color, melting point, and boiling point. Ductility is the property describing how easily a material can be drawn into a thin wire. Malleability is the property describing how readily a material can be pounded into thin sheets. Ductility and malleability allow metals, such as copper, to be made into many shapes and forms, as shown in Figure 3.1. Another physical property is solubility, which is the ability of a substance to dissolve in a liquid.

Elements also can be identified by how they react with each other chemically. A **chemical property** is the ability of a substance to combine with or change into one or more other substances. Sodium, for example, reacts violently with water, but magnesium hardly reacts with water at all.

Figure 3.1 Physical properties of metals, such as ductility and malleability, allow metals to be shaped into wire, coins, and tools.

Hydrogen is a flammable gas, reacting readily with oxygen in the air, but helium does not burn. Chemical properties can be used to identify the elements.

Every element has its own unique physical and chemical properties. Keep in mind, however, that the properties of an element may be different under different conditions. For example, at 1085°C, solid copper melts to become liquid copper. Obviously, some of the properties of liquid copper are different from the properties of solid copper. Nonetheless, these properties can be used to identify whether a given sample is copper.

☑ **CHECK FOR UNDERSTANDING** Name five examples of physical properties.

Table 3.1 • An Early Mendeleev Table

	I	II	III	IV	V	VI	VII	VIII		
I	H									
II	Li	Be	B	C	N	O	F			
III	Na	Mg	Al	Si	P	S	Cl			
IV	K	Ca	? = 44	Ti	V	Cr	Mn	Fe	Co	Ni
V	Cu	Zn	? = 68	? = 72	As	Se	Br			
VI	Rb	Sr	Yt	Zr	Nb	Mo	? = 100	Ru	Rh	Pd
VII	Ag	Cd	In	Sn	Sb	Te	J			
VIII	Cs	Ba	Di	Ce						
IX										
X			Er	La	Ta	W		Os	Ir	Pt
XI	Au	Hg	Tl	Pb	Bi					
XII				Th		U				

Mendeleev's Table

Mendeleev knew the properties of many elements. For example, fluorine (F), chlorine (Cl), and bromine (Br), react with metals to form salt. He decided to put these elements in the same column of his periodic table. When he did this he noticed that other elements also lined up according to their properties, as shown in Table 3.1. Hydrogen (H), lithium (Li), and sodium (Na) all react in a similar way and they all are in the same column of his table.

When an element did not fit where he thought it should be, Mendeleev left a gap in the table and assumed the gap would be occupied by an element that had not yet been discovered. In fact, Mendeleev was able to accurately predict the properties of several missing elements. For example, when germanium was discovered, its properties almost exactly matched his predictions for the missing element in column IV.

However, Mendeleev's table was not completely correct in its placement of some of the elements and many new elements were discovered in the following years. English chemist Henry Moseley was able to reinterpret the table in terms of atomic number, rather than atomic mass. Recall that the atomic number is the number of protons in an atom. The atomic number is different for each element and therefore, can be used to identify an element. For example, every carbon atom has six protons in its nucleus, while an oxygen atom always has eight protons, and a uranium atom has 92 protons. The **periodic law** states that when elements are arranged by increasing atomic number, there is a periodic repetition of their chemical and physical properties. The periodic law can be used to predict the properties of elements based on their positions in the periodic table. Figure 3.2 shows the modern version of the periodic table.

✓ **CHECK FOR UNDERSTANDING** How was Mendeleev's periodic table rearranged to correctly place the elements?

Isotopes and Atomic Mass

The periodic table gives the atomic mass of each element. Why aren't the atomic masses whole numbers? Recall that isotopes of an element have the same number of protons, but different numbers of neutrons. Each element can have more than one isotope. In section 2, you learned that carbon has three different naturally occurring isotopes. Each isotope has six protons but they have different numbers of neutrons. If you take the weighted average of the masses for carbon's isotopes, the result is an atomic mass of 12.011. No single carbon atom has this mass, but if we take a sample of many atoms, this is the average mass that would be measured.

Note that the chemical properties of isotopes of an element are the same because their chemical properties depend on how tightly the valence electrons are held by the nucleus. For example, C-12 and C-14 have the same positive charge in the nucleus, so the valence electrons behave similarly, and the isotopes are virtually identical in their chemical properties.

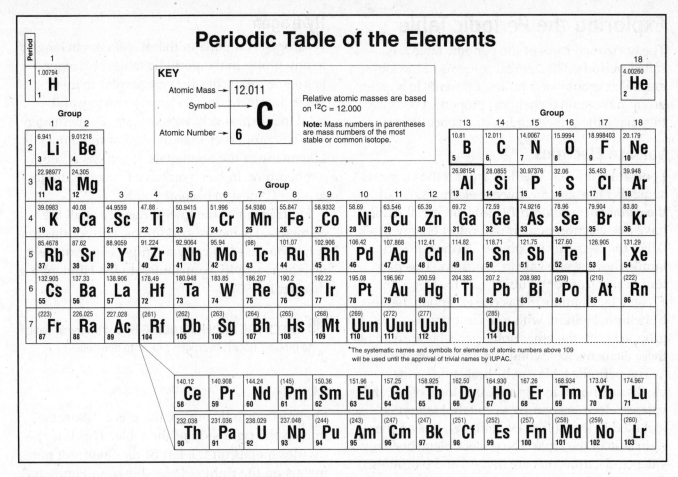

Periodic Table of the Elements

KEY

Atomic Mass → 12.011
Symbol → **C**
Atomic Number → 6

Relative atomic masses are based on $^{12}C = 12.000$

Note: Mass numbers in parentheses are mass numbers of the most stable or common isotope.

*The systematic names and symbols for elements of atomic numbers above 109 will be used until the approval of trivial names by IUPAC.

Figure 3.2 The modern periodic table arranges the elements by increasing atomic number.

It also is possible for an element to have different forms that have different properties. **Allotropes** are forms of an element in the same physical state (solid, liquid, or gas) that have different structures or properties. Two allotropes of solid carbon are diamond and graphite. Diamond is one of the hardest materials known, and graphite has flat layers that can slide apart easily. When a pencil is used to write, it allows layers of carbon to slide from the pencil onto the paper to produce writing.

✓ CHECK FOR UNDERSTANDING How do the isotopes of an element differ?

Quick Review

1 Elements in the columns of Mendeleev's table have similar
   (1) atomic masses
   (2) chemical properties
   (3) numbers of neutrons
   (4) atomic numbers

2 All of the following are examples of a physical property *except*
   (1) malleability   (3) flammability
   (2) solubility   (4) hardness

3 Fluorine-19 has
   (1) 19 protons
   (2) 19 neutrons
   (3) 9 protons
   (4) 9 neutrons

4 An atom with 32 protons and 28 neutrons is
   (1) germanium-60
   (2) germanium-32
   (3) germanium-28
   (4) germanium-30

5 State the periodic law.

6 What predictions did Mendeleev make based on his periodic table?

7 Explain the difference between an isotope and an allotrope.

Exploring the Periodic Table

The horizontal rows of the periodic table are called **periods**. The vertical columns of the table are called **groups** or families. Elements in a given group have similar chemical properties because they have the same number of valence electrons.

Valence Electrons

Look at Figure 3.3. The dots around the elements' symbols represent the valence electrons. All of the elements in column 1 (the alkali metal family) have one electron in their outermost energy level. All of the elements in column 17 (the halogen family) have seven valence electrons. This pattern also is true for columns 1, 2, 13, 14, 15, 16, 17, and 18. Column 18 has one exception, namely, helium. Helium, with two electrons, is grouped with the other noble gases because all of these elements have complete outer energy levels.

The periodic table can be broken up into blocks, as shown in Figure 3.4. In the s block, the valence electrons occupy s orbitals. Helium is included in the s block even though it is on the right side of the table. The p block elements have valence electrons that are in the s and p orbitals. The p block has six groups because the p orbitals can hold six electrons. For similar reasons, the d block spans ten groups and the f block spans 14 groups. In this way, valence electrons help to explain the organization of the periodic table.

✓ CHECK FOR UNDERSTANDING How many valence electrons do the halogens have?

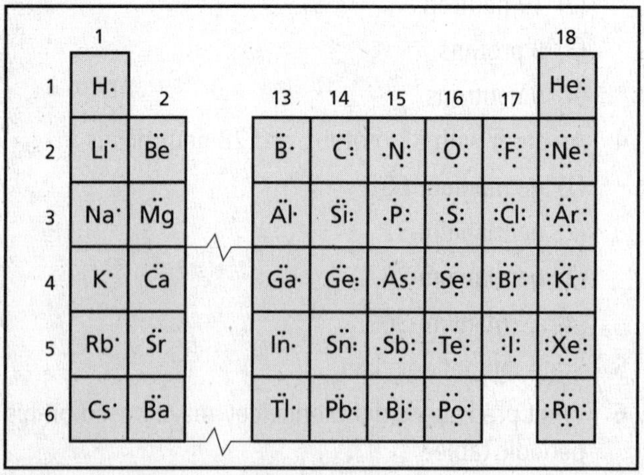

Figure 3.3 Except for helium, elements in the same column of the periodic table have the same number of valence electrons.

Hydrogen

Hydrogen is unique in that it does not belong to any group in the periodic table. Hydrogen has some properties that are similar to metals. For example, hydrogen is very reactive and combines explosively with oxygen. But hydrogen also has properties that are similar to nonmetals. Like many of the nonmetals, it is a gas at room temperature. In fact, you have to cool hydrogen to −259°C for it to become solid.

Hydrogen has the lowest density of all the elements at standard conditions, and for this reason it was used in early airships. Unfortunately, its high reactivity contributed to the Hindenburg disaster in 1937.

✓ CHECK FOR UNDERSTANDING How is hydrogen similar to metals? How is hydrogen similar to nonmetals?

Metals

On most periodic tables, there is a "staircase" line on the right side of the table. This line divides metals on the left of the line from nonmetals on the right side as shown in Figure 3.2, on page 39. **Metals** are elements that generally are solid at room temperature, shiny, good conductors of heat and electricity, malleable, and ductile. Some familiar examples of metals include silver, iron, gold, aluminum, lithium, potassium, and copper. Other less familiar examples of metals include sodium, calcium, and mercury, which is the only metal that is a liquid at room temperature. Notice that hydrogen, even though it does appear on the left side of the table, is not considered a metal.

✓ CHECK FOR UNDERSTANDING What properties are common among metals?

Elements in the first column of the periodic table, except for hydrogen, are called **alkali metals**. These elements are the most reactive metals. Notice in Figure 3.5 that they all have a single valence electron, so they form ions with a 1+ charge. They are so reactive that they are not found isolated in nature. The alkali metals tend to be soft and are easily cut. The cut surface is very shiny, but turns dull as the metal reacts with oxygen.

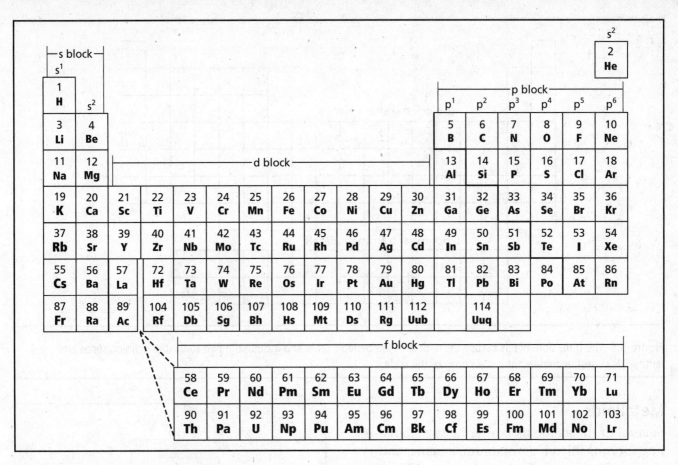

Figure 3.4 The periodic table can be organized into the s, p, d, and f blocks.

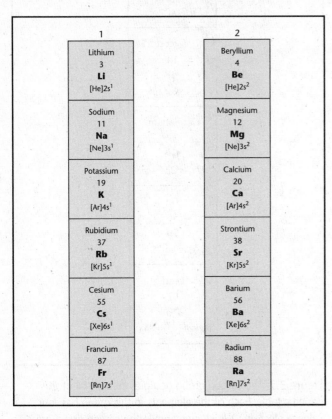

Figure 3.5 The alkali metals are in column 1. The alkaline earth metals are in column 2.

The elements in the second column of the periodic table are called **alkaline earth metals**. They are less reactive and harder than the alkali metals. Figure 3.5 shows that they each have two valance electrons, so they form ions with a 2+ charge. The alkaline earth metals readily react with nonmetals to form compounds. Like the alkali metals, they are solid at room temperature and also form an oxide coating when exposed to air.

Columns 3–12 of the periodic table contain elements called **transition metals**. These elements, shown in Figure 3.6 on page 42, have somewhat less predictable properties than the elements at either end of the table. The two rows at the bottom of the table are included in the transition metals. These inner transition metals include the lanthanide series and the actinide series. Notice that the lanthanide series elements fit between element 57 (lanthanum) and 72 (hafnium) while the actinide series fits between element 89 (actinium) and 104 (rutherfordium).

✓ **CHECK FOR UNDERSTANDING** Where are the transition metals located in the periodic table?

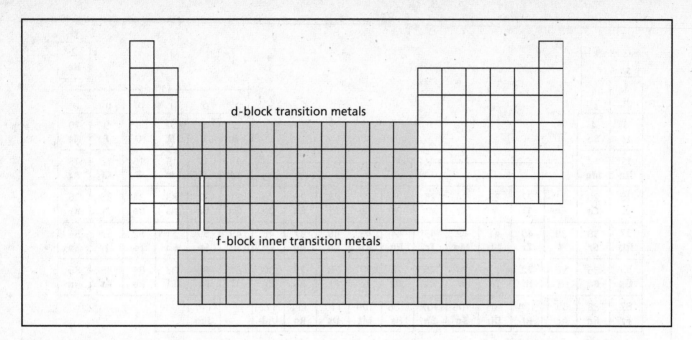

Figure 3.6 The transition metals occupy the middle of the periodic table and include the two rows (the actinide series and lanthanide series) underneath the main body of the table.

Metalloids

Several of the elements bordering the staircase line (boron, silicon, germanium, arsenic, antimony, tellurium) in Figure 3.2 on page 39 are called metalloids. **Metalloids** are elements that have physical and chemical properties of both metals and nonmetals. For example, they can conduct electricity, but not as well as metals and not as poorly as nonmetals. Sometimes metalloids are called semiconductors because of their in-between nature. The metalloids silicon and germanium are used to make microchips used in electronic devices, such as computers and calculators.

 **CHECK FOR UNDERSTANDING** Why are metalloids sometimes called semiconductors?

Nonmetals

In Figure 3.2 on page 39 the nonmetals are located to the right of the metalloids. **Nonmetals** are typically gases or dull, brittle solids that are poor conductors of heat and electricity. Examples include carbon, oxygen, sulfur, and chlorine. Bromine is the only nonmetal that is a liquid at room temperature.

The carbon group shown in Figure 3.7 has only one nonmetal—carbon. Notice that carbon is unique in that it is the only nonmetal with

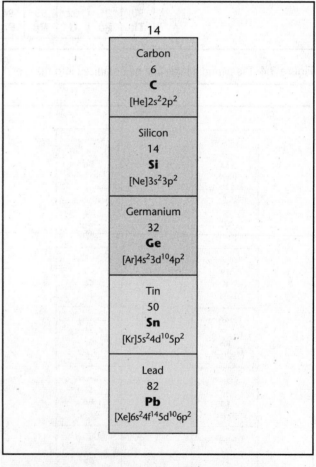

14

| Carbon |
| 6 |
| **C** |
| $[He]2s^22p^2$ |

| Silicon |
| 14 |
| **Si** |
| $[Ne]3s^23p^2$ |

| Germanium |
| 32 |
| **Ge** |
| $[Ar]4s^23d^{10}4p^2$ |

| Tin |
| 50 |
| **Sn** |
| $[Kr]5s^24d^{10}5p^2$ |

| Lead |
| 82 |
| **Pb** |
| $[Xe]6s^24f^{14}5d^{10}6p^2$ |

Figure 3.7 The carbon group occupies column 14 of the periodic table. Each of the elements in this group has four valence electrons. Which elements in the carbon group are metalloids?

four valence electrons. Carbon can form many different compounds, and in particular, it can form long chains and very large compounds. These properties explain why carbon is the basis of most compounds found in living cells. The study of the chemistry of carbon compounds found in living things is called organic chemistry.

Figure 3.8 shows the elements in the nitrogen group and the oxygen group (columns 15 and 16). In the nitrogen group the nonmetals are nitrogen and phosphorus, while the oxygen group contains the nonmetals oxygen, sulfur, and selenium. Both nitrogen and phosphorus are found in important organic compounds. The air you breathe consists of about 78 percent nitrogen (N_2) and 21 percent oxygen (O_2). Most living things need oxygen in order to survive. Oxygen is the most abundant element in Earth's crust, in part because it reacts with so many different elements. In combustion, something burns by reacting with oxygen. Because oxygen has six valence electrons, it readily accepts electrons to form an ion with a 2– charge. This is the basis

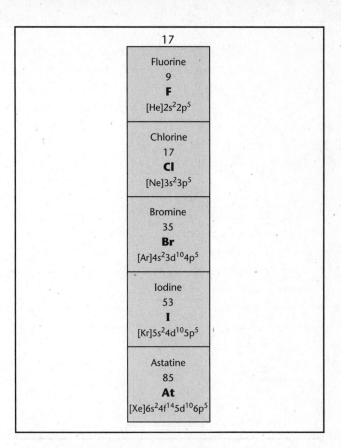

Figure 3.9 The halogens occupy column 17 of the periodic table. What do these elements have in common?

for many reactions, such as when a substance burns (combustion) or rusts (corrosion).

Figure 3.9 shows the elements in column 17, which are highly reactive elements called **halogens** or "salt formers". Astatine sometimes is not considered part of this group because it is radioactive and changes into another element almost instantly, so its chemical properties are very difficult to determine. The halogens are highly reactive and are used in many industrial applications. Chlorine is found in common table salt, and fluorine is added to water supplies to help prevent tooth decay.

The last column (column 18) of the periodic table, shown in Figure 3.10 on page 44, contains the **noble gases**. These elements are unreactive and sometimes are called inert gases. These gaseous elements are very stable because their outer energy sublevels are filled. The noble gases are nonflammable and are used in some situations for extinguishing fires. Helium has a very low density, which is why it commonly is used in toy balloons, as well as in large airships.

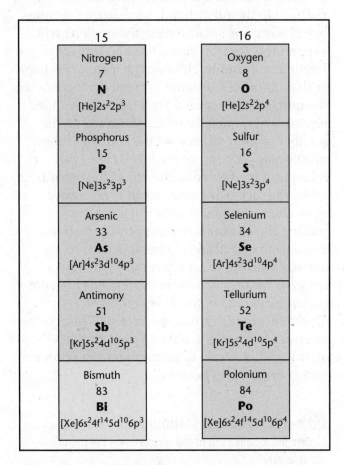

Figure 3.8 The nitrogen and oxygen groups occupy columns 15 and 16 of the periodic table.

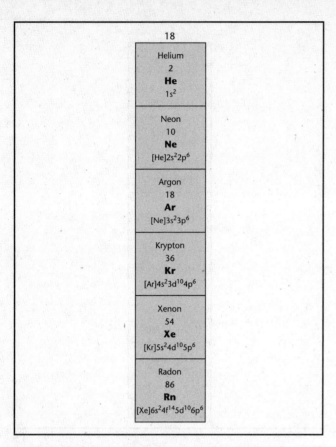

18
Helium 2 **He** $1s^2$
Neon 10 **Ne** $[He]2s^22p^6$
Argon 18 **Ar** $[Ne]3s^23p^6$
Krypton 36 **Kr** $[Ar]4s^23d^{10}4p^6$
Xenon 54 **Xe** $[Kr]5s^24d^{10}5p^6$
Radon 86 **Rn** $[Xe]6s^24f^{14}5d^{10}6p^6$

Figure 3.10 The noble gases in column 18 are the least reactive elements in the periodic table.

Quick Review

8 Elements with one valence electron are

(1) inert gases

(2) halogens

(3) alkali metals

(4) lanthanides

9 Elements with seven valence electrons are

(1) inert gases

(2) halogens

(3) alkali metals

(4) lanthanides

10 Which of the following is considered a metalloid?

(1) carbon

(2) calcium

(3) sulfur

(4) silicon

11 Sketch a simplified version of the periodic table and indicate the locations of groups, periods, metals, nonmetals, and metalloids.

Periodic Trends

There are many trends that can be observed in the properties of elements, both within a family and across the periods of the periodic table. These trends include atomic radius, ionic radius, ionization energy, and electronegativity.

Atomic Radius

In a family, moving down the column the atoms get larger. For example, hydrogen is the smallest atom in Group 1 and francium is the largest in Group 1. As you move across a period from left to right, generally the atoms get smaller. For example, by looking at Figure 3.11 you can observe that sodium is the largest atom in Period 3 and argon is the smallest.

There are two counteracting factors that determine the trends in atomic radius. As the number of protons increases from one element to another, the strength of the positive charge on the nucleus increases. Increasing the positive charge pulls the surrounding electrons further in toward the nucleus, decreasing the atom's radius. On the other hand, increasing the number of electrons surrounding the nucleus will expand the electron cloud, making the atom larger. For example, chlorine (element 17) is larger than fluorine (element 9) due to the increase in the number of electrons. The effect of the added electrons overrides the effect of increasing the number of protons because the added electrons must occupy a new energy level. However, when moving horizontally across the periodic table, the increasing number of protons overrides the increasing number of electrons, pulling the electrons in closer to the nucleus. Because the electrons are being added to an already existing energy level, they do not increase the atomic radius as much as if a completely new energy level were being filled. Thus, the atomic radius tends to decrease moving from left to right across a period, while atomic radius tends to increase moving down a group from top to bottom.

✓ **CHECK FOR UNDERSTANDING** What is one reason why the atomic radii of the elements on the periodic table vary?

Strategies for Success

Atoms of which of the following elements have the smallest atomic radius? Refer to the Properties of Selected Elements Regents Reference Table.

(1) silicon   (3) sulfur

(2) phosphorus   (4) carbon

(1) Silicon has an atomic radius of 1.32×10^{-10} m.

(2) Phosphorus has an atomic radius of 1.28×10^{-10} m.

(3) Sulfur has an atomic radius of 1.27×10^{-10} m.

(4) Chlorine has an atomic radius of 0.97×10^{-10} m.

After considering all the options, the correct answer is number 4 because chlorine has the smallest atomic radius out of the four choices.

Ionic Radius

When an atom loses or gains electrons, it becomes an ion. An **ion** is defined as an atom or group of atoms that gain or lose electrons to carry a positive or negative charge. There also are trends in the periodic table in the sizes of ions that elements form.

The vertical trend as you move down a group from top to bottom is the same as for the atomic radii of neutral atoms; that is, the ions are larger the farther down the column you go.

The horizontal trend for metals, which form positive ions, shows a decrease in size from left to right across the first column of the table. Nonmetals form negative ions, and their sizes also decrease from left to right moving across the columns on the right side of the table. The trends of ionic radii are shown in Figure 3.12 on page 46.

☑ **CHECK FOR UNDERSTANDING** How would you describe how atoms that tend to form negative ions hold on to their electrons?

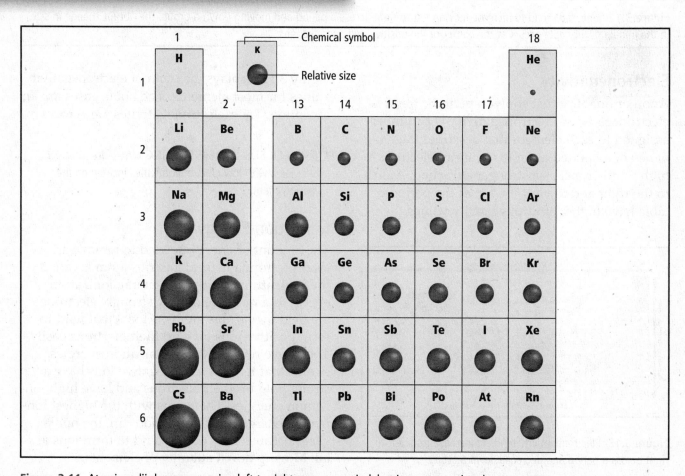

Figure 3.11 Atomic radii decrease moving left to right across a period, but increase moving down a group.

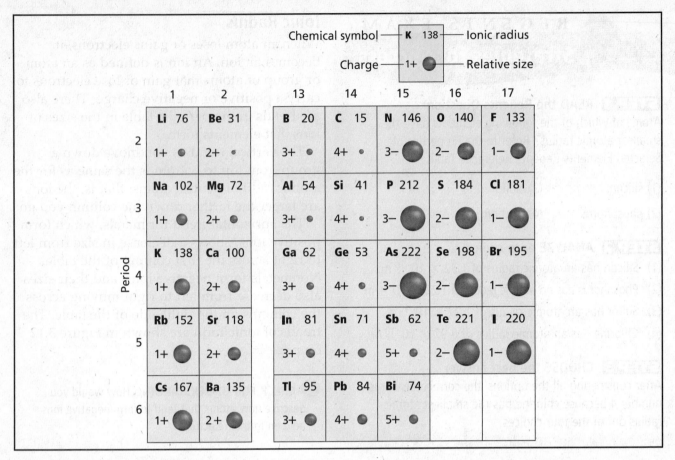

Figure 3.12 Ionic radii tend to increase moving left to right across a period and moving down a group. The abrupt change in size in the middle of the table occurs at the border of the positive and negative ions.

Electronegativity

Another quantity that shows a periodic trend is electronegativity. **Electronegativity** is a number assigned to each element that describes the tendency of a bonded atom to attract an electron. A high number means a stronger attraction. Atoms to the right and toward the top of the periodic table have higher electronegativity values.

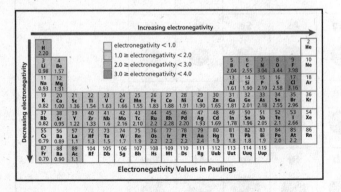

Figure 3.13 Electronegativity tends to increase from left to right across a period and decrease down a group.

Figure 3.13 displays the trend of electronegativity values for most elements. The noble gases are an exception. Their electronegativites are zero.

✓ **CHECK FOR UNDERSTANDING** Where are most elements with low electronegativities located on the periodic table?

Ionization Energy

The amount of energy needed to remove an electron from a neutral gaseous atom is called the **ionization energy**. In general, ionization energy is a measure of how strongly electrons are held by various atoms. Atoms that tend to form positive ions give up their electrons easily. They have relatively low ionization energies. Atoms that tend to form negative ions have a strong hold on their electrons and have high ionization energies. The atoms with the highest ionization energies in their periods are the noble gases because they do not tend to form ions at all. Moving down a family of elements,

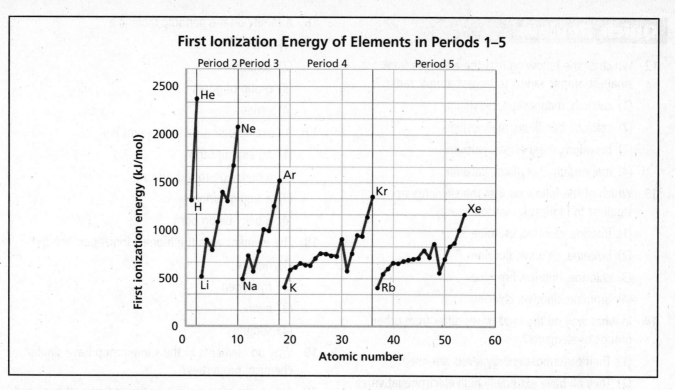

First Ionization Energy of Elements in Periods 1–5

Figure 3.14 The graph shows the first ionization energies for the first 55 elements. What is the periodic trend in ionization energy moving across a period?

the ionization energy decreases. This is because the electrons are farther from the nucleus in larger atoms and are not held as tightly. Moving across a period, the ionization energy generally increases because the added positive charge in the nucleus has a stronger attraction for the negative electrons. The graph in Figure 3.14 is repre-

sentative of the first ionization energies for the elements in Periods 1 through 5.

✓ **CHECK FOR UNDERSTANDING** What type of trend in ionization energy do you notice within the groups on the periodic table?

Example Problem 1

The trend along a period is that the first ionization energy increases with each successive element. Yet, the element gallium has a lower ionization energy level than zinc. Explain why.

1 Analyze the Problem

- Examine the electron configuration of both gallium and zinc.

Element	1s	2s	2p	3s	3p	3d	4s	4p
Zinc	2	2	6	2	6	10	2	
Gallium	2	2	6	2	6	10	2	1

2 Explain

Zinc's highest energy electron is in the 4s orbital, whereas gallium's highest energy electron is in an unfilled 4p orbital. The 4p orbital is higher in energy than the 4s orbital, so an electron in 4p is not as tightly held by the nucleus and can therefore be removed with less energy. Also, it is generally more difficult to remove an electron from a (with paired electrons) full orbital than from an unfilled orbital (with a single electron). Gallium has an unpaired 4p electron, so it has a lower first ionization energy.

3 Evaluate the Answer

- **Does the answer make sense?** Yes, electron configurations help to explain trends in first ionization energy.

12 Which of the following lists the elements from smallest atomic radius to largest atomic radius?

(1) calcium, magnesium, beryllium

(2) calcium, beryllium, magnesium

(3) beryllium, magnesium, calcium

(4) magnesium, beryllium, calcium

13 Which of the following lists the elements from smallest to highest ionization energy?

(1) fluorine, chlorine, bromine

(2) bromine, chlorine, fluorine

(3) chlorine, fluorine, bromine

(4) bromine, fluorine, chlorine

14 In what way do the inert gases differ from other groups of elements?

(1) Their outermost energy levels are filled.

(2) They all have extremely high electronegativities.

(3) They all have very high boiling points.

(4) They all have electronegativities equal to zero.

15 A period on the periodic table is a

(1) row

(2) column

(3) chemical family

(4) group

16 A family on the periodic table is a

(1) row

(2) column

(3) group of gases

(4) series

17 An example of a periodic event is

(1) an airplane trip

(2) a merry-go-round ride

(3) a tree growing

(4) a baby being born

18 The element with the highest ionization energy is

(1) helium

(2) hydrogen

(3) neon

(4) sodium

19 Why do elements in the same group have similar chemical properties?

20 A gaseous element is a poor conductor of heat and electricity and is extremely nonreactive. Is the element a metal, a nonmetal, or a metalloid? Where would the element be on the periodic table?

Part A

1 The elements from which two groups of the periodic table are most similar in their chemical properties?

  (1) 1 and 2
  (2) 1 and 17
  (3) 2 and 17
  (4) 17 and 18

2 Elements in the modern periodic table are arranged according to their

  (1) atomic number
  (2) atomic mass
  (3) relative activity
  (4) relative size

3 As elements of Group 15 of the periodic table are considered in order from top to bottom, the metallic character of the atoms of each successive element generally

  (1) decreases
  (2) increases
  (3) remains the same

4 As the elements in Group 15 are considered in order of increasing atomic number, which sequence in properties occurs?

  (1) nonmetal → metalloid → metal
  (2) metalloid → metal → nonmetal
  (3) metal → metalloid → nonmetal
  (4) metal → nonmetal → metalloid

5 Which statement is true about the properties of the elements in any one period of the periodic table?

  (1) They are determined by the number of neutrons.
  (2) They are determined by the number of electrons in the first principal energy level.
  (3) They change in a generally systematic manner.
  (4) They change in a random, unpredictable manner.

6 Which statement describes the elements in Period 3?

  (1) Each successive element has a greater atomic radius.
  (2) Each successive element has a lower electronegativity.
  (3) All elements have similar chemical properties.
  (4) All elements have valence electrons in the same principal energy level.

7 Which trends appear as the elements in Period 3 are considered from left to right?

  (1) Metallic character decreases, and electronegativity decreases.
  (2) Metallic character decreases, and electronegativity increases.
  (3) Metallic character increases, and electronegativity decreases.
  (4) Metallic character increases, and electronegativity increases.

8 As the atoms in Period 3 are considered from left to right, the atoms generally show

  (1) an increase in radius and an increase in ionization energy
  (2) an increase in radius and a decrease in ionization energy
  (3) a decrease in radius and an increase in ionization energy
  (4) a decrease in radius and a decrease in ionization energy

9 In Period 3, from left to right in order, each successive element will

  (1) decrease in electronegativity
  (2) decrease in atomic mass
  (3) increase in number of protons
  (4) increase in metallic character

10 Which element exhibits both metallic and non-metallic properties?

  (1) bismuth   (3) silver
  (2) helium   (4) tellurium

Part B–1

11 Which elements are both classified as metalloids?

(1) germanium and arsenic

(2) bismuth and polonium

(3) boron and carbon

(4) silicon and phosphorus

12 Given the reactions

$2X(s) + 2H_2O(l) \rightarrow 2X^+(aq) + 2OH^-(aq) + H_2(g)$

$2Y(s) + 2H_2O(l) \rightarrow 2Y^+(aq) + 2OH^-(aq) + H_2(g)$

the unknowns, X and Y, are most likely

(1) metallic elements in the same group

(2) metallic elements in the same period

(3) nonmetallic elements in the same group

(4) nonmetallic elements in the same period

13 In which two atoms do both nuclides contain the same number of neutrons?

(1) $^{20}_{10}Ne$ and $^{40}_{18}Ar$ (3) $^{24}_{12}Mg$ and $^{26}_{12}Mg$

(2) $^{65}_{29}Cu$ and $^{65}_{30}Zn$ (4) $^{14}_{6}C$ and $^{16}_{8}O$

14 Which noble gas has the highest first ionization energy?

(1) radon   (3) neon

(2) krypton   (4) helium

15 Which of these metals loses electrons most readily?

(1) calcium   (3) potassium

(2) magnesium   (4) sodium

16 In which area of the periodic table are the elements with the strongest nonmetallic properties located?

(1) lower left   (3) lower right

(2) upper left   (4) upper right

Part B–2

17 Based on the periodic table, explain why magnesium and calcium have similar chemical properties.

18 In the 19th century, Dmitri Mendeleev predicted the existence of a then unknown element X with a mass of 72. He also predicted that this element would have properties similar to both metals and nonmetals. On the modern periodic table, what is the group number and period number of element X?

19 Explain why elements in the modern periodic table are arranged according to atomic number rather than atomic mass.

20 Which group of the periodic table contains atoms with a stable outer electron configuration?

Part C

21 Use first ionization energies and the number of valence electrons to explain why Group 2 elements are less reactive than Group 1 elements.

22 As a neutral sulfur atom gains two electrons, what happens to the radius of the atom?

23 After a neutral sulfur atom gains two electrons, what is the resulting charge of the ion?

Base your answers to questions 23 and 24 on the information below.

Given: Samples of sodium, argon, astatine, and rubidium

24 Which two of the given elements have the most similar chemical properties?

25 Explain your answer in terms of the periodic table of elements.

4 Bonding

anion

cation

covalent bond

delocalized electrons

electron-dot structure

electron sea model

ionic bond

Lewis structure

metallic bond

molecule

octet rule

polar covalent

polyatomic ion

Understanding the types of bonds within a substance will help you see why each compound has its own unique properties that distinguish it from all others. These properties include melting point, boiling point, hardness, malleability, solubility, and conductivity. The interactions (bonds) between ions, atoms, or molecules determine what each of these properties are for a substance.

Bonding and Physical Properties

All matter is made up of elements. Most matter, however, is not composed of individual, isolated atoms. In fact, most of the world around us is made of compounds that contain atoms bonded to each other. In some cases, there are relatively few atoms making up a given substance. A molecule of water, for example, has only three atoms. One type of sugar is glucose, which has the formula $C_6H_{12}O_6$. This relatively simple molecule has 24 atoms. Other substances, such as DNA, (deoxyribonucleic acid), can have more than a billion atoms bonded. Figure 4.1 shows representations of glucose and DNA molecules.

The nature of the bonds holding the atoms together has a tremendous effect on the properties and uses of each compound. Most compounds fit in one of two major categories: ionic compounds or molecular compounds.

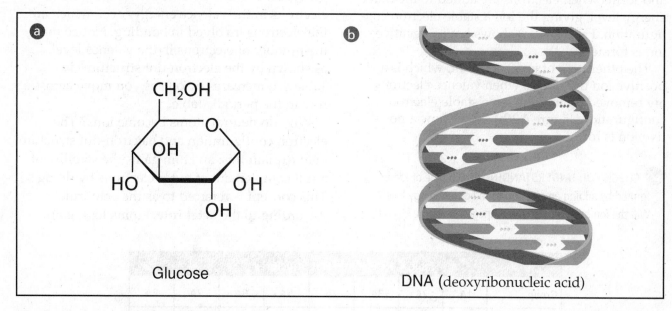

Glucose

DNA (deoxyribonucleic acid)

Figure 4.1 (a) Carbon, oxygen, and hydrogen bond together in the compound glucose. (b) In human DNA, more than a billion atoms bond together in a double-helix structure.

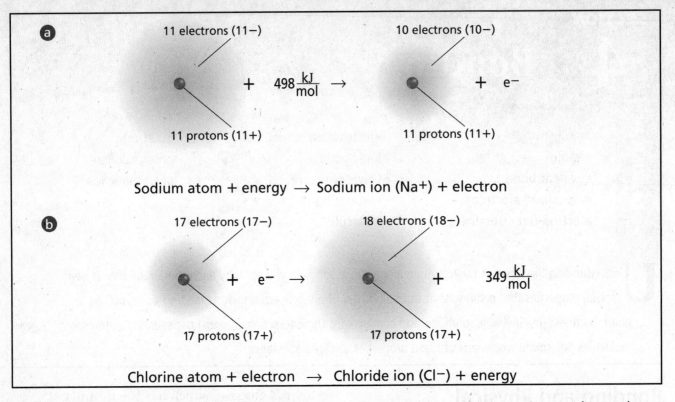

Sodium atom + energy → Sodium ion (Na+) + electron

Chlorine atom + electron → Chloride ion (Cl−) + energy

Figure 4.2 **(a)** A neutral atom gains one or more valence electrons to form a negative ion. The ion contains more electrons than protons, so the overall charge is negative. **(b)** A neutral atom loses one or more valence electrons to form a positive ion. The ion contains more protons than electrons, so the overall charge is positive.

Ionic Bonds

Ionic compounds include common table salt, NaCl, but there are thousands of other ionic compounds as well. All of these substances are made up of positive and negative ions. One type of ion is an **anion,** which has a negative charge and forms when electrons are added to the outer energy level, giving the ion a stable electron configuration. Figure 4.2(a) shows how a negative ion is formed.

The other type of ion is a **cation,** which is a positive ion that forms when valence electrons are removed, giving the ion a stable electron configuration. Figure 4.2(b) shows how a positive ion is formed.

✓ **CHECK FOR UNDERSTANDING** Which type of ion is formed by adding an electron to the outer energy level? Will the ion have a positive or a negative charge?

One way to represent the valence electrons of an atom is to use electron-dot structures. An **electron-dot structure** is a model that uses dots and lines to show how electrons are arranged in molecules. A line or a pair of dots represents bonding pairs of electrons. These diagrams provide a useful way of showing only the electrons in the valence energy level, which are the electrons involved in bonding. Notice that the number of electrons in the valence level, as shown by the electron-dot structures in Table 4.1, increases by one as you move across a row in the periodic table.

Why do neutral atoms become ions? The electron configuration and electron-dot structure help explain this: an atom gains the stability of a full complement of outer electrons by doing so. This concept is referred to as the octet rule. According to the **octet rule,** atoms lose, gain,

Table 4.1 • Electron-Dot Structures							
Group	1A	2A	3A	4A	5A	6A	7A	8A
Diagram	Li·	Be̤	B̤·	C̤:	·N̤·	·O̤:	:F̤:	:Ne̤:

or share electrons in order to acquire a full set of eight valence electrons (which is generally the stable electron configuration of a noble gas). The electron configuration of an ion is known as pseudonoble because the ion has a noble-gaslike configuration. A common misconception is that the ion becomes a noble gas. Note that the nucleus is unaffected by changes in the outer electron cloud, so it carries a positive charge that is not fully balanced by the negative charge of the electrons.

 CHECK FOR UNDERSTANDING What is the octet rule?

Example Problem 1

Indium, a rare, soft metal, was widely used during World War II to coat bearings in high-performance aircraft. What is the electron-dot structure for indium?

1 Analyze the Problem
- You are given the element indium (In). Look at the periodic table to determine the total number of electrons each atom has. To determine the number of valence electrons the atom has, write out the electron configuration.
- Then draw the electron-dot structure using the number of valence electrons and the rules for electron-dot structures.

2 Solve for the Unknown
From the periodic table, indium has an atomic number of 49, which means it has 49 electrons. Determine the electron configuration of an indium atom using noble gas notation.

$(Kr)5s^2 4d^{10} 5p^1$

The electron in the orbitals related to the atom's highest principle level are the two 5s and the one 5p electrons. These three electrons represent indium's three valence electrons. Draw the electron-dot structure for indium.

$\cdot \overset{\cdot}{In} \cdot$

3 Evaluate the Answer
- **Does the answer make sense?** The correct symbol for indium (In) has been used, and the rules for drawing the electron-dot structures have been correctly applied.

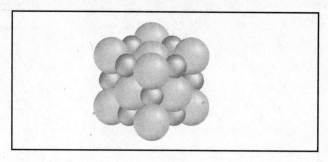

Figure 4.3 Sodium chloride is an ionic compound. Each ion is surrounded by six oppositely charged ions.

The electrostatic attraction between oppositely charged ions causes them to cling together, forming an ionic bond. An **ionic bond** is the electrostatic force that holds oppositely charged particles together in an ionic compound. The pattern that many ions organize themselves into when in solid form is an ionic crystal. A table salt crystal is illustrated in Figure 4.3.

When an atom becomes an ion, the size of the atom changes. If an atom gains an electron and becomes a negative ion, its atomic radius increases. This is due to the attractions and repulsions of the subatomic particles present in every atom. As more electrons are added to an atom, there is more repulsion among the electrons, so the atom becomes larger. When electrons are removed from an atom, the atom's radius decreases. There is a decrease in electron repulsion and the nucleus pulls the electrons closer.

The physical properties of ions are responsible for the characteristics shared by ionic compounds. All ionic compounds are solids at room temperature. As solids, they are not conductors of electricity. On the other hand, many ionic compounds dissolve in water, making the solution a good conductor because the ions are free to move. In liquid state, ionic compounds also are good conductors because ions are free to move under the influence of electric forces.

Molecular Bonds

In molecular compounds, electron pairs are shared between atoms. The chemical bond that results from this sharing of valence electrons is known as a covalent bond. A **covalent bond** is very different from an ionic bond in which electrons spend little or no time around the cation. A **molecule** forms when two or more atoms are covalently bonded.

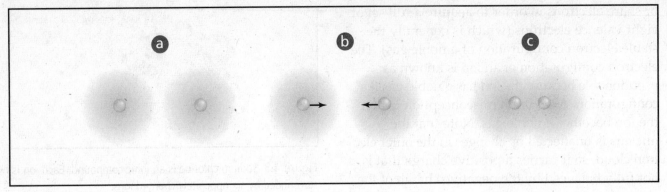

Figure 4.4 The force between two atoms results from electron-electron repulsions, nucleus-nucleus repulsions, and nucleus-electron attractions. **(a)** At a distance, the force between the two atoms is very small. **(b)** As two fluorine atoms approach, the electron clouds repel, but the nucleus of each atom attracts the electron cloud of the other atom. **(c)** At a specific distance, the attractive forces balance the repulsive forces, and a stable bond results.

When two atoms approach each other, as shown in Figure 4.4(a), their positively charged nuclei repel and their negatively charged electron clouds repel. But each nucleus also attracts the electron cloud of the other atom. At a distance the attractive forces are greater than the repulsive forces, as shown in Figure 4.4(b). As a result, the atoms come close to each other and gain stability from the sharing of electrons. But if the atoms were to come too close together, the repulsive force between the nuclei would push them apart. The distance between the two bonding nuclei when they are in the most stable arrangement is called the bond length, as shown in Figure 4.4 (c).

Figure 4.5 shows some simple molecules that form when atoms bond covalently. Look carefully at the electron-dot structure shown for water. This is a **Lewis structure,** a model that uses an electron-dot diagram to show how electrons are arranged in molecules. Pairs of dots or lines represent bonding pairs of electrons. The oxygen atom starts with six valence electrons. After the bond forms, it has a stable octet. Notice that the oxygen atom gains two electrons, and each hydrogen atom gains one electron. The water molecule is stable because each atom within it has gained stability by sharing electrons.

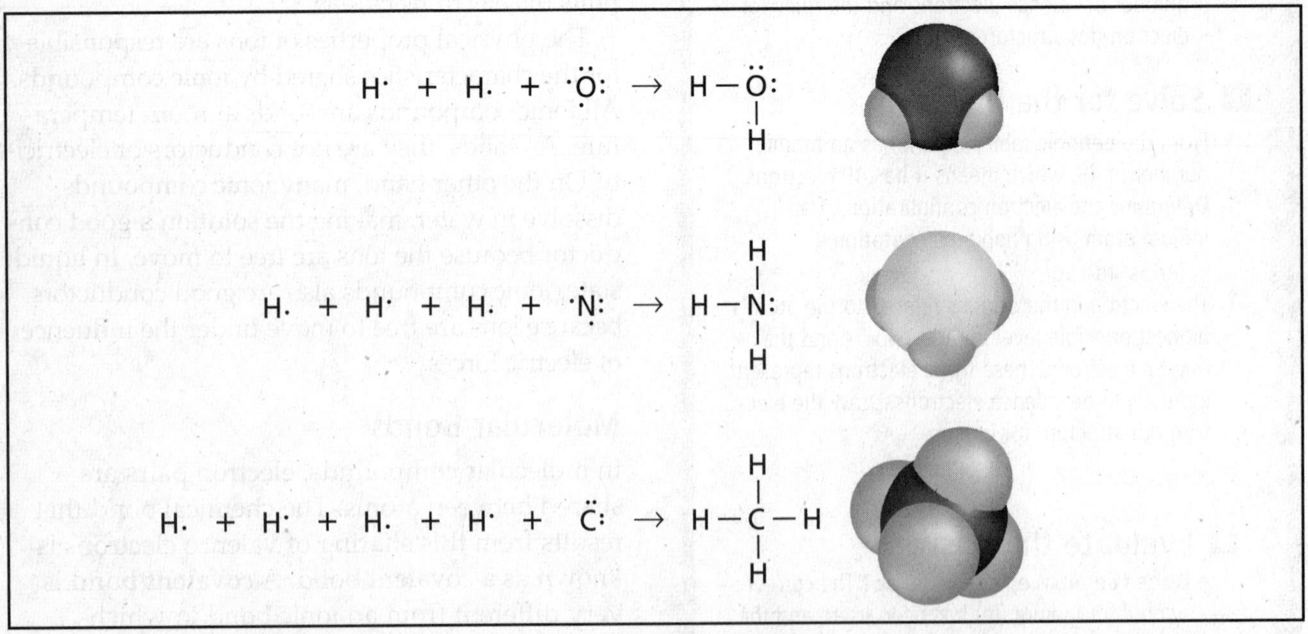

Figure 4.5 These chemical equations show how atoms share electrons to become stable. The electron-dot structures for the molecules show that all atoms in the molecules are stable according to the octet rule.

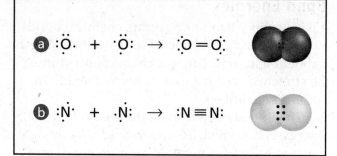

Figure 4.6 Multiple bonds form when more than one pair of electrons are shared. **(a)** The two pairs of electrons shared by oxygen atoms form a double bond. **(b)** Nitrogen shares three pairs of electrons, forming a triple bond.

Covalent bonds can involve one, two, or three pairs of electrons. If one pair of electrons is shared, it is called a single bond. If two electron pairs are shared, it is called a double bond, and if three pairs are shared, the result is a triple bond, as shown in Figure 4.6.

Nonmetals, such as hydrogen, chlorine, and fluorine, can bond covalently to produce diatomic molecules (H_2, F_2, and Cl_2). These compounds are made of a single type of atom, bonded together in small, neutral groups of atoms. In contrast, ionic compounds form from two or more different elements that bond together in an extended array known as a crystal lattice. Ionic compounds do not contain any molecules.

Because bonding is all about the formation of stable electron configurations for atoms or ions, we can see why the noble gases usually do not form compounds and generally are unreactive. The noble gases already have complete valence configurations and therefore, do not gain stability from combining with other atoms.

Ionic compounds sometimes have more complex anions or, more rarely, cations that are known as **polyatomic ions.** A polyatomic ion is the type of ion that is composed of two or more atoms that act as a single unit with a net charge. A polyatomic ion is formed by a small cluster of covalently bonded atoms. Table 4.2 lists common polyatomic ions.

Metallic Bonds

There is a third type of bond, a **metallic bond,** in which metallic cations are attracted to delocalized electrons. **Delocalized electrons** are electrons involved in metallic bonding that are free to move easily from one atom to the next throughout the metal and are not attached to a particular atom. Instead, the valence electrons in metals are shared in a "mobile sea of electrons," while the positive ions that remain are fixed. This model, known as the **electron sea model,** proposes that all atoms in a metallic

Table 4.2 • Common Polyatomic Ions				
Ion	**Name**	**Ion**	**Name**
NH_4^+	Ammonium	IO_4^-	Periodate
NO_2^-	Nitrate	$C_2H_3O_2^-$	Acetate
NO_3^-	Nitrate	$H_2PO_4^-$	Dihodrogen phosphate
HSO_4^-	Hydrogen sulfate	CO_3^{2-}	Acetate
OH^-	Hydroxide	SO_3^{2-}	Sulfite
CN^-	Cyanide	SO_4^{2-}	Sulfate
MnO_4^-	Permanganate	$S_2O_3^{2-}$	Thiosulfate
HCO_3^-	Hydrogen carbonate	O_2^{2-}	Peroxide
ClO^-	Hypochlorite	CrO_4^{2-}	Chromate
ClO_2^-	Chlorite	$Cr_2O_7^{2-}$	Dichromate
ClO_3^-	Chlorate	HPO_4^{2-}	Hydrogen phosphate
ClO_4^-	Perchlorate	PO_4^{3-}	Phosphate
BrO_3^-	Bromate	AsO_4^{3-}	Arsenate
IO_3^-	Iodate		

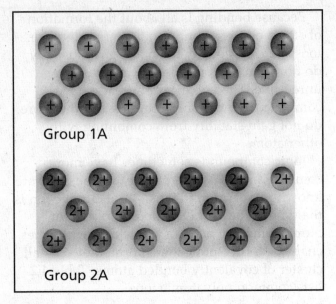

Figure 4.7 The valence electrons in metals are evenly distributed among the metallic cations. Attractions between the positive cations and negative "sea" hold the metal atoms together in a lattice structure.

solid contribute valence electrons. Figure 4.7 shows the even distribution of valence electrons among the metallic cations in a metal.

✔ **CHECK FOR UNDERSTANDING** Why do some electrons move freely in a metal?

Network Covalent Solids

Some solid substances contain atoms bonded together in a network of covalent bonds. These solids tend to be poor conductors of heat and electricity, are not malleable, have high melting points, are insoluble in most solvents, and are extremely hard. These solids are called network covalent solids.

One of the most familiar examples of a network covalent solid is a diamond, which contains a network of carbon atoms. The atoms bond to form a crystal that is the hardest known substance and has a very high melting point. Quartz and graphite are two other examples of solids with network covalent bonds.

✔ **CHECK FOR UNDERSTANDING** What are characteristics of network covalent solids?

Bond Energies

Like a rubber band or a spring, chemical bonds are elastic and can stretch. Similar to breaking a rubber band or a spring, a chemical bond must be stretched well beyond its normal length in order to be broken.

When bonds between atoms are broken, energy is absorbed. To understand why, imagine two balls held together by a spring. If you want to pull the balls apart, it will take energy to overcome the attractive force exerted by the spring. In the same way, it takes energy to pull atoms apart. The energy needed to pull atoms apart completely is called the bond dissociation energy. The stronger a bond is a compound, the greater the bond dissociation energy.

Not all bond types are of equal strength. Ionic bonds tend to be much stronger than covalent bonds. Covalent bonds in network covalent solids, however, can be very strong because they have a highly stable geometry. In the case of graphite, the bonds are very strong within a layer, but much weaker between layers. This type of bonding explains why graphite rubs off so easily, which makes it ideal for pencil leads and for lubricating machinery.

Not surprisingly, double and triple covalent bonds are stronger than single covalent bonds. The shorter the bond length, the stronger a covalent bond is. A double bond between carbon atoms (C=C) is about twice the strength of a single bond (C−C) because the double bond is shorter in length. Similarly, a triple bond is about three times the strength of a single bond.

Properties of Compounds

Ionic compounds tend to have very high melting points because of their high bond strength. The melting point of NaCl, for example, is 801°C. Ionic compounds also tend to form very distinct three-dimensional crystal shapes. They are very hard and brittle. When they crack under pressure, they tend to crack along characteristic lines or faces. In the liquid state, or when dissolved in water, ionic compounds can conduct electricity because the ions are free to move about.

Covalent compounds are quite different from ionic substances. They tend to have low melting points. Many covalent compounds do not ionize when dissolved in water, in which case they do not conduct an electric current.

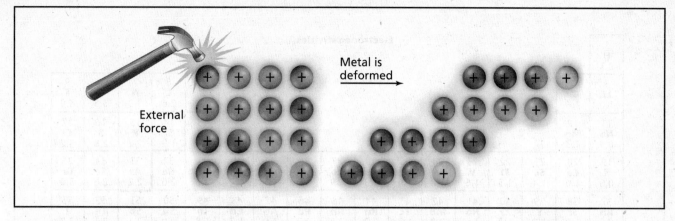

Figure 4.8 An applied force causes metal ions to move through delocalized electrons, making metals malleable and ductile.

Many exist as liquids or gases at room temperature. Covalent compounds, if solid at room temperature, tend to be softer than ionic compounds.

The electron sea model can explain many properties of metallic solids, including malleability and ductility, as shown in Figure 4.8. Because the metal cations can move within the sea of electrons, a metal is easily deformed and can retain its new shape even after the deforming force is removed. The cations simply lock into place in their new positions.

Metals are also good conductors because free electrons can flow readily through the metal. When an electric current is applied to a metal, the electric force pushes or pulls on the free electrons. Because these electrons are only held in place very weakly, the charges can flow with little resistance. This is the essence of a good conductor, and in fact, the best conductors generally are metals.

✓ CHECK FOR UNDERSTANDING How do ionic compounds differ from covalent compounds?

Quick Review

1 An atom loses electrons to form a(n)
   (1) cation   (3) molecule
   (2) anion   (4) metal

2 Ionic compounds consist of
   (1) cations bonded to cations
   (2) anions bonded to anions
   (3) cations bonded to anions
   (4) molecules

3 When an atom forms an ion, its electron configuration is similar to
   (1) a noble gas   (3) hydrogen
   (2) a metal   (4) a nonmetal

4 In a molecule, electrons are
   (1) transferred from one atom to another
   (2) attracted to the atoms in the molecule from the surrounding environment
   (3) equally shared between two atoms
   (4) completely lost by one atom

5 A polyatomic ion is
   (1) an atom with a positive charge
   (2) an atom with a negative charge
   (3) a neutral atom
   (4) a group of atoms acting as a single ion

6 A metal is a good conductor of electricity because
   (1) it contains tightly bonded electrons
   (2) it has a freely moving sea of electrons
   (3) it is shiny
   (4) it is malleable

7 Which type of bond can form a multiple bond?
   (1) ionic bonds
   (2) covalent bonds
   (3) metallic bonds

8 Explain why noble gases usually do not form bonds with other atoms.

9 Would you expect ionic or covalent compounds to have a higher melting point? Why?

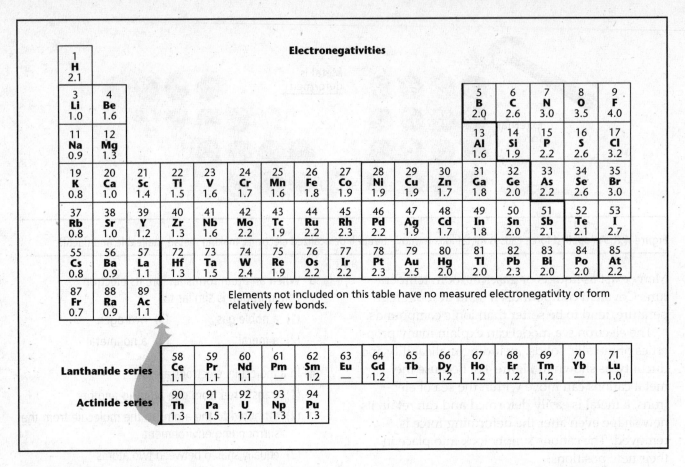

Figure 4.9 Electronegativity values are not measured quantities. They are assigned values that compare the abilities of atoms to attract shared electrons (relative to fluorine's attraction for shared electrons).

Electronegativity and Bonding

Recall that electronegativity is a measure of how strongly an atom attracts electrons. Therefore, electronegativities can be used to predict which type of bond will form between two atoms. Figure 4.9 lists the electronegativity of each of the elements.

Nonpolar Molecules

Consider the molecule of hydrogen, H_2, shown in Figure 4.10(a) on page 59. The two atoms in this molecule are identical, so they share the electrons equally. The covalent bond that results is called nonpolar because charge is spread more or less evenly throughout the molecule. In this simple case, the electronegativities of the two atoms involved in the bond are exactly equal. When atoms with similar electronegativities bond together, they exert a similar pull on the electrons, and the covalent bond that forms will tend to be nonpolar.

Polar Molecules

When two atoms have very different electronegativities, the shared electrons are attracted more toward one atom than the other. The resulting bond is **polar covalent,** a covalent bond in which the atoms at each end of the bond have a slight electric charge. Typically, one end of the molecule will have a slight positive charge and the other end will have a slight negative charge. This type of bond sometimes is called a dipole because, like a magnet, it has two poles.

Consider the bond between hydrogen and chlorine in the HCl molecule shown in Figure 4.10(b). The chlorine atom has a much greater electronegativity than the hydrogen atom, so the chlorine atom has a slight negative charge. The hydrogen atom has a slight positive charge. These charges are "partial charges," which are less than whole-number charges found on ions.

If the bonds in a molecule are polar, does the molecule have to be polar? If a molecule is asymmetrical, then it can be polar if it contains

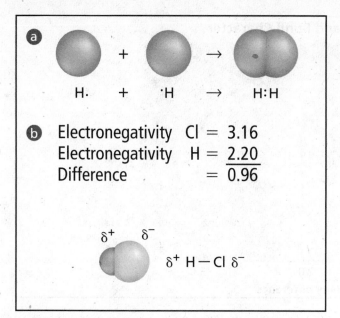

Electronegativity Cl = 3.16
Electronegativity   H = 2.20
Difference   = 0.96

δ^+ δ^-

δ^+ H — Cl δ^-

Figure 4.10 **(a)** By sharing a pair of electrons, these hydrogen atoms have a full outer electron energy level and are stable. **(b)** In a molecule of HCl, chlorine has the higher electronegativity, so the shared electron pair is with the chlorine atom more often than it is with the hydrogen atom. The δ^+ and δ^- symbols indicate the partial charge at each end of the molecule.

polar bonds. But if a molecule is symmetrical, it usually is nonpolar, regardless of the polarity of its bonds. For example, H_2O is a polar molecule because it has a 104.5° bond angle, and the H–O bond is polar. But CO_2 is a nonpolar molecule because it is a linear molecule, so the two C–O dipoles cancel their effect.

The polar covalent bonds within a molecule produce an attraction between one molecule and another, as shown in Figure 4.11. These intermolecular forces hold the molecules together and help to determine the properties of the compound.

☑ **CHECK FOR UNDERSTANDING** When atoms with similar electronegativities are involved in a bond, which type of covalent bond occurs?

Bond Character

Each element is given an electronegativity value from 0 to 4, depending on how strongly the bonding electrons are attracted to the atom. This scale is based on fluorine having the highest electronegativity, 4.0. The electronegativities that have been assigned to other atoms are based relative to fluorine. This scale for electronegativity, developed by Linus Pauling, is referred to as the Pauling scale.

The electronegativity difference between two bonded atoms determines the degree of polarity in the bond. Nitrogen, N_2, has an electronegativity difference of zero because the atoms are identical. Therefore, the bond between two nitrogen atoms is 100 percent covalent, or nonpolar. Water, on the other hand, is a polar molecule because it is asymmetrical and it has a larger electronegativity difference (1.24). The percent ionic character of a bond depends on the electronegativity difference of the atoms that form it.

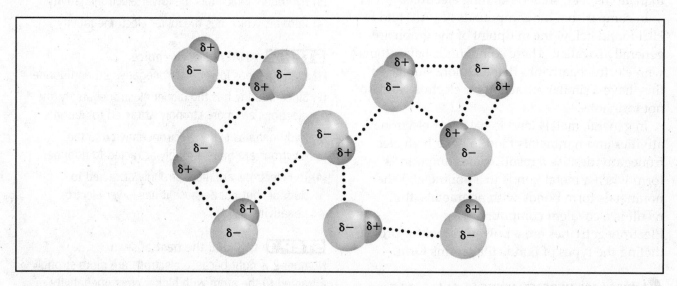

Figure 4.11 In hydrogen chloride gas, HCl(g), the partially positive hydrogen atom in one molecule is attracted to the partially negative chlorine atom in another molecule. This figure shows the attractions among several molecules.

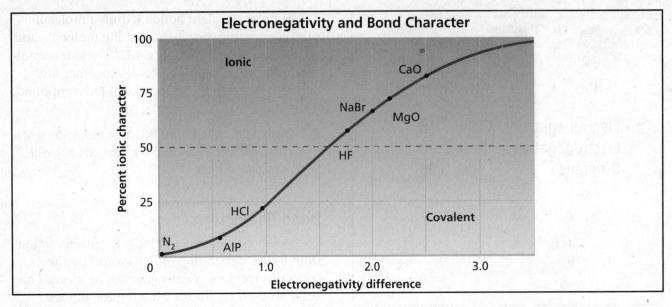

Electronegativity and Bond Character

Figure 4.12 This graph shows that the percent ionic character of a bond depends on the difference in electronegativity between the atoms that form the bond. Bonds that have percent ionic character above 50 percent are mostly ionic. What is the percent ionic character of a pure covalent bond?

Generally, if the electronegativity difference is great enough, the compound is not molecular. Instead, the compound is ionic, and it contains only ionic bonds. This is illustrated in the graph in Figure 4.12, which plots the percent ionic character versus electronegativity difference. As the electronegativity difference increases, the percent ionic character increases. If the percent ionic character is greater than 50 percent, the bond is considered ionic. You can see the positions of four ionic compounds: HF, NaBr, MgO, and CaO. These compounds have anions and cations rather than atoms with shared bonding electrons.

In comparison, the compounds N_2, AlP, and HCl found below the midpoint of the graph are generally covalent. These compounds have atoms with electronegativities that are more similar, so they have a similar attraction for electrons and do not form ions.

In general, metals tend to have low electronegativities and nonmetals tend to have high electronegativities. As a result, ionic compounds form when a metal bonds to a nonmetal. When nonmetals form bonds with nonmetals, the result is a covalent compound. Electronegativities are a powerful tool for predicting the types of bonds that atoms form.

✓ **CHECK FOR UNDERSTANDING** In which part of Figure 4.12 are you likely to find ionic compounds? Where would covalent compounds be found?

10 Which of the following has the bond with the most nonpolar character?

(1) F_2 (3) CaO

(2) HCl   (4) CCl_4

11 Which of the following has the most ionic character?

(1) F_2 (3) CaO

(2) HCl   (4) CCl_4

12 Metals tend to have _____ electronegativities while nonmetals tend to have _____ electronegativities.

(1) low, high   (3) high, low

(2) low, low   (4) high, high

13 Using Figure 4.12 and a chart of electronegativities, what percent ionic character is the bond between sodium and chlorine?

(1) about 20 percent

(2) about 30 percent

(3) about 60 percent

(4) about 70 percent

14 The bond between H and Cl in HCl is referred to as a(n)

(1) ionic bond

(2) covalent bond

(3) dipole

(4) symmetrical bond

15 A bond between potassium and bromine should be

(1) ionic

(2) covalent

(3) polar covalent

(4) need more information to evaluate

16 An example of a compound that shows about 50 percent ionic character is

(1) N_2 (3) CaC

(2) Li_2O (4) H_2S

17 Why do some polar molecules have an attraction for each other?

18 How is the electronegativity difference used to determine the type of bond between two atoms?

Part A

1 Element X is in Group 2 and element Y is in Group 17. What happens when a compound is formed between these two atoms?
   (1) X loses electrons to Y to form an ionic bond.
   (2) X loses electrons to Y to form a covalent bond.
   (3) X gains electrons from Y to form an ionic bond.
   (4) X gains electrons from Y to form a covalent bond.

2 Which particles may be gained, lost, or shared by an atom when it forms a chemical bond?
   (1) protons   (3) neutrons
   (2) electrons   (4) nucleons

3 When ionic bonds are formed, metallic atoms tend to
   (1) lose electrons and become negative ions
   (2) lose electrons and become positive ions
   (3) gain electrons and become negative ions
   (4) gain electrons and become positive ions

4 Electronegativity is a measure of an atom's ability to
   (1) attract the electrons in the bond between the atom and another atom
   (2) repel the electrons in the bond between the atom and another atom
   (3) attract the protons of another atom
   (4) repel the protons of another atom

5 Which statement best describes the substance that results when electrons are transferred from a metal to a nonmetal?
   (1) It contains ionic bonds and has a low melting point.
   (2) It contains ionic bonds and has a high melting point.
   (3) It contains covalent bonds and has a low melting point.
   (4) It contains covalent bonds and has a high melting point.

6 Which physical characteristic of a solution may indicate the presence of a transition element?
   (1) its density
   (2) its color
   (3) its effect on litmus
   (4) its effect on phenolphthalein

7 Which formula represents an ionic compound?
   (1) NaCl   (3) HCl
   (2) N_2O (4) H_2O

8 What occurs when a coordinate covalent bond is formed between nitrogen and hydrogen in the ammonium ion, NH_4^+?
   (1) Hydrogen provides a pair of electrons to be shared with nitrogen.
   (2) Nitrogen provides a pair of electrons to be shared with hydrogen.
   (3) Hydrogen transfers a pair of electrons to nitrogen.
   (4) Nitrogen transfers a pair of electrons to hydrogen.

9 Which type of bond is formed when an atom of potassium transfers an electron to a bromine atom?
   (1) metallic
   (2) ionic
   (3) nonpolar covalent
   (4) polar covalent

10 Which atom will form an ionic bond with a bromine atom?
   (1) nitrogen   (3) oxygen
   (2) lithium   (4) carbon

11 In which compound do atoms form bonds by sharing electrons?
   (1) H_2O (3) CaO
   (2) Na_2O (4) MgO

12 Which molecule contains a triple covalent bond between its atoms?

(1) N_2 (3) F_2

(2) O_2 (4) H_2

13 Which compound is described correctly?

(1) $BaCl_2$ is covalent and a polar molecule.

(2) H_2O_2 is covalent and crystalline.

(3) H_2O is ionic and a polar molecule.

(4) NaCl is ionic and crystalline.

14 Two fluorine atoms are held together by a covalent bond. Which statement correctly describes this bond?

(1) It is polar and forms a polar molecule.

(2) It is polar and forms a nonpolar molecule.

(3) It is nonpolar and forms a polar molecule.

(4) It is nonpolar and forms a nonpolar molecule.

Part B–1

15 Which electron-dot diagram represents a molecule that has a polar covalent bond?

(1) H×C̈l:

(3) :C̈l×C̈l×

(2) Li⁺[×C̈l:]⁻

(4) K⁺[×C̈l:]⁻

16 Given the reaction
Cl(g) + Cl(g) → Cl_2 + energy
which statement best describes the reaction?

(1) A bond is formed and energy is absorbed.

(2) A bond is formed and energy is released.

(3) A bond is broken and energy is absorbed.

(4) A bond is broken and energy is released.

17 Which species does not have a noble gas electron configuration?

(1) Na^+ (3) Ar

(2) Mg^{2+} (4) S

18 Which electron-dot diagram symbol represents an atom of argon in the ground state?

(1) Är: (3) ·Är:

(2) ·Är: (4) :Är:

Part B–2

19 How does the size of a barium ion compare to the size of a barium atom?

20 The table below shows the normal boiling point of four compounds.

Compound	Normal Boiling Point (°C)
HF(l)	19.4
$CH_2C(l)$	−24.2
$CH_2F(l)$	−78.6
HCl(l)	−83.7

Which compound has the strongest intermolecular forces?

21 If the electronegativity difference between the elements in compound NaX is 2.0, what is element X?

22 Which of these formulas contains the most polar bond and why: H–Br, H–Cl, H–F, H–I?

23 Use electronegativities in the Chemistry Reference Tables to predict the type of bond formed between copper and chlorine. What would you need to know to determine whether the compound produced is a polar compound?

Part C

Base your answers to questions 24 through 27 on the information below.

Each molecule listed below is formed by sharing electrons between atoms when the atoms within the molecule are bonded together.

Molecule A: Cl_2

Molecule B: CCl_4

Molecule C: NH_3

24 Draw the electron-dot (Lewis) structure for the NH_3 molecule.

25 Explain why CCl_4 is classified as a nonpolar molecule.

26 Explain why NH_3 has stronger intermolecular forces of attraction than Cl_2.

27 Explain how the bonding in KCl is different from the bonding in molecules A, B, C.

Base your answers to questions 28 through 30 on the information below.

Testing of an unknown solid shows that it has the properties listed below.

a low melting point

b nearly insoluble in water

c nonconductor of electricity

d relatively soft solid

28 State the type of bonding that would be expected in the particles of this substance.

29 Explain in terms of attractions between particles why the unknown solid has a low melting point.

30 Explain why the particles of this substance are nonconductors of electricity.

Avogadro's number
coefficient
combustion reaction
decomposition reaction
double-replacement
  reaction
empirical formula

excess reactant
formula unit
limiting reactant
molar mass
mole
molecular formula
oxyanion

percent composition
precipitate
single-replacement
  reaction
stoichiometry
structural formula
synthesis reaction

A list of ingredients on a cereal box indicates how much there is of each ingredient in a unit serving. In the same way, a chemical formula indicates which elements are contained in a compound, and how much there is of each element. In stoichiometry, chemists use chemical formulas and equations to determine the quantity of each chemical that participates in a reaction. Stoichiometry is a powerful tool that allows chemists to turn abstract chemistry knowledge into concrete applications.

Naming Compounds

Recall that a compound is a pure substance that consists of two or more different elements that are chemically combined. The properties of the constituent elements no longer are present, and the new substance has its own, unique physical and chemical properties, which can be used to identify it. The elements that make up a compound occur in a fixed ratio of atoms, and therefore, in a fixed mass ratio as well. The IUPAC (International Union of Pure and Applied Chemistry) system of nomenclature provides a method of naming compounds based on which elements are combined and in what ratio.

Two different compounds may be formed from the same elements, but the elements are combined in different proportions. Two compounds also may be formed of the same elements and in the same ratio, but with the atoms arranged differently. In both cases, the IUPAC name will serve to differentiate these compounds from each other.

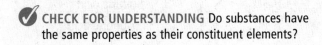 CHECK FOR UNDERSTANDING Do substances have the same properties as their constituent elements?

Ionic Compounds

Recall that an ionic compound consists of anions and cations bonded in a crystal array. The simplest ratio of ions in an ionic compound is called a **formula unit.** You can use formula units to name these compounds.

In a binary ionic compound, which consists of only two elements, the name starts with the cation and ends with the anion. The anion is modified by adding *–ide*. For example, $CaCl_2$ is named calcium chloride.

Recall that polyatomic ions contain more than one atom. Table 5.1 lists some of the most common polyatomic ions. Ammonium is a cation. All the rest are **oxyanions**, which are polyatomic ions composed of an element, usually a nonmetal, bonded to one or more oxygen atoms.

Table 5.1 • The Most Common Polyatomic Ions	
NH_4^+	Ammonium
NO_3^-	Nitrate
$C_2H_3O_2^-$	Acetate
OH^-	Hydroxide
CO_3^{2-}	Carbonate
SO_4^{2-}	Sulfate
PO_4^{3-}	Phosphate

Table 5.2 • Prefixes in Covalent Compounds			
Prefix	Number of Atoms	Example	Name
Mono-	1	CO	Carbon monoxide
Di-	2	SO_2	Sulfur dioxide
Tri-	3	SO_3	Sulfur trioxide
Tetra-	4	SiF_4	Silicon tetrafluoride
Penta-	5	PCl_5	Phosphorus pentachloride
Hexa-	6	SF_6	Sulfur hexafluoride
Hepta-	7	Cl_2O_7	Chlorine heptaoxide
Octa-	8	$Ba(OH)_2 \cdot 8H_2O$	Barium hydroxide octahydrate

A name ending in –*ate* designates a compound with an oxyanion. To designate the oxyanion that has one less oxygen atom, use the ending –*ite* instead. For example, $NaNO_3$ is named sodium nitrate, and $NaNO_2$ is named sodium nitrite.

Recall that an oxidation number is the charge of a monatomic ion. Stock notation indicates the oxidation number of transition metals, as well as of nonmetals, all of which can have multiple oxidation states. The oxidation state is either the charge (the result obtained by actually gaining or losing electrons) or it is a "bookkeeping" method of allocating electrons to one species or another. In stock notation, the name of a metal cation is followed by a Roman numeral to indicate the metal's oxidation state. For example, FeO is named iron(II) oxide because it contains Fe^{2+} ions. Fe_2O_3 is named iron(III) oxide because it contains Fe^{3+} ions.

Sometimes it is helpful to write the ions as part of a compound separately before writing the actual name. One example is the oxygen series of ions.

oxide	O^{2-}
peroxide	O_2^{2-}
superoxide	$O2-$

Another is the series of polyatomic ions of chlorine.

chloride ion	Cl^-
hypochlorite ion	ClO^-
chlorite ion	ClO_2^-
chlorate ion	ClO_3^-
perchlorate ion	ClO_4^-

For example, the compound $NaClO_4$ is named sodium perchlorate.

☑ **CHECK FOR UNDERSTANDING** What does it mean when the name of the element is followed by a Roman numeral?

Covalent Compounds

In molecular compounds, the atoms are held together by covalent bonds. These compounds are represented by a **molecular formula**. A molecular formula shows the actual numbers of atoms of each element in one molecule or formula unit of the substance. Figure 5.1(b) shows you how to name a compound if the formula is known and if it has been determined whether the compound is an ionic compound or a molecular compound.

In a binary molecular compound, the name of the compound starts with the name of the first element in the formula. The second element name is modified by adding the suffix –*ide* and using one of the standard prefixes shown in Table 5.2. The prefix indicates the number of atoms of the element. For example, a molecule of carbon monoxide (CO) contains one oxygen atom. A molecule of carbon dioxide (CO_2) contains two oxygen atoms. Memorizing the standard prefixes will help you write the correct names for compounds.

Acids have their own fairly detailed method of nomenclature. However, you should memorize the formulas for these five most common acids, shown in Table 5.3. You most likely will encounter these acids in the laboratory.

Table 5.3 • Table of Most Common Acids	
HCl	Hydrochloric acid
HNO_3	Nitric acid
$HC_2H_3O_2$	Acetic acid
H_2SO_4	Sulfuric acid
H_3PO_4	Phosphoric acid

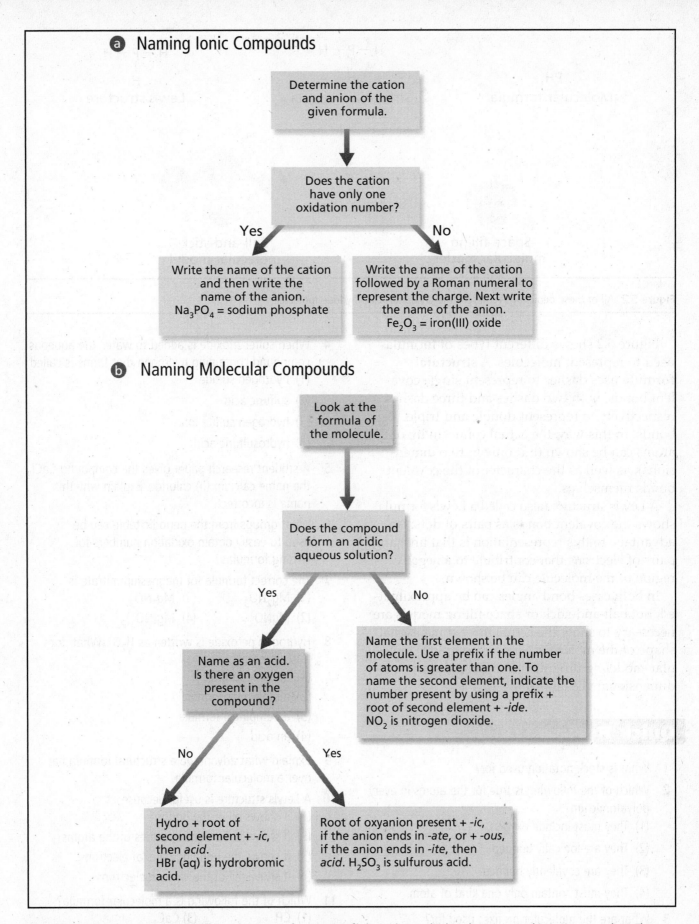

a Naming Ionic Compounds

Determine the cation and anion of the given formula.

Does the cation have only one oxidation number?

Yes

Write the name of the cation and then write the name of the anion.
Na_3PO_4 = sodium phosphate

No

Write the name of the cation followed by a Roman numeral to represent the charge. Next write the name of the anion.
Fe_2O_3 = iron(III) oxide

b Naming Molecular Compounds

Look at the formula of the molecule.

Does the compound form an acidic aqueous solution?

Yes

Name as an acid. Is there an oxygen present in the compound?

No

Name the first element in the molecule. Use a prefix if the number of atoms is greater than one. To name the second element, indicate the number present by using a prefix + root of second element + -ide.
NO_2 is nitrogen dioxide.

No

Hydro + root of second element + -ic, then acid.
HBr (aq) is hydrobromic acid.

Yes

Root of oxyanion present + -ic, if the anion ends in -ate, or + -ous, if the anion ends in -ite, then acid. H_2SO_3 is sulfurous acid.

Figure 5.1 The procedure for identifying the name of a compound depends on whether the compound is ionic or covalent. The diagrams summarize how to name **(a)** ionic compounds and **(b)** molecular compounds.

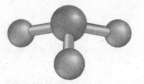

H — P — H
    |
    H
PH$_3$
Molecular formula Structural formula

H — P̈ — H
    |
    H
Lewis structure

Space-filling
molecular model

Ball-and-stick
molecular model

Figure 5.2 All of these depictions represent the phosphorous trihydride molecule.

Figure 5.2 shows different types of formulas used to represent molecules. A **structural formula** uses dashes to represent single covalent bonds, with two dashes and three dashes respectively to represent double and triple bonds. In this way, the actual connectivity of the atoms can be shown (but only in two dimensions), as well as the character of the covalent bonds themselves.

A Lewis structure (also called a Lewis formula) shows the covalent bonds as pairs of dots. An advantage to this representation is that unshared pairs of electrons that contribute to a negative region of the molecule can be shown.

In both cases bond angles can be approximated, but ball-and-stick or space-filling models are necessary to show the actual three-dimensional shape of the molecule. Modern computer molecular-modeling programs also can assist in three-dimensional visualization.

Quick Review

1 What is stock notation used for?

2 Which of the following is true for the atoms in every polyatomic ion?
  (1) They must include oxygen.
  (2) They are ionically bonded.
  (3) They are covalently bonded.
  (4) They must contain only one kind of atom.

3 What are the molecular prefixes used for? Explain how they are used.

4 When sulfer trioxide is added to water, the aqueous compound containing hydrogen that forms is called
  (1) hydrogen sulfide
  (2) sulfuric acid
  (3) hydrogen sulfite ion
  (4) hydrosulfuric acid

5 A student research paper gives the compound CaCl$_2$ the name calcium (II) chloride. Explain why this name is incorrect.

6 What groups from the periodic table can be used to easily obtain oxidation numbers for writing formulas?

7 The correct formula for magnesium nitrate is
  (1) Mg$_2$NO$_3$ (3) Mg$_2$NO$_3$
  (2) MgNO$_3$ (4) Mg(NO$_3$)$_2$

8 Hydrogen peroxide is written as H$_2$O$_2$. What does this represent?
  (1) an ionic formula
  (2) a molecular formula
  (3) an empirical formula
  (4) an acid

9 Explain what advantage a structural formula has over a molecular formula.

10 A Lewis structure is useful because
  (1) it shows all of the bonds
  (2) it shows the oxidation states of the atoms
  (3) it shows the bonding pairs of electrons
  (4) it shows all of the valence electrons

11 Which of the following is a molecular formula?
  (1) CH   (3) CaC$_2$
  (2) CaCO$_3$ (4) CO$_2$

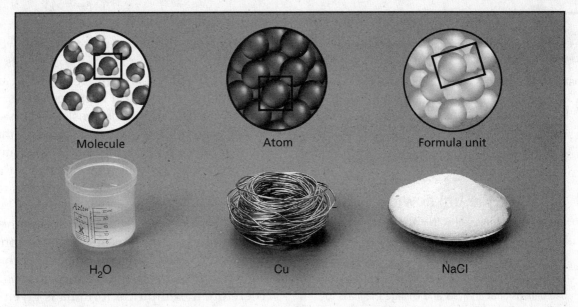

Figure 5.3 The amount of each substance shown is 6.02×10^{23} or one mole of representative particles. The representative particle for each substance is shown in a box.

Mole Calculations

Very small particles that make up matter, and which are too small to count or mass individually, are defined as "representative particles." Some examples are atoms, molecules, ions, and the subatomic particles: electrons, protons, and neutrons. Representative particles also can be formula-units in an ionic compound, although these are not actual particles that exist independently of the crystal.

The Mole

Chemists needed a unit with which to designate a defined number of representative particles for use in calculations. Avogadro's studies of gases in the early 1800s resulted in the defined value **Avogadro's number**, 6.02×10^{23}, which in turn was defined as the number of representative particles in a mole of those particles. A **mole** is the SI base unit used to measure the amount of a substance.

Figure 5.3 shows some of the representative particles used to count moles in different types of materials. The representative particle in water is the molecule H_2O. In copper, the representative particles are copper atoms. In sodium chloride, the representative particle is the formula unit ($NaCl$).

✓ **CHECK FOR UNDERSTANDING** What is Avogadro's number and what does it represent?

Molar Mass

The atomic mass of each element on the periodic table is the mass, in grams, of one mole (Avogadro's number) of atoms of that element.

To obtain the formula mass for an ionic compound, or the molecular mass of a molecular compound, add up all of the atomic masses of the elements. This result also is called the **molar mass**, which gives the mass, in grams, of one mole of that substance.

The mole roadmap, in Figure 5.4, is a diagram that chemists use to calculate numbers of representative particles, masses of substances, and volumes of gases. All calculations among the outside variables must be made by going through the center, which contains the mole.

In doing mole calculations, dimensional analysis is generally used as follows:

1 Obtain the atomic masses from the periodic table and use one more significant digit in the molar masses than is present in the given quantity. This minimizes rounding errors.

2 Convert the mass of the given to moles, but keep an extra significant digit in the result.

3 Use the mole ratio to compute the moles of the desired substance.

4 Finally, use a mole-to-mass conversion to obtain the final mass. In this last step we would round our answer to the number of significant digits we were given originally.

Example Problem 1 on page 70 shows how to find the molar mass of a compound.

What is the molar mass of ammonium phosphate?

1 Analyze the Problem

- Determine the formula for ammonium phosphate and number of ammonium ions in the compound.
- Use dimensional analysis to find the amount of representative particles of ammonium.

2 Solve for the Unknown

The formula of this salt is $(NH_4)_3PO_4$, so one formula unit contains three ammonium ions.

Find the molar mass:

$3(14.0) + 12(1.0) + 31.0 + 4(16.) = 149 \text{ g}$

Use dimensional analysis and change the mass to moles and the moles to representative particles, in this case, formula units.

$$2.56 \text{ g } (NH_4)_3PO_4 \times \frac{(1 \text{ mol}/149 \text{ g})}{6.022 \times 10^{23} \text{ particles/mol}}$$

$$\times \frac{3 \text{ } NH_4^+}{1 \text{ formula unit}}$$

$= 0.310 \times 10^{23} = 3.10 \times 10^{22}$ ammonium ions

3 Evaluate the Answer

- **Does the answer make sense?** You can verify the answer by calculating the number of phosphate ions. The ratio of ammonium ions to phosphate ions is 3:1, as it should be.

Empirical Formulas

An **empirical formula** represents the lowest whole-number mole ratio of the elements of a compound. Almost all ionic compounds are represented by an empirical formula. This is because ionic compounds consist of a crystal lattice of alternating cations and anions in the ratio given by the empirical formula. You cannot identify a single particle that represents the compound, but nonetheless, the ratio of ions is fixed and is given by the empirical formula.

For instance, with sodium chloride there are alternating sodium ions and chloride ions, but no specific unit of the crystal exists with only one sodium ion and one chloride ion. Therefore the empirical formula is given by the ionic formula, which is the simplest whole-number ratio of ions.

By comparison, hydrogen peroxide exists as a molecule consisting of two hydrogen atoms held together by covalent bonds. Therefore, the molecular formula is H_2O_2, which represents this unit, the molecule, whereas its empirical formula would be HO. The subscripts in the molecular formula are always a whole-number multiple of the subscripts in the empirical formula.

☑ **CHECK FOR UNDERSTANDING** What is the difference between a molecular formula and an empirical formula?

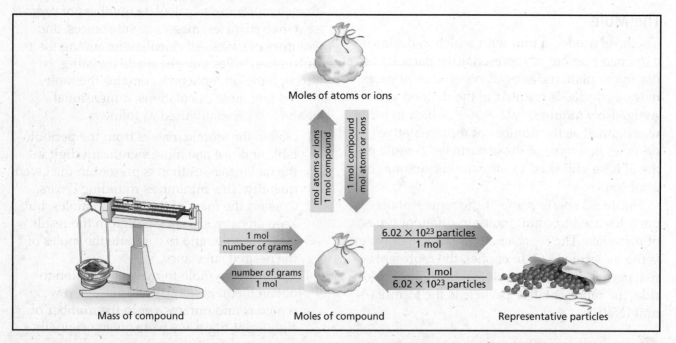

Figure 5.4 In complicated stoichiometry problems, look at this diagram first to map a path to finding the solution. In most problems, different quantities are first converted to moles, which is why the mole is in the center of the diagram.

Determining Empirical Formulas

To determine the empirical formula of a compound, it is necessary to find the mass of each element present in a sample of the compound, then convert each mass to moles. Dividing the moles of each element by the smallest value will yield ratios from which a whole-number ratio of each element may be obtained.

Since the data often is obtained from experimental results that have measurement errors, slight rounding will be necessary in order to produce whole numbers. In addition, ratios may be obtained, that are fractions, which must be manipulated with a multiplier to obtain a whole-number ratio. It is a common mistake to round to the nearest whole number, but this should not be done.

For example, data for carbonic acid might be as follows:

H   1.1 g = 1.1 mol

C   5.9 g = 0.49 mol

O   24.2 g = 1.51 mol

It would be an error to round the 1.51 mol of oxygen to 2 mol. In this case, all of the quantities should be doubled:

H   2 × 1.1 mol = 2.2 mol

C   2 × 0.49 mol = 0.98 mol

O   2 × 1.51 mol = 3.02 mol

Then round off to the nearest whole number to arrive at the correct formula: H_2CO_3.

If the substance is molecular, an additional step must be taken to obtain the molecular formula, which will be a whole-number multiple of the empirical formula. Usually, a mass spectrometer is used to obtain the molar mass of the compound. Then the formula mass is calculated, based upon the empirical formula. Dividing the molar mass by the formula mass tells how many multiples of the empirical formula the actual molecule contains. From this multiplier the molecular formula can be determined.

✓ CHECK FOR UNDERSTANDING What does an empirical formula represent?

Example Problem 2

In an experiment, a student found that 6.19 grams of phosphorus reacted with 8.04 grams of oxygen. What is the empirical formula of the compound formed? An additional experiment finds that the compound has a molar mass of 283.9 amu. What is the molecular formula of this compound?

1 Analyze the Problem

- You are given the masses of the reactants and must first determine the empirical formula. Then use the molar mass to determine the molecular formula.

2 Solve for the Unknown

Find the empirical formula

Change the mass of phosphorus to moles and keep an extra significant digit.

$$6.19 \text{ g P} \left(\frac{1 \text{ mol P}}{30.97 \text{ g P}} \right) = 0.1999 \text{ mol P atoms}$$

Change the mass of oxygen to moles.

Use the atomic mass of oxygen atoms, not of molecules.

$$8.04 \text{ g O} \left(\frac{1 \text{ mol P}}{16.00 \text{ g O}} \right) = 0.5025 \text{ mol O atoms}$$

Divide the largest moles by the smallest moles.

$$\frac{0.5025 \text{ mol O}}{0.1999 \text{ mol P}} = \frac{2.5137 \text{ mol O}}{1 \text{ mol P}}$$

2.5 mol O : 1 mol P is the simplest ratio. To obtain a whole-number ratio, double the fraction. 5 mol O : 2 mol P, and write the resultant empirical formula as P_2O_5.

Find the molecular formula

Determine the formula mass:

(2)(30.97 amu) + 5(16.00 amu) = 141.94 amu).

Divide the obtained molecular mass (molar-mass) by the formula mass:

$$\frac{283.9 \text{ amu}}{141.9 \text{ amu}} = 2.0007 \rightarrow 2 : 1$$

Therefore, double all of the subscripts to get the molecular formula: P_4O_{10}.

3 Evaluate the Answer

- **Does the answer make sense?** Using the molecular formula to calculate the molar mass results in the same molar mass as the experimental compound.

Percent Composition

The **percent composition** of a compound is a listing of the percent by mass of each element in the compound. To calculate the percent composition, divide the atomic mass of the element whose percent you wish to know by the molar mass of the substance containing it. Then multiply by 100 percent. In water, for example, there are 2.0 g of hydrogen in 18 g of water. The percent composition of hydrogen is:

$$\frac{2.0 \text{ g H}}{18 \text{ g H}_2\text{O}} \times 100\% = 11\% \text{ H}$$

Percent composition can be used to find the formula of a compound, as shown in Figure 5.5. You simply assume that the percentages given for the substance represent the number of grams in a 100-g sample of the substance. Then use the mass of each element in the 100-g sample to find the number of moles of each element. Finally, converting to whole-number ratios gives the empirical formula.

✓ **CHECK FOR UNDERSTANDING** How do you calculate the percent composition of a compound?

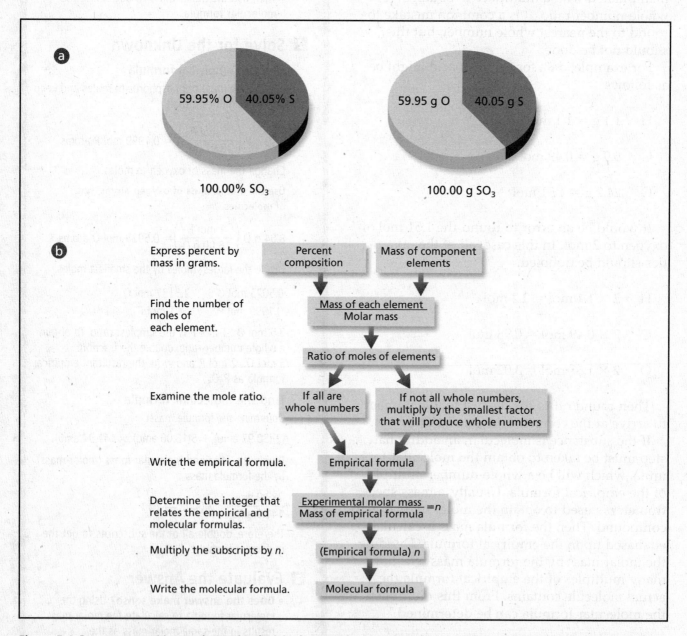

Figure 5.4 Percent composition can be used to find the formula of a compound. **(a)** First assume that each percentage represents the number of grams in a 100-g sample. **(b)** Calculate the number of moles of each element to find the molecular formula. If the molar mass is known, the empirical formula can then be calculated.

STEP 1 READ the Regents Questions …

A compound is analyzed and found to contain 75% carbon and 25% hydrogen by mass. What is the compound's empirical formula?

(1) CH

(3) CH_3

(2) CH_2

(4) CH_4

STEP 2 ANALYZE each choice …

(1) The formula given has a total formula mass of 13 amu. The percent composition of hydrogen is calculated by taking the total mass of hydrogen and dividing by the total formula mass and then multiplying by 100 percent:

$$\% \text{ H} = \frac{1.0 \text{ amu}}{13 \text{ amu}} \times 100\%$$

$$= 7.7\%$$

(2) For this answer, the percent composition of hydrogen is calculated in the same way as above, except that the total formula mass is 14 amu:

$$\% \text{ H} = \frac{2.0 \text{ amu}}{14 \text{ amu}} \times 100\%$$

$$= 14\%$$

(3) We can evaluate this answer by solving for the percent composition of carbon in the same manner as was done for hydrogen. The percent of carbon equals the total mass of carbon divided by the total formula mass multiplied by 100 percent:

$$\% \text{ C} = \frac{12.0 \text{ amu}}{15 \text{ amu}} \times 100\%$$

$$= 80\%$$

(4) The percent composition of carbon for the last choice can be calculated in the same manner as the previous example:

$$\% \text{ C} = \frac{12.0 \text{ amu}}{16 \text{ amu}} \times 100\%$$

$$= 75\%$$

STEP 3 CHOOSE the best answer …

After considering all the options, the correct answer is number 4 because it gives the percent composition of carbon that matches the one given in the problem.

12 Explain the relationship between atomic mass and molar mass.

13 Representative particles can be

(1) metals

(3) nonmetals

(2) formula units

(4) equations

14 Describe how you would convert from atoms of an element to grams of an element, using the mole.

15 Explain how you would calculate the percent composition of $CaCO_3$.

16 The percent of hydrogen in sulfuric acid, H_2SO_4, is about

(1) 2%

(3) 10%

(2) 5%

(4) 12%

17 Explain why the number of particles in a mole is such a large number.

18 Write three examples of empirical formulas.

19 Analysis of a colorless, odorless liquid gives 11 percent hydrogen and 89 percent oxygen. Does this substance have to be water? Explain.

20 Explain the difference between an empirical and a molecular formula. Can they ever be the same?

Classifying Chemical Reactions

Classifying equations by type of chemical reaction assists us in both balancing them, and in understanding the nature of the chemical system under consideration. Table 5.4 on page 74 summarizes four types of reactions.

Synthesis Reactions

Synthesis reactions are easy to identify; two or more reactants, often elements, form one product. Synthesis reactions are typically exothermic. Burning is a special case of a synthesis reaction in which oxygen reacts with another substance. If more than one product is formed, and if the reaction is used to produce energy in the form of heat and light, it usually is called a **combustion reaction**. Combustion reactions also are used to determine the composition of an unknown substance, usually a hydrocarbon or some other organic substance containing carbon, hydrogen, and oxygen.

Table 5.4 • Classifying Reactions		
Type of Reaction	**General Format**	**Example Reaction**
Synthesis	A + B → AB	$2K(s) + Cl_2(g) → 2KCl(s)$
Decomposition	AB → A + B	$2HgO(s) → 2Hg(l) + O_2(g)$
Single-Replacement	A + BX → AX + B	$CaNO_3(aq) → Ca(s) + LiNO_3(aq)$
Double-Replacement	AY + BX → AX + BY	$2NaOH(aq) + CuCl_2(aq) → 2NaCl(aq) + Cu(OH)_2(s)$

Decomposition Reactions

Decomposition reactions are defined as a chemical reaction that occurs when a single compound breaks down into two or more elements or new compounds. One reactant produces (yields) two or more products. Often the reactant is heated. This designation is made with a delta symbol over the yields arrow. Sometimes a catalyst is used to aid in decomposition. This substance is placed over the yields arrow to indicate that it is neither a reactant nor a product. Decomposition reactions are typically endothermic.

Single-Replacement Reactions

Single-replacement reactions consist of an element and a compound on each side of the equation. The more active element replaces the less active element in the compound. Table 5.4 shows the activity series, which is used to determine which element is more active. Metals can replace metals from salts, or replace hydrogen in acids or in water, and nonmetals can replace nonmetals in salts.

Double-Replacement Reactions

Double-replacement reactions involve the exchange of cations and anions. The "driving force," for these reactions to occur is that an uncharged particle is formed, which pulls ions from solution. In other words one set of cations and anions in the solution, combine to form a compound, leaving another set of cations and anions in solution. This can occur in three ways:

1 A precipitate is formed. A **precipitate** is a solid produced by a reaction in solution.
2 A gas is formed.
3 A molecular substance is formed.

A precipitate is designated with either a down-arrow or an (s) after that substance. A gas is designated with either an up-arrow or (g) after that substance.

✓ CHECK FOR UNDERSTANDING What is the "driving force" in a double-replacement reaction?

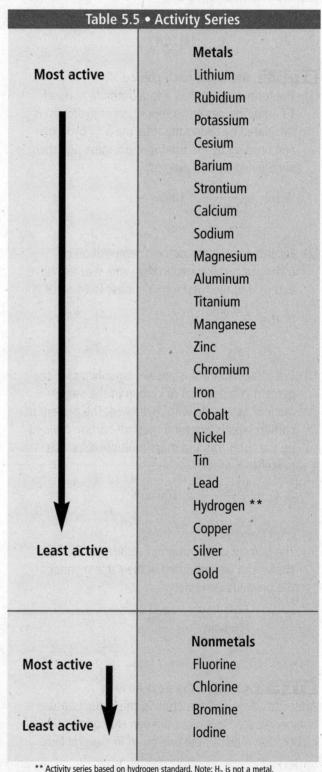

Table 5.5 • Activity Series

Metals

Most active

Lithium
Rubidium
Potassium
Cesium
Barium
Strontium
Calcium
Sodium
Magnesium
Aluminum
Titanium
Manganese
Zinc
Chromium
Iron
Cobalt
Nickel
Tin
Lead
Hydrogen **
Copper
Silver
Gold

Least active

Nonmetals

Most active

Fluorine
Chlorine
Bromine
Iodine

Least active

** Activity series based on hydrogen standard. Note: H_2 is not a metal.

21 How are synthesis and decomposition reactions related?

22 How can synthesis and combustion reactions be related?

23 Explain how a single-replacement and a double-replacement reaction are different.

24 Use an activity series to determine which of the following shows the correct order of increasing activity.
    (1) Au, Fe, H, Mg
    (2) Mg, H, Au, Fe
    (3) H, Au, Fe, Mg
    (4) Au, H, Fe, Mg

25 A decomposition reaction often needs all but
    (1) heat
    (2) another reactant
    (3) time to react
    (4) a catalyst

26 Explain why burning a hydrocarbon for an energy source would not be both a combustion reaction and a synthesis reaction.

27 Zinc reacts vigorously with sulfur to produce lots of heat and light. Is this a combustion reaction? Explain.

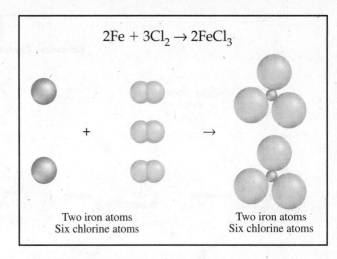

$$2Fe + 3Cl_2 \rightarrow 2FeCl_3$$

Two iron atoms
Six chlorine atoms

Two iron atoms
Six chlorine atoms

Figure 5.6 You can tell this equation is balanced because there are equal numbers of each type of atom on each side of the equation.

Stoichiometry

Chemical reactions can be represented by chemical equations like the one in Figure 5.6. A chemical equation is a statement that uses chemical formulas to show the identities and relative amounts of the reactants and products in a chemical reaction. A chemical reaction is a powerful tool that chemists use to determine the amount of each reactant that is needed and the amount of each product that will be produced.

You can think of a reaction as a recipe. Suppose you are cooking pancakes. The recipe tells you the correct amount of each ingredient (sugar, flour, eggs, etc) that you will need to gather beforehand. The recipe also tells you how many pancakes you can expect to make if you use the given amount of ingredients.

The first step in stoichiometry is to balance the equation. In Table 5.6, notice the numbers in front of each substance. These numbers in front of a reactant or product are called **coefficients**. Each coefficient in a balanced equation represents the number of atoms, molecules, or formula-units in the case of ionic compounds, that participate in the reaction.

Each coefficient can be multiplied by Avogadro's number, the number of representative particles in a mole, so the coefficients also show the number of moles of each substance involved in that reaction. This allows you to determine the mass relationships for all of the reactants and products once you are given the mass of one reactant or product.

Table 5.6 • Relationships Derived from a Balanced Chemical Equation				
Iron	**+**	**Oxygen**	**→**	**Iron(III) oxide**
$4Fe(s)$	+	$3O_2(g)$	→	$2Fe_2O_3(S)$
4 atoms Fe	+	3 molecules O_2	→	2 formula units Fe_2O_3
4 moles	+	3 moles O_2	→	2 moles Fe_2O_3
223.4 g Fe	+	96.0 g O_2	→	319.4 g Fe_2O_3
		319.4 g reactants	→	319.4 g product

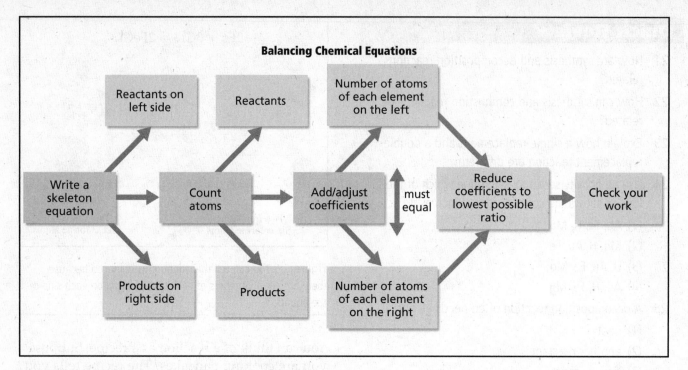

Figure 5.7 This chart represents one process for balancing equations.

This process is called **stoichiometry**, from the Greek word, *stoichio*, for elements, and *metry*, to measure; therefore, literally meaning "to measure elements." For example, you can see in Table 5.6 that four atoms of iron reacts with three molecules of oxygen to produce two formula units of Fe_2O_3. If you multiply by the respective molar masses of iron, oxygen, and iron oxide. you find that 223.4 g of iron reacts with 96.0 g of oxygen to produce 319.4 g of Fe_2O_3. But the process does not work unless the equations are balanced.

Balancing Equations

When you start a stoichiometry problem, first you need to balance the equation for the given reaction. It is not hard to determine if an equation is balanced. In a balanced equation, all of the atoms that react, the reactants, are shown on the left. The products that are formed are shown on the right. Because every atom that reacts must appear in the products, coefficients are used to balance equations, which really means to balance the number of atoms on each side of the equation. This is necessary in order to obey the law of conservation of matter. However, keep in mind that correct formulas must be written for all constituents before

balancing with coefficients, and the subscripts in the formulas are not again touched during the balancing process.

It takes a bit more skill to balance an unbalanced equation. Balancing equations is a skill that, like most skills, can be developed and improved. Some equations balance easily by inspection, while other equations require some manipulation. Equation balancing is a skill acquired through practice.

Figure 5.7 shows a procedure for correctly balancing a chemical equation. The steps may vary, but usually include the following:

1 Classify the reaction and predict the products.
2 Write correct formulas for all substances, using subscripts.
3 Balance atoms using coefficients.
4 Recheck and add equation symbols.

Sometimes chemists eliminate the ions that remain in a solution from both sides of the equation, writing only the ions that react. These abbreviated equations are called net ionic equations. A net ionic equation is an ionic equation that includes only the particles that participate in the reaction. The ions that are omitted are called spectator ions.

For example, suppose a reaction forms a precipitate:

$$2CaOH(aq) + CuCl_2(aq) \rightarrow 2CaCl(aq) + Cu(OH)_2(s)$$

Notice that both the left and right sides contain Ca^+ and Cl^- ions. In other words, these ions do not react. Omitting these ions gives the unbalanced net ionic equation:

$$OH^-(aq) + Cu^{2+}(aq) \rightarrow Cu(OH)_2(s).$$

To balance this equation, you need to balance both the atoms and the charges. Placing the coefficient 2 in front of $OH^-(aq)$ will give you

$$2OH^-(aq) + Cu^{2+}(aq) \rightarrow Cu(OH)_2(s).$$

✓ **CHECK FOR UNDERSTANDING** What are the four steps in balancing a chemical equation?

Mass-Mass Conversions

Look at Figure 5.8 on page 78. You can use this "mole roadmap" to find the mass of an unknown. The steps are not always the same, but generally the procedure is straight forward. In mass-mass stoichiometry, you are given the mass of a reactant or product, and you are asked to find the mass of one of the other species in the reaction equation. Generally, you will need to convert mass to moles, and then convert moles to mass. The following is a list of steps for doing mass-to-mass stoichiometry.

1 Write a balanced equation for the reaction.

2 Label the known and unknown quantities above those substances in the equation.

3 Write the molar masses below each of the substances.

4 To begin the solution process, write the given value over "1." This clearly delineates where the divisor line will be located throughout the computation.

5 Use dimensional analysis to go from mass to moles, to mole ratio, and moles to mass. Do this in successive steps on your calculator.

6 Make sure that each value is clearly labeled with both the units and the formula of the substance it represents. This will ensure that you put the correct values in the correct places during your computation.

7 Label your final result with units and the correct chemical formula.

Example Problem 3

How many grams of water vapor are produced when 6.0 grams of hydrogen react completely with oxygen?

1 Analyze the Problem

- You are given the mass of one of the reactants, hydrogen, and you are asked to find the mass of the product, water. You do not need to know the mass of oxygen.
- First, write the complete equation for the balanced reaction.
- Then convert the given mass of hydrogen to moles of hydrogen.
- Then use the equation to determine the number of moles of water that will be produced.
- Finally, convert the moles of water produced to mass of water produced.

Known:
mass of H_2 = 6.0 g

Unknown:
mass of H_2O

2 Solve for the Unknown

Write the balanced equation.

$$2H_2(g) + O_2(g) \rightarrow 2H_2O(g)$$

Convert mass of hydrogen to moles of hydrogen.

$$6.0 \text{ g } H_2O \times \frac{1 \text{ mol}}{2.0 \text{ g } H_2} = 3.0 \text{ mol } H_2$$

Use the equation to determine the number of moles of H_2O produced.

H_2 and H_2O have the same coefficient in the balanced equation, so 3 mol of H_2O are produced when 3 mol of H_2 react.

Convert the moles of water produced to mass of water produced.

$$3.0 \text{ mol } H_2O \times \frac{18 \text{ g } H_2O}{1 \text{ mol } H_2O} = 54 \text{ g } H_2O$$

3 Evaluate the Answer

- **Does the answer make sense?** You know that in 1 mol of H_2O has a mass of 18 g and contains 2.0 g H_2. Therefore it is reasonable that 3.0 mol H_2 would produce three times as much water, or 54 g.

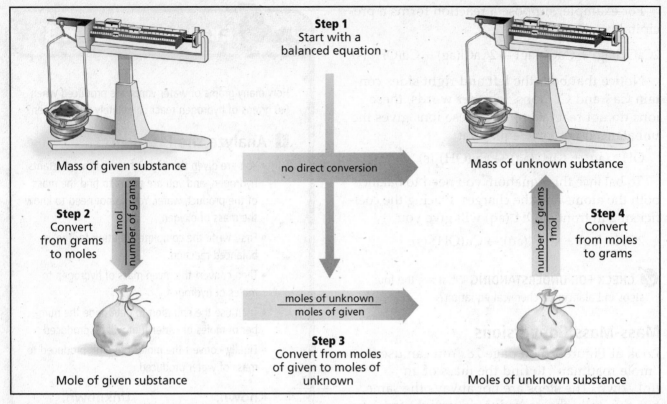

Figure 5.8 This roadmap is helpful for determining the mass of an unknown in a stoichiometry problem.

Conservation of Energy

In any chemical or physical reaction, an accompanying energy change always occurs. We know from the law of conservation of energy that the total energy present must be accounted for in both the reactants and the products, just like we did with the mass. Energy absorbed will be found in the bond energies of the products, while energy released comes from the bond energies of the reactants. Summing these two terms yields the overall energy change for the chemical reaction. Energy is conserved because any energy released or absorbed was or is contained in the potential energy of the chemical bonds of the substances whose compositions were changed in the reaction.

Energy also is conserved in physical changes, and energy absorbed or evolved will have been converted to or from the potential energy involved in the phase change or in the solution process.

✔ **CHECK FOR UNDERSTANDING** Why is energy conserved in a chemical reaction?

Excess Reactants and Limiting Reactants

When compounds and/or elements react, all the mass of the reactants must be present in the products, as seen in Figure 5.9. If one reactant is used in excess, that excess also will be present

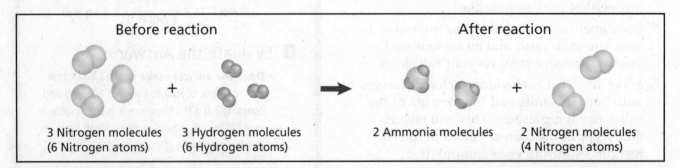

Figure 5.9 In this reaction, two ammonia molecules are produced, leaving two unused nitrogen molecules. Since this nitrogen is left over, it is the excess reactant. What is the limiting reactant?

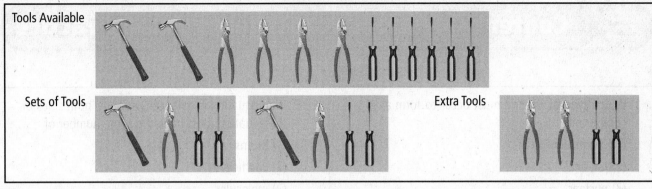

Figure 5.10 In this analogy for limiting reactants, there are not enough hammers to produce three complete sets of tools.

among the products. An **excess reactant** is a reactant that remains after a chemical reaction stops. This is a very important point to understand, and is used extensively in chemical experiments and calculations. Note that it is really just another aspect of the law of conservation of mass.

If there is an excess of one of the reactants, then another reactant will be the limiting reactant. A **limiting reactant** is totally consumed during a chemical reaction and therefore, limits the extent of the reaction. A limiting reactant determines the amount of each of the products.

Figure 5.10 shows an analogy for limiting reactants. Suppose the tools shown will be used to fill toolboxes at a manufacturer. How many boxes can be produced? Only two sets of tools can be produced because there are only two hammers. In this case, the hammer is the limiting reactant.

Balancing Charge in Net Ionic Equations

Electrons can be transferred among atoms, but all the electrons must be accounted for. This is done when balancing redox (oxidation-reduction) equations as discussed in Section 8. The net sum of all negative and positive charge must appear on both sides of a chemical equation. This means that if an equation is written in ionic form, all the charges must balance, as they do in this reaction:

$$NH_4^+ + NaOH \rightarrow NH_4OH + Na^+$$

Quick Review

28 If an equation is balanced, it means that

(1) there must be a limiting reactant

(2) there must be an excess reactant

(3) the coefficient ratios give the mass ratios

(4) the coefficient ratios give the mole ratios

29 Explain how a net ionic equation can be more useful than the complete equation.

30 How would you determine which product is the precipitate in a double-replacement reaction?

31 Sucrose has a molar mass of 342 grams/mol. This means that

(1) 3.00 mol of sucrose has a mass of 1026 g

(2) 342 g of sucrose contains 1.806×10^{24} molecules

(3) 3.00 g of sucrose = 0.100 mole

(4) 1.00 mol of sucrose = 100.00 g

32 The formula for sulfuric acid is H_2SO_4 and its molar mass is 98 grams/mole. This means that

(1) 98 g of sulfuric acid has two atoms of hydrogen

(2) 98 g of sulfuric acid has 4 mol of sulfate ion

(3) 9.8 g of sulfuric acid has 0.10 mol of H_2SO_4

(4) there are 6.02×10^{23} atoms in 98 g of H_2SO_4

33 If the law of conservation of energy says that energy cannot be created or destroyed in ordinary chemical and physical reactions, explain how energy can seem to disappear in some instances, like when you heat an ice cube and it doesn't get hot?

34 If you react 16 grams of oxygen with 4.0 grams of hydrogen, you'll

(1) obtain 20. g of water

(2) have 2.0 g of hydrogen as the excess reactant

(3) have 2.0 g of hydrogen as the limiting reactant

(4) have 4.0 g of oxygen as the excess reactant

35 Explain why forming bonds is exothermic and breaking bonds is endothermic.

36 Give at least two reasons why a chemist might want to have one of the reactants in a particular reaction be in excess.

Content Questions for Regents Exam Practice

Part A

1 Which type of change must occur to form a compound?

(1) chemical

(2) physical

(3) nuclear

(4) phase

2 The molecular formula of a compound is represented by X_3Y_6. What is the empirical formula of this compound?

(1) X_3Y (3) XY_2

(2) X_2Y (4) XY_3

3 Which structural formula is incorrect?

(1)

(3)

(2)

(4)

4 An example of an empirical formula is

(1) CH_4

(2) C_2H_4

(3) $C_2H_4(OH)_2$

(4) $C_6H_{12}O_6$

5 When an equation is correctly balanced, it must show conservation of

(1) charge but not of mass

(2) mass but not of charge

(3) both charge and mass

(4) neither charge nor mass

6 If an equation is balanced properly, both sides of the equation must have the same number of

(1) atoms

(2) coefficients

(3) molecules

(4) moles of molecules

7 Given the unbalanced equation:

$Al(s) + O_2(g) \rightarrow Al_2O_3(s)$

When this equation is correctly balanced using smallest whole numbers, what is the coefficient of $O_2(g)$?

(1) 6   (3) 3

(2) 2   (4) 4

8 A compound whose empirical formula is NO_2 could have a molecular mass of

(1) 23   (3) 92

(2) 39   (4) 120

9 Given the incomplete equation:

$2N_2O_5(g) \rightarrow$

Which set of products completes and balances the incomplete equation?

(1) $2N_2(g) + 3H_2(g)$

(2) $2N_2(g) + 2O_2(g)$

(3) $4NO_2(g) + O_2(g)$

(4) $4NO(g) + 5O_2(g)$

10 Given the unbalanced equation:

$N_2(g) + H_2(g) \rightarrow NH_3(g)$

When the equation is balanced using *smallest* whole-number coefficients, the ratio of moles of hydrogen consumed to moles of ammonia produced is

(1) 1:3   (3) 3:1

(2) 2:3   (4) 3:2

11 Given the unbalanced equation:

$$\_CaSO_4 + \_AlCl_3 \rightarrow \_Al_2(SO_4)_3 + \_CaCl_2$$

What is the coefficient of $Al_2(SO_4)_3$ when the equation is completely balanced using the smallest whole-number coefficients?

(1) 1   (3) 3

(2) 2   (4) 4

12 The empirical formula of a compound is CH_2. Which molecular formula is correctly paired with a structural formula for this compound?

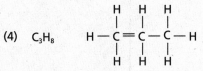

(1) C_2H_4

(2) C_2H_4

(3) C_3H_8

(4) C_3H_8

13 Given the balanced equation:

$$2Na + S \rightarrow Na_2S$$

What is the total number of moles of S that reacted when 4.0 moles of Na were completely consumed?

(1) 1.0 mol

(2) 2.0 mol

(3) 0.5 mol

(4) 4.0 mol

14 Given the balanced equation:

$$Fe(s) + CuSO_4(aq) \rightarrow FeSO_4(aq) + Cu(s)$$

What total mass of iron is necessary to produce 1.00 mole of copper?

(1) 26.0 g

(2) 55.8 g

(3) 112 g

(4) 192 g

15 What is the total number of moles of sulfur atoms in 1 mole of $Fe_2(SO_4)_3$?

(1) 1

(2) 15

(3) 3

(4) 17

16 One mole of O_2 has approximately the same mass as one mole of what element?

17 What is the gram formula mass of NH_4Cl?

18 A compound was analyzed and found to contain 75 percent carbon and 25 percent hydrogen by mass. What is the compound's empirical formula?

19 What is the percent by mass of carbon in $HC_2H_3O_2$?

20 MgO and Co are two substances commonly found in nature, however, only one of these substances can be decomposed chemically. Which one can be decomposed chemically and why?

21 A hydrate is a compound that includes water molecules within its crystal structure. During an experiment to determine the percent by mass of water in a hydrated crystal, a student found the mass of the hydrated crystal to be 4.10 grams. After heating to constant mass, the mass was 3.70 grams. What is the percent by mass of water in this crystal?

22 Given the unbalanced equation:

_____N$_2$(g) + _____O$_2$(g) → _____N$_2$O$_5$(g)

What is the balanced equation when using smallest whole numbers?

23 Given the reaction between two different elements in the gaseous state:

Box A below represents a mixture of the two reactants before the reaction occurs. The product of this reaction is a gas. In box B, draw the system after the reaction has gone to completion, based on the law of conservation of matter.

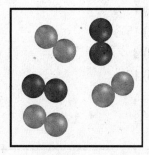

Box A
System Before Reaction

Box B
System After Reaction

Base your answers to questions 24 through 26 on the information below.

Barium chloride is a hydrated compound that contains water molecules within its crystalline structure. Its chemical formula is BaCl$_2$•2H$_2$O. Barium chloride contains 2 moles of water for each 1 mole of barium.

24 What is the gram formula mass of BaCl$_2$•2H$_2$O?

25 Show a correct numerical setup for calculating the percent composition by mass of water in this compound.

26 What is the percent composition by mass of water in BaCl$_2$•2H$_2$O?

Physical Behavior of Matter

VOCABULARY

activation energy
boiling point
catalyst
chemical change
chromatography
collision theory
combined gas law
dipole-dipole forces
distillation
enthalpy

freezing point
gas
Henry's law
Hess's law
heterogeneous mixture
homogeneous mixture
hydrogen bond
kinetic-molecular theory
law of conservation of energy
liquid

mixture
molarity
physical change
solid
solute
solution
solvent
specific heat
states of matter
substance

Everywhere you look there is an amazing variety of matter, and almost every kind of matter occurs naturally in different forms that have different physical properties. Liquid water, for example, has very different properties from solid ice or gaseous steam, yet all three are composed of the same basic building block—water molecules. In this section, you will investigate how physical changes affect the properties of matter.

Classifications of Matter

Look at the classifications of matter shown in Figure 6.1. A **substance** is a pure form of matter that has a uniform composition and consists entirely of only one kind of matter. Substances have one representative particle: atom, molecule, or formula unit. A substance can be either an element or a compound. Recall that an element is composed only of atoms with the same atomic number. Compounds are chemical combinations of two or more elements.

Anything that is not a substance is called a **mixture**, which is a physical blend of two or more pure substances in which each substance

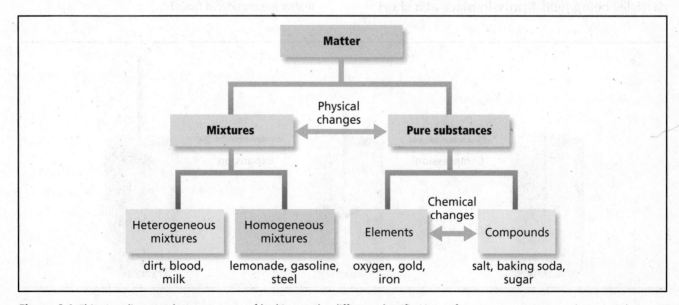

Figure 6.1 This tree diagram shows one way of looking at the different classifications of matter.

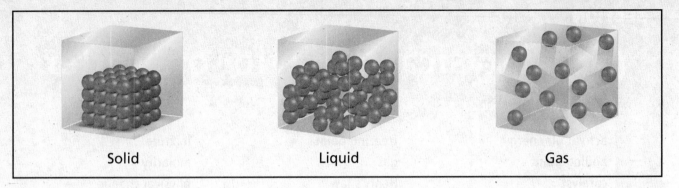

Solid   Liquid   Gas

Figure 6.2 The particles in a solid are in a rigid, orderly arrangement. The particles in a liquid have some freedom to move and create different arrangements. Particles in the gas phase are completely separated and can create an almost infinite number of arrangements.

retains its individual properties. If a mixture is uniform at the particle level and has a single phase, it is called a **solution**, or a **homogeneous mixture**. If it is not uniform and the individual substances are distinguishable, it is called a **heterogeneous mixture**.

States of Matter

States of matter are the physical forms in which all matter naturally exists on Earth—most commonly as a solid, a liquid, or a gas. Figure 6.2 shows the representative particles in solids, liquids, and gases.

Solids generally are incompressible under normal conditions, and have a fixed shape. They can be crystalline, with a definite geometric arrangement of atoms, molecules, or ions, or amorphous (without shape). These macroscopic properties are a result of the constituent particles being held firmly in place at a short and definite distance by attractive forces. At the microscopic level, the particles can vibrate only in place.

Liquids are incompressible and take the shape of their containers. These properties are a result of attractive forces holding the particles together at a fixed distance, yet enabling them to move more freely. Therefore, the particles can flow.

Gases are compressible and expand to occupy the volume of the container in which they are enclosed, as shown in Figure 6.3. The particles of a gas have negligible attractive forces holding them to other gas particles and are not at fixed distances from each other. The particles can move freely around in relation to each other. Gases, like liquids, are fluids; they can flow.

☑ **CHECK FOR UNDERSTANDING** Which two states of matter are considered fluids?

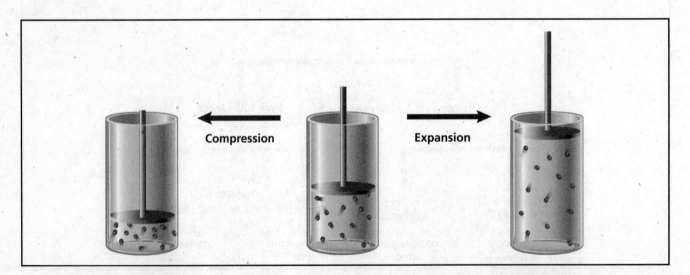

Compression   Expansion

Figure 6.3 A gas can expand or be compressed; the particles fill the volume of the container in which they are enclosed.

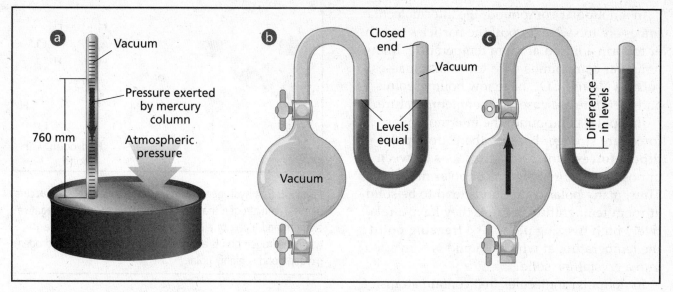

Figure 6.4 (a) A simple barometer is used to measure air pressure. **(b)** A manometer is used to measure the pressure of an enclosed gas. **(c)** The levels of the mercury are no longer equal once a gas is introduced.

Gases exert pressure on the container holding them, but they also exert pressure in our atmosphere, which can be measured by a barometer as shown in Figure 6.4(a). A simple barometer measures the pressure exerted by the atmosphere on a column of mercury. The air pressure balances the pressure of the column of mercury. Note that an open end must face the atmosphere.

A manometer measures the pressure exerted by a gas. In the manometer shown in Figure 6.4(b), the levels of mercury are equal because there is a vacuum on each side of the U-shaped tube. A gas is introduced and the stopcock is opened, as shown in Figure 6.4(c). The levels of the mercury change because the pressure is greater in the side of the tube containing the gas. The difference in the levels of mercury is used to determine the pressure of the enclosed gas.

There is a fourth state of matter, called plasma, in which atoms have lost some or all of their electrons. A plasma, like a gas, is a fluid, but the particles in it are mostly electrons and ions rather than neutral atoms or molecules. Although plasma is not common on Earth, most of the universe consists of hydrogen and helium in the plasma state. On Earth, the most familiar examples of plasma include lightning, gas-discharge tubes (neon lights), and fluorescent lightbulbs.

✓ **CHECK FOR UNDERSTANDING** What are three phases of matter and how does each differ from the others?

Intermolecular Forces

Intermolecular forces are electric forces of attraction among the molecules in a molecular compound. You can use a knowledge of intermolecular forces and polarity to predict the properties of a substance.

Recall that if two atoms are covalently bonded, their shared electrons are more likely to be found in the electron cloud of the atom with the greater electronegativity. The bond is a polar bond if a significant dipole forms. But a molecule may not be polar even if it contains polar bonds. A molecule is polar only if it has polar bonds and the molecule is asymmetrical.

The intermolecular forces in nonpolar compounds are weak because there is no net charge on each molecule and there are no dipoles. Thus, nonpolar compounds tend to be gases with relatively low boiling points. Why?

A substance changes from a liquid to a gas at its boiling point. The **boiling point** is defined as the temperature at which a liquid's vapor pressure is equal to the external or atmospheric pressure. Temperature is a measure of the average kinetic energy of particles in a sample of matter. At higher temperatures, particles move faster, on average. At the boiling point, the particles move fast enough to overcome the intermolecular forces, and so the substance changes from a liquid to a gas. This is called a change of state.

In a nonpolar compound, the intermolecular forces are too weak to pull the particles together to form a liquid at room temperature. Many nonpolar compounds with low molar masses, such as N_2 and CO_2, have low boiling points and therefore are gases at room temperature.

In a polar compound, the intermolecular forces are stronger because there are **dipole-dipole forces**, which are attractions between oppositely charged regions of polar molecules. Thus, many polar compounds tend to be solid at room temperature because they have a relatively high freezing point. The **freezing point** is the temperature at which a liquid is converted into a crystalline solid.

In nonpolar molecules that contain atoms of high atomic mass, temporary dipoles can form due to the large electron cloud, which repels the bonded atom's electron cloud. This temporarily exposes more of the nuclear charge of the more massive atom, which, in turn, attracts the electron cloud of a second molecule, as shown in Figure 6.5. These temporary attractive forces that are weaker than dipole-dipole forces are called dispersion forces. Dispersion forces help to explain the higher boiling points of these substances.

Hydrogen bonds are strong dipole-dipole attractions among molecules that contain a hydrogen atom bonded to a small, highly electronegative atom with at least one lone electron pair. Hydrogen bonds among water molecules are shown in Figure 6.6. These attractions are particularly important in biological systems.

✔ **CHECK FOR UNDERSTANDING** How do nonpolar molecules with high atomic masses form temporary dipoles?

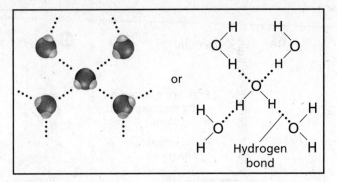

Figure 6.6 A hydrogen bond is an attractive force that occurs between a hydrogen that is bonded to a more electronegative element and a pair of electrons on an adjacent molecule. In water, hydrogen bonds are quite strong because the hydrogen-oxygen bond is highly polar.

Physical and Chemical Changes

A **physical change** is a type of change that alters the physical properties of a substance but does not change its composition. Physical changes include changes of state and dissolution. In both cases, a rearrangement of existing particles occurs without a change in identity of the substances involved. Physical changes often are reversible, as shown in Figure 6.7.

In a **chemical change**, also called a chemical reaction, new substances with different physical and chemical properties are produced. Many chemical changes are difficult to reverse.

Chemical properties are descriptions of what a substance will or will not react with to undergo a chemical change. Typically the description includes such phrases as *reacts with*, or *burns*, or *decomposes upon heating*.

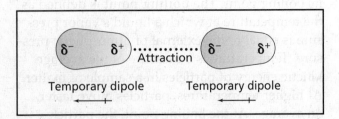

Figure 6.5 The temporary dipole has partial negative ($\delta-$) and partial positive ($\delta+$) charges of equal magnitude. These dipoles allow for the attraction between molecules, as shown by the dotted line. Do only polar molecules have dipoles?

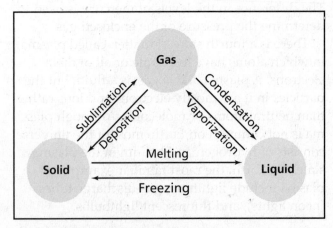

Figure 6.7 These are the six possible phase changes among the three states of matter shown above. What phase changes can occur between gases and solids? What phase changes can occur between solids and liquids?

A chemical change usually is identified by the way new substances are formed. The following changes are evidence that a chemical change may have occurred:

1 A precipitate forms.
2 A gas forms (effervescence).
3 A color change occurs.
4 A change in odor occurs.
5 A discernible energy change occurs; heat and/or light is given off or absorbed.

In any given chemical change, you would not expect all of these changes to occur, and in some cases, one of these changes will occur when there is no chemical change.

✓ **CHECK FOR UNDERSTANDING** Why is water freezing considered a physical change?

Separating Mixtures

Each component in a mixture retains its own physical and chemical properties. The components can be separated from the mixture by an appropriate laboratory operation based upon those differing physical properties. Some common methods of separation include:

1 Filtration, in which solids are separated from a mixture based on differences in the size of the particles, some of which do not pass through the pores of a filter,
2 Decantation, in which a less-dense liquid or solution is drawn off from components of greater density, usually in a separatory funnel,
3 **Distillation**, a technique of physically separating a homogeneous mixture based on differences in the boiling points of the substances involved,
4 Crystallization, in which a substance comes out of solution as a solid when the solution is cooled or is allowed to evaporate,
5 **Chromatography**, which is a technique used to separate the components of a mixture based on the tendency of each component to travel or be drawn across the surface of another material, and
6 Extraction, in which a component of a mixture is removed because it tends to form a solution with another substance.

Chemical separation also is possible and sometimes is used. However, a second chemical reaction would be necessary to regenerate the substance that had been separated out.

1 Choose the substance from the following:
   (1) saltwater   (3) air
   (2) brass   (4) table salt

2 Is a mineral found on a gemology expedition likely to be a substance? Explain your reasoning.

3 If you had a very small sample of a substance to analyze, why would it be preferable to use physical properties to identify it? Explain.

4 Choose a physical change from the following:
   (1) synthesizing   (3) burning
   (2) dissolving   (4) decomposing

5 Choose the property from this list that is *not* a physical property:
   (1) solubility   (3) density
   (2) color   (4) electronegativity

6 Which of the following is *not* likely to be evidence of a chemical change?
   (1) A solid disappears when it is added to a liquid.
   (2) A solid changes color when it is heated.
   (3) A precipitate forms when two liquids are mixed together.
   (4) Gas bubbles form when a solid is added to a liquid.

7 List some common laboratory processes used for separating mixtures.

8 Which of the following is *not* a method used to separate a mixture?
   (1) filtration
   (2) distillation
   (3) decomposition
   (4) chromatography

9 A plasma consists of which kinds of particles?
   (1) mostly positive ions
   (2) mostly electrons
   (3) mostly neutral particles
   (4) approximately equal numbers of electrons and positive ions

10 The boiling point of methane is $-161.48°C$, while pentane boils at $36.06°C$. Which substance has stronger intermolecular forces? Explain.

Table 6.1 • Some Types and Examples of Solutions			
Type of Solution	Example	Solvent	Solute
Gas			
Gas in gas	Air	Nitrogen (gas)	Oxygen (gas)
Liquid			
Gas in liquid	Carbonated water	Water (liquid)	Carbon dioxide (gas)
Gas in liquid	Ocean water	Water (liquid)	Oxygen gas (gas)
Liquid in liquid	Antifreeze	Water (liquid)	Ethylene glycol (liquid)
Liquid in liquid	Vinegar	Water (liquid)	Acetic acid (liquid)
Solid in liquid	Ocean water	Water (liquid)	Sodium chloride (solid)
Solid			
Liquid in solid	Dental amalgam	Silver (solid)	Mercury (liquid)
Solid in solid	Steel	Iron (solid)	Carbon (solid)

Solutions

There are many types of solutions, including a solid in a solid (an alloy is a solution of metals), a solid in a liquid, a liquid in a liquid, and a gas in a gas. The solid, or lesser volume of liquid, that is dissolved in a liquid or solid is designated as the **solute.** The substance that dissolves a solute to form a solution is called the **solvent.** The solvents and solutes of some common solutions are shown in Table 6.1.

Solutions in water are called aqueous solutions. When ionic solutes dissolve in water, the polar water molecules pull both negative and positive ions from the crystal into solution, as shown in Figure 6.8(a). With molecular solutes, the water molecules pull solute molecules into solution. Then the water molecules surround the solute molecules, as shown in Figure 6.8(b).

There are other kinds of mixtures intermediate between a solution and a heterogeneous mixture that are called colloids. Their classification is based upon the particle size of the solute. Examples of colloids are sols, aerosols, gels, emulsions, and foams.

✓ CHECK FOR UNDERSTANDING What combinations of matter can be used to create a solution?

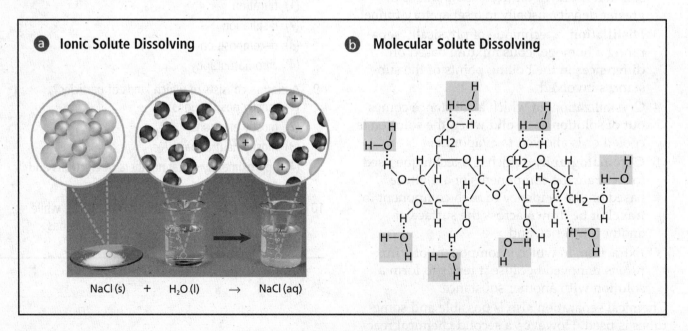

Figure 6.8 (a) Ionic solids, such as sodium chloride (NaCl), dissolve to form ions in aqueous solution. **(b)** Molecular solutes like sucrose ($C_{12}H_{22}O_{11}$) dissolve and then are surrounded by several water molecules.

Concentration

Table 6.2 shows the ratios used to designate the composition of a mixture: percent by mass, percent by volume, mole-fraction, molarity, molality, and ppm, ppb, and ppt (parts per million, billion, and trillion respectively). Percent can be seen as equivalent to parts per hundred (pph).

Mole-fraction is used extensively with gases. To calculate mole-fraction, divide the moles of a given gas by the total number of moles in the mixture. Similarly, the moles of a solid or liquid solute can be divided by the sum of the moles of solute and solvent to obtain its mole-fraction.

Molarity, M, is defined as the moles of solute per liter of solution. Molality, m, is defined as the moles of solute per kilogram of solvent. For dilute solutions in water these are very nearly the same value. If you were to add more solute to a liquid and it would keep dissolving, the solution is considered unsaturated. When the solution has dissolved all of the solute that is possible, the solution is considered saturated.

Parts per million (ppm) is a very common designation for trace amounts of nutrients, as well as for pollutants. The very small amount present is expressed as a mass-fraction or as a volume-fraction, which then is multiplied by 10^6, 10^9, or 10^{12}, to get ppm, ppb, or ppt, respectively. For example, if the amount of carbon dioxide in the atmosphere is given as 360 ppm, it means that the volume-fraction of CO_2 is $\frac{360}{1,000,000}$.

☑ **CHECK FOR UNDERSTANDING** In what ways can the composition of a mixture be expressed?

Table 6.2 • Concentration Ratios

Concentration Description	Ratio
Percent by mass	$\dfrac{\text{kilograms of solute}}{\text{kilograms of solution}} \times 100$
Percent by volume for a liquid	$\dfrac{\text{liters of solute}}{\text{liters of solution}} \times 100$
Molarity	$\dfrac{\text{moles of solute}}{\text{liters of solution}}$
Molality	$\dfrac{\text{moles of solute}}{\text{kilograms of solvent}}$
Mole-fraction	$\dfrac{\text{moles of solute}}{\text{moles of solute + moles of solvent}}$

Example Problem 1

A soft drink company has just released a new product containing only 20.0 grams of sugar as opposed to 41.6 grams of sugar in an ordinary 12-fluid-ounce can of soda. The amount of soda that the sugar is dissolved into in the new and old cans is 0.3400 kilograms and 0.3184 kilograms, respectively. What is the difference in the percent by mass of sugar in the two different soda cans?

1 Analyze the Problem

- You are given the amount of sugar dissolved into the respective amount of soda. The percent by mass of a solute is the ratio of the solute's mass to the solution's mass, which is the sum of the masses of the solute and the solvent.

Known:	Unknown:
New Soda:	
Solute mass = 20.0 g	Percent by mass = ?
Solvent mass = 0.3400 kg	
Old Soda:	
Solute mass = 41.6 g	Percent by mass = ?
Solvent mass = 0.3184 kg	

2 Solve for the Unknown

Find the mass of solution for each soda.
Mass of solution = grams of solute + grams of solvent

New soda
340.0 g + 20.0 g = 360.0 g
Old soda
318.4 g + 41.6 g = 360.0 g

Substitute the unknown values into the percent-by-mass equation.

$$\text{Percent by mass} = \frac{\text{Mass of solute}}{\text{Mass of solution}} \times 100$$

New soda
$$\frac{20.0 \text{ g}}{360.0 \text{ g}} \times 100 = 5.56\%$$

Old soda
$$\frac{41.6 \text{ g}}{360.0 \text{ g}} \times 100 = 11.6\%$$

Subtract the percent by mass of the old soda by the percent by mass of the new soda.

11.6% − 5.56% = 6.0% difference

3 Evaluate the Answer

- **Does the answer make sense?** Since the new soda has about half the amount of sugar, the new soda also should have about half the percent by mass of sugar.

Solubility

A mixture has no fixed composition. However, the maximum ratio of solute to solvent in a solid or liquid solution generally is limited by the solubility of that solute in that solvent. Solubility is defined as the maximum amount of solute that will dissolve in a given amount of solvent at a specific temperature and pressure. Solubility usually is measured in grams of solute per 100 g of solvent. The factors that affect solubility include the polarity of the solute and solvent, temperature, and (for gases) pressure.

Effect of Polarity on Solubility

How does polarity of the solute and solvent affect solubility? The guiding principle for solubility is "like dissolves like." Polar solvents dissolve polar and ionic compounds best. Nonpolar solvents dissolve nonpolar molecular compounds best. For example, sodium chloride is an ionic compound that dissolves readily in water, which is a polar molecule. But sodium chloride does not dissolve readily in oil because the oil molecules are nonpolar.

Varying degrees of solubility are seen with polar compounds dissolving in nonpolar or polar solvents. Table 6.3 shows how to determine solubility based on which ions an ionic compound contains. You can see from the table that all nitrate compounds, for example, are soluble, and that many carbonate compounds are insoluble.

Polarity also affects the solubility of gases. Ammonia gas, for example, consists of polar molecules. Ammonia has a much greater solubility in water than nonpolar gases, such as carbon dioxide or oxygen.

With a liquid in a liquid, the term miscibility is used to designate whether a given liquid will mix with another. Generally it is said that liquids are miscible if they are capable of mixing in any proportion. Gases, by definition, are miscible in all proportions, since it can be assumed they exist as separate and independent particles that require no energy to separate.

✓ CHECK FOR UNDERSTANDING Why do polar solutes tend to dissolve readily in polar solvents?

Table 6.3 • Solubility Guidelines for Aqueous Solutions

Ions that Form Soluble Compounds	Exceptions	Ions that Form Insoluble Compounds	Exceptions
Group 1 ions (Li^+, Na^+, etc.)		Carbonate (CO_3^{2-})	when combined with Group 1 ions or ammonium (NH_4^+)
Ammonium (NH_4^+)		Chromate (CrO_4^{2-})	when combined with Group 1 ions, Ca^{2+}, Mg^{2+}, or ammonium (NH_4^+)
Nitrate (NO_3^-)		Phosphate (PO_4^{3-})	when combined with Group 1 ions or ammonium (NH_4^+)
Acetate ($C_2H_3O_2^-$ or CH_3COO^-)		Sulfide (S^{2-})	when combined with Group 1 ions or ammonium (NH_4^+)
Hydrogen carbonate (HCO_3^-)		Hydroxide (OH^-)	when combined with Group 1 ions, Ca^{2+}, Ba^{2+}, Sr^{2+}, or ammonium (NH_4^+)
Chlorate (ClO_3^-)			
Perchlorate (ClO_4^-)			
Halides (Cl^-, Br^-, I^-)	when combined with Ag^+, Pb^{2+}, and Hg_2^{2+}		
Sulfates (SO_4^{2-})	when combined with Ag^+, Ca^{2+}, Sr^{2+}, Ba^{2+}, and Pb^{2+}		

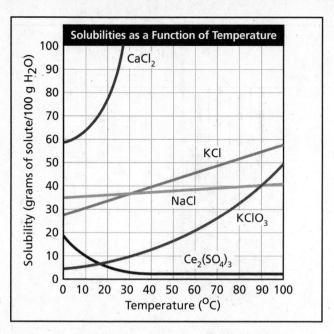

Figure 6.9 These solubility curves indicate the maximum amount of solute that dissolves in water at each temperature.

Effect of Temperature and Pressure on Solubility

Temperature is an important factor in determining the solubility of a solute. The solubility of a gas in water decreases as the water temperature increases. The solubility of the gas decreases because the solute particles are moving faster, on average, at higher temperatures, so they escape more readily from the solution. For example, the solubility of oxygen decreases as the water temperature increases. As a result, aquatic animals and plants are stressed because there is less dissolved oxygen for them to take in. A more familiar example is the buildup of carbon dioxide gas in a can of soda that is left outside on a hot day. As the soda heats up, carbon dioxide comes out of solution into the air space above the soda. When the can opens, the pressurized carbon dioxide gas escapes suddenly.

The solubility of a solid in a liquid also depends on temperature. For many solid solutes, as temperature increases, so does solubility. The solubility of specific solids in liquids generally is obtained either in a table of values given at several temperatures, or using a graph of solubility versus temperature. Figure 6.9 shows solubility curves for several compounds.

✔ CHECK FOR UNDERSTANDING In Figure 6.9, which is more soluble at 70°C, KCl or $KClO_3$? How many grams of NaCl can dissolve into 100 grams of water at 90°C?

The rate at which a solid solute dissolves can be increased by agitation, by breaking up of the solute to increase its surface area, and generally, by increasing the temperature of the solvent.

Pressure is a factor that primarily affects the solubility of gases, as shown in Figure 6.10. **Henry's law** states that the solubility of a gas is directly proportional to the pressure upon it. You can think of the increased pressure as forcing the gas molecules in between the solvent molecules.

✔ CHECK FOR UNDERSTANDING How does pressure affect the solubility of gases?

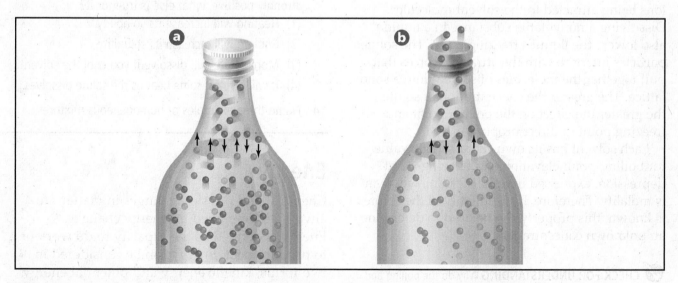

Figure 6.10 (a) In a sealed soda bottle, the carbon dioxide (CO_2) remains in solution because of the constant high pressure. (b) When the bottle is opened, the pressure drops, reducing the solubility of the CO_2 and creating bubbles.

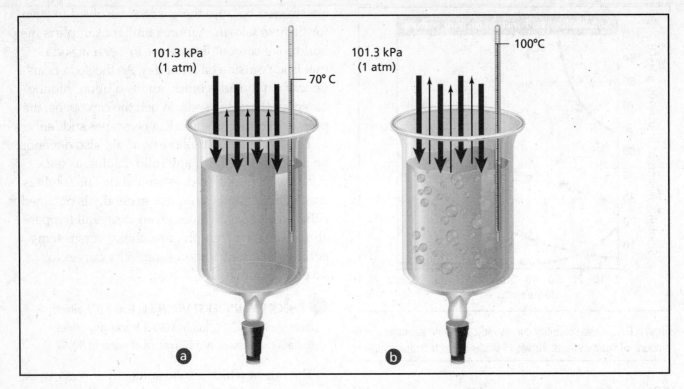

Figure 6.11 (a) The vapor pressure exerted by water increases as temperature increases. **(b)** When the vapor pressure of a liquid reaches atmospheric pressure, the liquid begins to boil. The boiling point of water is 100°C at standard pressure (1 atm).

Effect of Solutes on Boiling Point and Freezing Point

Colligative properties are factors that determine how the properties of a liquid solution, such as boiling point and freezing point, change depending on the concentration of the solute particles. Dissolving a nonvolatile substance, like a salt, in a liquid raises the boiling point, as shown in Figure 6.11. This can be attributed to the solute ions being attracted to the solvent molecules. Dissolving a nonvolatile substance in a liquid also lowers the liquid's freezing point. The solute particles interfere with the attractive forces that pull together the molecules of solvent into a solid lattice. The greater the concentration of solute, the greater the effect on the boiling point and freezing point in direct proportion.

Each solvent has its own characteristic value for boiling-point elevation and freezing-point depression, expressed in units of °C/m, where m is molality. Therefore, if the identity of the solute is known, this property can be used to determine an unknown concentration.

✓ **CHECK FOR UNDERSTANDING** Why do the boiling and freezing points of a solvent change if a nonvolatile substance is dissolved into the solvent?

Quick Review

11 Choose the solution from the following:
   (1) table salt   (3) water
   (2) brass   (4) mercury

12 Explain how a dissolved solute increases the boiling point and decreases the freezing point of the solvent.

13 If the heat of solution for a particular solute is strongly positive, what else is true for it?
   (1) Heating will increase its solubility.
   (2) Cooling will increase its solubility.
   (3) More solute will dissolve if you cool the solvent.
   (4) It will give off some heat as the solute dissolves.

14 Name three examples of homogeneous mixtures.

Energy

Chemical and physical changes in matter are always accompanied by energy changes. Energy is defined as the capacity to do work or to produce heat. Energy can be considered in two forms, kinetic energy and potential energy. Kinetic energy is defined as energy of motion. For example, falling water has kinetic energy.

It can do work, for example, by turning a water wheel. If you lift water to a greater height, you increase its potential energy, which is stored energy, or energy of position. After raising the water, it has a greater potential to do work.

Types of Energy

There are several other kinds of energy that you encounter every day. Mechanical energy can be converted into potential energy, for example, by compressing a spring or by lifting an object to a greater height. Mechanical energy can be transferred from one system to another, but it does not include any internal energy associated with the structure of the system. Internal energy includes thermal energy, which is the energy from moving atoms, molecules, and ions.

Chemical energy is the energy stored in chemical bonds, which is released when bonds are formed. For example, when a car engine burns gasoline, energy stored in chemical bonds in the gasoline is released, and this energy can be used to make the car move. Electric energy is related to the position of an electric charge in an electric field. This energy is provided by batteries and electric power companies. Nuclear energy is the energy stored in the arrangement of the particles in the nucleus. Nuclear energy is used in electric power plants and submarines.

Radiant energy refers to the energy of electromagnetic radiation, which is the energy carried by photons. Radiant energy radiates, or spreads outward, as it moves through space. Most of Earth's energy comes to you in the form of radiant energy from the Sun.

✔ **CHECK FOR UNDERSTANDING** Which type of energy is released when bonds are formed? Which type of energy is carried by photons?

Heat

Heat is energy that is in the process of flowing from a warmer object to a cooler object. Energy always is absorbed or released in any physical or chemical change. Recall that if heat is absorbed during a change, the change is endothermic. If heat is released, the change is exothermic.

Thermal energy is an extensive property of a system, which means its value is greater or lesser in proportion to the mass of the system. For example, a pot of tea has more thermal energy than a cup of tea when both are at the same temperature.

Temperature

Temperature is a measure of the average kinetic energy of particles composing a system. Temperature is an intensive property, which means it is independent of the mass of the system. For example, a chess piece and a chess board are both at room temperature, even though they have different masses.

The Celsius (Centigrade) scale is based upon the normal freezing point of water, defined as 0°C, and the normal boiling point of water, defined as 100°C, both at standard atmospheric pressure. The Kelvin scale begins at absolute zero, the point where all particle motion is at a minimum. Absolute zero, 0 K, is approximately –273°C. The SI system defines the Kelvin scale by adding 273.15° to the Celsius temperature. Note that no degree symbol is used with kelvins.

In the Fahrenheit temperature scale, freezing water is normally 32°F and boiling water is normally 212°F. The formula for converting units is $°C = \frac{5}{9}(°F - 32)$.

The three temperature scales are shown in Figure 6.12. Temperature is measured with mercury or alcohol thermometers, or with a thermocouple, which consists of two dissimilar metals wound about each other. The voltage change in the thermocouple is used to calculate the temperature change.

✔ **CHECK FOR UNDERSTANDING** Why is 273° added to the Celsius temperature to convert to the Kelvin temperature scale?

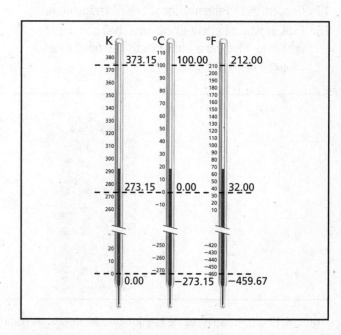

Figure 6.12 Kelvin, Celsius, and Fahrenheit are three common temperature scales.

Law of Conservation of Energy

As a ball falls, its potential energy decreases because its height decreases, but its kinetic energy increases because it moves faster. The potential energy is converted to kinetic energy, but the total energy does not change. **The law of conservation of energy** states that in any chemical or physical process, energy may change from one form to another but it is neither created nor destroyed. It is useful to think in terms of a system, which is a specific region or subset of the universe. A system may lose or gain energy, but the total energy of a system and its surroundings does not change.

Sometimes the law of conservation of energy may seem to be violated because energy is changed to a form that cannot be used. For example, if you glide along flat ground on inline skates, you have kinetic energy. Because the wheels have friction, eventually you come to a stop. The kinetic energy that you started with seems to be lost. But the "lost energy" is converted to thermal energy that heats your surroundings, and so the law of conservation of energy has not been violated.

Quick Review

15 Using your knowledge of bonding, explain the difference between the solvation of an electrolyte and the solvation of a nonelectrolyte.

16 List some examples of potential energy, then list some examples of kinetic energy, and explain how they are different.

17 Convert 98.6° Fahrenheit to a Celsius temperature.

18 Explain why a battery sitting on a shelf and not connected to anything is not correctly described as an example of electric energy.

19 When water (or any other fluid) freezes, it can be said that this process is
    (1) endothermic, because it is cold
    (2) exothermic, because it gives off heat
    (3) neither exothermic nor endothermic because the temperature stays the same

20 Energy that is in the process of flowing from a warmer object to a cooler object is defined as:
    (1) heat   (3) temperature
    (2) thermal energy   (4) specific heat

The Kinetic-Molecular Theory

The **kinetic-molecular theory (KMT),** explains the properties of ideal gases in terms of the energy, size, and motion of their particles. It is assumed that the particles of an ideal gas collide with each other and with the walls of their container without losing kinetic energy. These collisions are called *elastic.* Figure 6.13(b) shows many collisions between a particle and the container walls. Because the collisions are elastic, the particle is not slowed down by these collisions.

Another assumption about ideal gases is that there are no attractive forces among the gas particles, which would affect their energy exchange during collisions. A third assumption is that the distances among particles are so great that the actual volume occupied by the particles is negligible. In other words, they behave as point masses.

The gas laws quantitatively describe the behavior of ideal gases. The gas laws hold true to a large extent for real gases, depending upon the nature of the gas (its molar mass and polarity), and the temperature and pressure of the system.

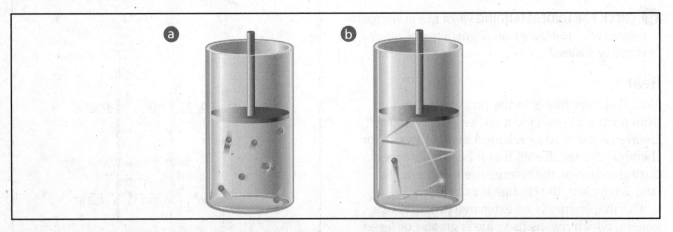

Figure 6.13 (a) According to the kinetic-molecular theory, gas-particle collisions are elastic. This means that each collision can transfer energy from one particle to another, but overall there is no change in the total energy of the system. **(b)** What happens to the speed of a particle after many elastic collisions with the walls of the container?

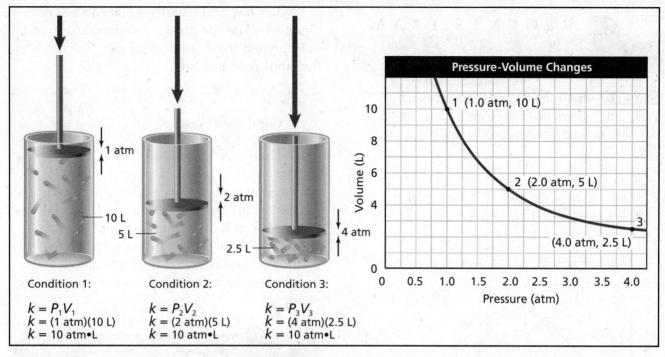

Condition 1:

$k = P_1V_1$
$k = (1\ atm)(10\ L)$
$k = 10\ atm \cdot L$

Condition 2:

$k = P_2V_2$
$k = (2\ atm)(5\ L)$
$k = 10\ atm \cdot L$

Condition 3:

$k = P_3V_3$
$k = (4\ atm)(2.5\ L)$
$k = 10\ atm \cdot L$

Figure 6.14 The gas particles in this cylinder display the inverse relationship between pressure and volume. As pressure increases, volume decreases. As pressure decreases, volume increases.

Boyle's Law

You know from pumping up a bicycle tire that compressing a gas will cause the pressure exerted by the gas to increase. Boyle's law states that at constant temperature the volume of a gas varies inversely with its pressure, as shown in Figure 6.14.

Boyle's Law $V = \dfrac{\text{constant}}{P}$ or $V_1P_1 = V_2P_2$

✓ **CHECK FOR UNDERSTANDING** A sealed bottle of gas is placed inside a sealed container in a vacuum. What happens to the gas pressure in the bottle when it is opened?

Charles's Law

When a gas is heated at constant pressure, the space that gas occupies will increase, as depicted in Figure 6.15. Charles's law states that at a constant pressure, the volume of a gas varies directly with the Kelvin temperature:

Charles's Law $V = (\text{constant})T$ or $\dfrac{V_1}{T_1} = \dfrac{V_2}{T_2}$

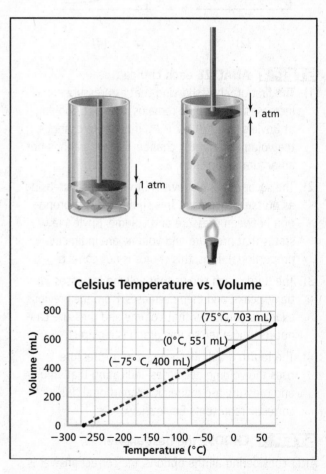

Figure 6.15 The gas particles in the cylinder display a direct relationship between temperature and volume. As temperature increases, volume increases.

STEP 1 **READ the Regents Questions …**

Which graph below best represents the relationship described between pressure and volume in Boyle's law?

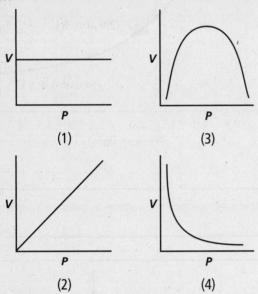

(1)

(3)

(2)

(4)

STEP 2 **ANALYZE each choice …**

(1) The first graph is showing that as pressure increases, the volume remains constant. Looking at Boyle's law, $V_1P_1 = V_2P_2$, if pressure changes, the volume also must change. So this graph is not an accurate depiction.

(2) The second graph shows that volume is increasing as pressure increases. This shows a direct proportion between pressure and volume. Boyle's law states that pressure and volume are indirectly proportional. Thus, this choice is not correct.

(3) The third graph shows that volume increases initially, peaks, and then decreases. From the previous example you know that volume and pressure cannot rise together, so this graph is incorrect.

(4) The fourth graph illustrates that as pressure rises the volume decreases, indicating that volume and pressure are indirectly proportional. This correctly represents Boyle's law.

STEP 3 **CHOOSE the best answer …**

After considering all the options, the correct answer is number 4. It correctly depicts Boyle's law, that pressure and volume are inversely proportional.

Boyle's law and Charles's law can be combined to relate the pressure, temperature, and volume of a fixed quantity of gas. The result is the **combined gas law**.

Combined Gas Law $$\frac{P_1V_1}{T_1} = \frac{P_2V_2}{T_2}$$

The combined gas law allows you to compare the initial and final states of a gas. If you know the initial conditions and two of the three variables in the final state, you can solve for the unknown variable in the final state. Note that temperature must be in kelvins for this equation to apply.

Example Problem 2

A balloon holds 1.00 liters of air at a temperature of 298 K and a pressure of 1.10 atmospheres. The balloon is left in a car on a hot day, and the temperature rises to 320. K while the gas pressure increases to 1.20 atmospheres. What is the volume of the balloon under these conditions?

1 Analyze the Problem

- You are given the initial volume, temperature, and pressure of a gas and asked what the new volume is when the temperature and pressure change.

Known:
$V_1 = 1.00$ L
$P_1 = 1.10$ atm
$T_1 = 298$ K
$P_2 = 1.20$ atm
$T_2 = 320.$ K

Unknown:
$V_2 = ?$ atm

2 Solve for the Unknown

Use the combined gas law to solve for V_2

$$\frac{V_1P_1}{T_1} = \frac{V_2P_2}{T_2}$$

$$V_2 = \frac{V_1P_1T_2}{P_2T_1}$$

$$= \frac{(1.00 \text{ L})(1.10 \text{ atm})(320. \text{ K})}{(1.20 \text{ atm})(298 \text{ K})}$$

$$= 0.984 \text{ L}$$

3 Evaluate the Answer

- **Are the units correct?** The answer is expressed in liters, a unit of volume.

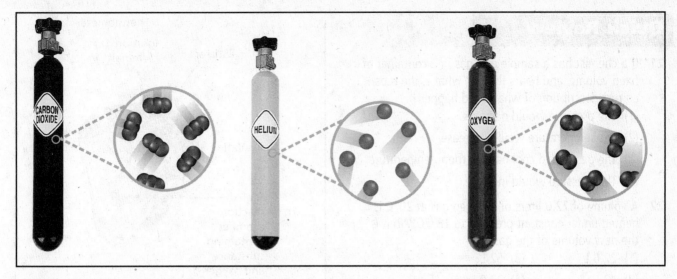

Figure 6.16 Gases in these tanks are at equal pressure and equal volume. Therefore, according to Avogadro's principle, the tanks contain equal numbers of particles.

Avogadro's Hypothesis

By making careful measurements of masses of reactants and products and the volumes of gases involved, Avogadro concluded that equal volumes of gas, at the same conditions of temperature and pressure, contain the same number of particles (atoms or molecules), as shown in Figure 6.16. This is consistent with the fact that temperature is the measure of the average kinetic energy of the particles. According to the formula, $E_k = \frac{1}{2}mv^2$, where E_k is the kinetic energy, m is the mass and v is the velocity, particles with more mass will move slower on average. Because the volume and pressure are not related to the molar mass (point masses are assumed), the composition of the particles must not matter.

Avogadro went on to use this principle to prove the diatomic nature of hydrogen, nitrogen, oxygen, and chlorine. If one volume each of hydrogen and chlorine react to form one volume of hydrogen chloride gas, the pressure in the reaction vessel should decrease by one-half; it did not. This is consistent with the fact that diatomic molecules of hydrogen and chlorine reacting would produce two volumes of HCl. This same analysis can be done for water vapor and for ammonia gas. This work by Avogadro helped to establish an even more quantitative basis for chemistry.

Recall that a mole of a gas contains an Avogadro's number of particles. The volume this occupies at standard conditions (STP), 273 K and 101.3 kPa, is 22.4138 L. This is defined as the molar volume, V_m, and is used in stoichiometric calculations involving gases. Remember that to use this value for the molar volume, the combined gas law must be used to convert to and from STP.

✔ **CHECK FOR UNDERSTANDING** What is the molar volume of any gas at STP?

The Ideal Gas Law

The relationship between temperature in kelvins and pressure can be described by the ideal gas law equation:

$PV = nRT$

In this equation R, the universal gas constant, is equal to 0.0821 L•atm/mol•K. The ideal gas law assumes that intermolecular forces are negligible. A nonideal gas composed of polar molecules will have greater intermolecular forces acting during collisions than an ideal gas. This will tend to contract the volume (or lower the pressure) of the nonideal gas somewhat. At low temperatures, the molecules are moving more slowly on average, which gives attractive forces more time to have an effect, also lowering the pressure or volume. At high pressures, the molecules will be pressed closer together, giving more opportunity for them to interact and contracting the gas further. And finally, molecules of high molar mass will, by definition, be larger than point masses and so will take up appreciable volume themselves, especially when close together. Therefore, gases tend to behave most ideally at high temperatures and low pressures.

21 If a chemist has a sample of a gas in a container of fixed volume, and heats the gas, what is the most correct description of what could happen?

(1) The pressure would decrease.

(2) The temperature would decrease.

(3) The gas would cool back to room temperature.

(4) The pressure would increase.

22 A volume of 22.0 liters of nitrogen gas at 20°C is heated under constant pressure to 167°C. What is the new volume of the gas?

(1) 22.0 L   (3) 52 L

(2) 43 L   (4) 33.0 L

23 Without doing any calculations on paper or a calculator, what pressure would 121.6 kilopascals be closest to?

(1) 1 atm

(2) 1.2 atm

(3) 740 mm Hg

(4) 790 mm Hg

24 Explain why it is necessary to have the concept of an "elastic collision" when describing the behavior of gas molecules. What would happen if this particular phenomenon were not occurring?

25 An ideal gas is defined to have all of the following characteristics except

(1) the particles occupy no volume

(2) the particles stick briefly to the sides of the container

(3) the particles bounce off of each other without sticking together

(4) as particles bounce off of each other, some are going very fast and some are going very slow

26 A gas in a 20-liter container is kept under a pressure of 100.0 kilopascals at a temperature of 273 K. The gas temperature is lowered to 91 K. The pressure is increased to 150 kilopascals. What is the new volume of the gas?

(1) 44 L   (3) 30 L

(2) 7.3 L   (4) 4.4 L

27 Describe how pressure is measured with a mercury barometer, and why the English units of pressure, "millimeter of Hg," do not have the physics units of force per area.

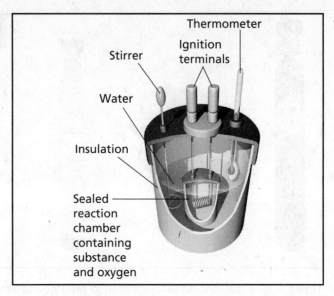

Figure 6.17 This diagram shows the components of a bomb calorimeter.

Thermochemistry

Thermochemistry is the application of thermodynamics to the field of chemistry. Thermochemistry deals with the energy changes that take place in chemical reactions, phase changes, and the formation of solutions, and the corresponding changes in physical properties.

Specific Heat

Calorimetry is used in thermochemistry. Energy changes are measured precisely by monitoring the temperature change of a known mass of surrounding material called a heat sink. In the calorimeter shown in Figure 6.17, the sample and oxygen are placed in a sealed chamber and ignited. Then the resulting heating of the water can be used to measure the sample's specific heat.

The **specific heat** of a substance is the quantity of heat, in joules, that is absorbed when 1 g of a substance is raised 1°C. Specific heats of several common substances are listed in Table 6.4. The specific heat of water is 4.18 J/g•°C. It takes 4.18 J of energy to raise the temperature of 1 g of water by 1° C.

To find the heat absorbed or released as a substance changes temperature, multiply the mass, specific heat, and change in temperature.

Specific Heat $q = mC\Delta T$

Table 6.4 • Specific Heats of Common Substances at 298 K (25°C)	
Substance	**Specific Heat J/g•°C**
Water(l) (liquid)	4.18
Water(s) (ice)	2.03
Water(g) (steam)	2.01
Ethanol(l) (grain alcohol)	2.44
Aluminum(s)	0.897
Granite(s)	0.803
Iron(s)	0.449
Lead(s)	0.129
Silver(s)	0.235
Gold(s)	0.129

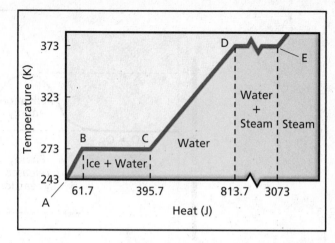

Figure 6.18 As water is heated, it changes from a solid to a liquid to a gas. During the phase changes, temperature is constant.

For example, how much energy is needed to raise the temperature of 100. g of water by 5.0°C? The specific heat of water is 4.18 J/g•°C.

$q = mC\Delta T$

$\quad = (100.\ g)(4.18\ J/g•°C)(5.0°C)$

$\quad = 2100\ J$

☑ **CHECK FOR UNDERSTANDING** How much energy is absorbed as 2.0 grams of water is cooled by 1°C?

Phase Changes

At the molecular level, thermal energy is a measure of the random motion of particles: atom, molecules, or ions. Energy needs to be absorbed to increase this motion, and energy is released when this motion decreases. These changes will result in a change in temperature.

During a phase change, however, no temperature change occurs because the thermal energy is used to change the physical state, rather than increase the average kinetic energy of the particles. Look at Figure 6.18, which shows the stages of the process in which ice changes to steam as water is heated at a steady rate. You can see that the temperature is consistent at 273 K, while solid ice changes to liquid water, and again at 373 K, while liquid water changes to steam. Each substance has its own characteristic heat of fusion, H_f, and heat of vaporization, H_v, given in kilojoules per mole.

To find the heat absorbed as a given mass melts, multiply the mass by the heat of fusion.

Heat of Fusion $q = mH_f$

To find the heat absorbed as a liquid vaporizes, multiply the mass by the heat of vaporization.

Heat of Vaporization $q = mH_v$

☑ **CHECK FOR UNDERSTANDING** Which portions of the graph in Figure 6.18 represent phase changes?

Energy (Enthalpy) Diagrams

Enthalpy is defined as the heat content of a system at constant pressure. A change in enthalpy is a more specific way of describing a change in energy. This term is necessary because if a change in pressure occurs, work will be done on or by the system in question, and the energy measured via calorimetry will not represent the total change in energy of the chemical system.

Typically, heats of reaction are measured in an enclosed calorimeter, where precise temperature measurements can be taken before and after the reaction. The temperature change, along with the known mass of water in the calorimeter and the specific heat of water, can be used to determine the energy released or absorbed.

Heats of combustion are determined with a bomb calorimeter, which is sealed to withstand pressure increases, and which provides a source of oxygen for the combustion reaction to occur.

An enthalpy diagram, also known as a potential energy diagram, can be used with both physical and chemical changes to visualize the change in energy that occurs during a physical change or a chemical change.

Thermochemistry • **99**

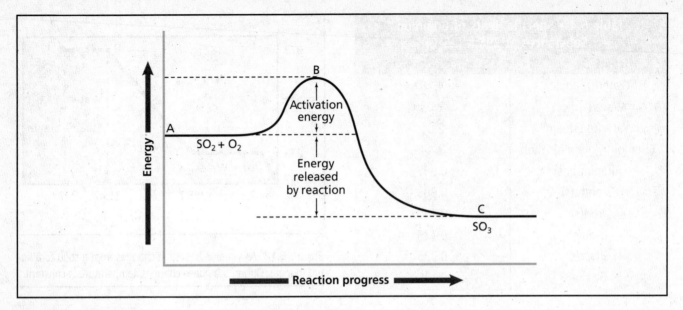

Figure 6.19 The graph shows energy changes for the reaction between SO_2 and $O_2(g)$. The size of the hill on the graph indicates how much energy is needed to cause the reaction to occur.

Figure 6.19 shows the potential energy diagram for the reaction in which sulfur and oxygen combine to produce sulfur trioxide. The reactants, $2S(s) + 2O_2(g)$, start off at energy level A. When reactants combine, they create an unstable intermediate called an activated complex. In order for a reaction to occur, it must have sufficient **activation energy**, which is the minimum amount of energy required by reacting particles in order to form the activated complex. The activation energy increases the

energy to level B. Then energy is released and the energy level drops to level C when the product, SO_3, forms. The total change in energy, from level A to level C, equals ΔH, the enthalpy change for the reaction.

At higher temperatures, the reaction rate increases because increasing the temperature increases the average kinetic energy of the particles. Therefore, more particles have the activation energy, and the reaction will proceed faster. A rule of thumb is that every 10-K increase in temperature doubles the rate of a chemical reaction, as seen in Figure 6.20.

✔ **CHECK FOR UNDERSTANDING** What does an enthalpy diagram show?

Hess's Law

Hess's law can be used to determine heats of reaction that are hard to measure experimentally. The law says that the sum of the heats of reaction of the products, minus the sum of the heats of the reactants, equals the heat of reaction. Therefore, an algebraic solution, using experimental values, can be used to determine an unknown heat of reaction. Values are always given, used, and determined at standard conditions, which is defined as 1 atm and 298 K. Note that this is not the same as STP, which is defined as 1 atm and 273 K.

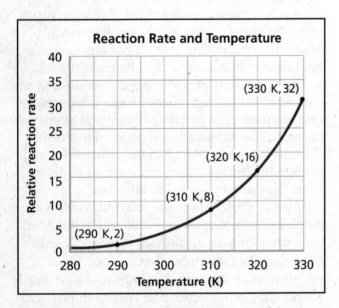

Figure 6.20 As the temperature increases, more of the reactants particles have the activation energy. Thus, the reaction rate increases.

Ammonia gas does not normally burn, but using a platinum catalyst, it can be oxidized to produce nitrogen monoxide (nitric oxide). This oxide then can be used to make nitric acid. Calculate the heat of reaction per mole of ammonia for this process.

1 Analyze the Problem

- First, write an unbalanced equation.
  $$NH_3 + O_2 \rightarrow NO + H_2O$$
- Then balance it.
  $$4NH_3 + 5O_2 \rightarrow 4NO + 3H_2O$$
- Next you need the heats of formation of all species, so you will seek a suitable table of heats of formation of selected compounds.

  1 Note that these all will be at standard state.
  2 Always include the positive sign when it occurs.
  3 The heat of formation of an element is zero by definition.

Substance	ΔH_f° (kJ/mol)
NH_3	-46.19
NO	$+90.37$
H_2O	-285.84
O_2	0

It would be helpful, but not necessary, to draw an enthalpy diagram to help you visualize the energies that you will add together.

2 Solve for the Unknown

Hess's law says that the heat of reaction equals the sum of the heats of formation of the products minus the sum of the heats of formation of the reactants.

Products:

$4NO$	$(4)(+90.37\ kJ) = +361.48\ kJ$
$3H_2O$	$(3)(-285.84\ kJ) = -857.52\ kJ$

Reactants:

$4NH_3$	$(4)(-46.19\ kJ) = -184.76\ kJ$

Now subtract the heat of formation of the 4 moles of ammonia from the sum of the heats of formation of the two products:

$$-361.48\ kJ + (-857.52\ kJ) - (-184.76\ kJ) = -311.28\ kJ$$

However, the problem asks for the heat of reaction per mole of ammonia, so you must divide the result by 4.

$$\frac{-311.28\ kJ}{4\ mol\ NH_3} = -77.82\ kJ/mol\ NH_3$$

3 Evaluate the Answer

- **Does the answer make sense?** Recheck the equation for correct coefficients, then see that they are correctly applied. Check the signs to make sure you did not mistakenly reverse any. Values precise to the hundredth place were used throughout.
- **Are the units reasonable?** The answer has the correct units of kilojoules per mole of ammonia, as was called for.

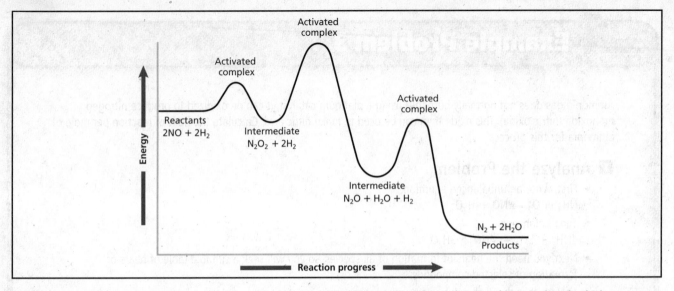

Figure 6.21 In the reaction $2NO(g) + 2H_2(g) \rightarrow N_2(g) + 2H_2O(g)$, there are two intermediate products produced, which are represented by the valleys in the coordinate diagram above. The peaks in energy represent the points at which an activated complex has been formed. The middle peak represents the highest energy needed in the reaction.

The KMT and Collision Theory

Collision theory states that atoms, ions, and molecules must collide in order to react. It may take several intermediate stages, each with its own activated complex, to produce the products, as shown in Figure 6.21. If reacting particles do not have the activation energy at any stage, the reaction will not occur spontaneously.

Because reactants must collide to form an activated complex, and the KMT describes the motion of representative particles, the KMT is necessary to describe conditions that favor the occurrence of a reaction. Higher pressures, lower volumes, and higher temperatures all favor the occurrence of a reaction by making it more likely that favorable collisions will form an activated complex.

For example, heating may be necessary to cause a reaction to occur. This commonly is seen when ignition is needed to start a fire, and when the heat of friction is needed to ignite a match.

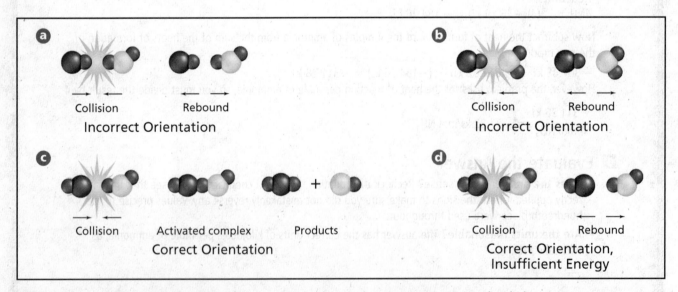

Figure 6.22 For a reaction to take place, molecules must combine in the correct orientation and with the minimum energy required. The collisions in **(a)** and **(b)** do not result in a reaction because the molecules are not in the correct orientation. The molecules in **(c)** are in the correct orientation when they collide, and a reaction occurs. The molecules in **(d)** are also in the correct orientation on collision, but do not react because of insufficient energy.

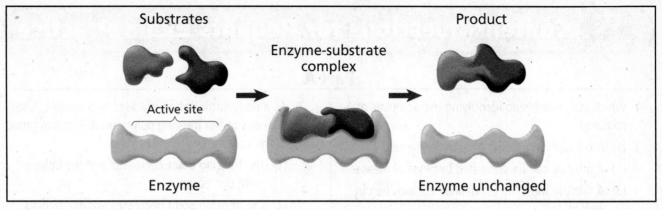

Figure 6.23 An enzyme is a biological catalyst that helps the substrates come together in the proper orientation to form the enzyme-substrate complex.

In addition, larger molecules such as proteins, with very large molar masses, have definite characteristic shapes. Collisions among reactants must be with the proper orientation for a reaction to occur, as shown in Figure 6.22.

Catalysts are substances that speed up a reaction by lowering activation energies without being consumed. Because a catalyst molecule is not a reactant, it is not used up and can catalyze reactions again and again. An inhibitor is a substance that slows down a reaction or prevents a reaction from happening. A catalyst's function is to lower the activation energy by changing the orientation of the reacting particles or by providing a substrate upon which the particles can react. Enzymes are highly specific, powerful biological catalysts whose function is to temporarily bind to protein molecules, like a lock-and-key mechanism, as seen in Figure 6.23. This changes the protein's shape, which makes the formation of the activated complex more likely.

✔ **CHECK FOR UNDERSTANDING** How does a catalyst speed up a reaction?

Quick Review

28 When a chemist uses a calorimeter, he or she is
 (1) measuring the time it takes to reach a certain temperature
 (2) measuring the amount of heat directly
 (3) measuring the heat transferred
 (4) measuring the solubility

29 Explain why it is not possible to determine the absolute enthalpy of a substance.

30 A 25.0-gram piece of aluminum is heated to 200.°C and placed into a beaker of water. If the final temperature of the aluminum is 65.0°C, how much heat was transferred to the water?

31 How much heat is released when 24.9 grams of propanol (C_3H_7OH) is burned? The heat of combustion, ΔH_{comb}, is -2010 kilojoules per mole.

32 Use reactions a and b to determine the ΔH for this single-replacement reaction:

$Cl_2(g) + 2HBr(g) \rightarrow 2HCl(g) + Br_2$
a $H_2(g) + Cl_2(g) \rightarrow 2HCl(g)$ $\Delta H = -185$ kJ
b $H_2(g) + Br_2(g) \rightarrow 2HBr(g)$ $\Delta H = -73$ kJ

33 Use the heats of reaction table in the Regents Reference Table to determine the change in enthalpy for each of these reactions at 101.3 kilopascals and 298 kelvins.
a $2NO(g) + O_2(g) \rightarrow 2NO_2(g)$
b $4NH_3(g) + 7O_2(g) \rightarrow 4NO_2 + 6H_2O(g)$

34 A chemical change can take place between two molecules only if
 (1) they collide in the correct orientation
 (2) they have the proper kinetic energy
 (3) the species are inert

35 A catalyst
 (1) is consumed in a chemical reaction
 (2) prevents a chemical reaction from taking place
 (3) increases the activation energy of a reaction
 (4) increases the rate of a chemical reaction

Part A

1 Which statement is an identifying characteristic of a mixture?

(1) A mixture can consist of a single element.

(2) A mixture can be separated by physical means.

(3) A mixture must have a definite composition by weight.

(4) A mixture must be homogeneous.

2 Which phase change at STP represents sublimation?

(1) $CO_2(s) \rightarrow CO_2(g)$ (3) $CO_2(l) \rightarrow CO_2(g)$

(2) $H_2O(s) \rightarrow H_2O(l)$ (4) $H_2O(l) \rightarrow H_2O(s)$

3 The particles of a substance are arranged in a definite geometric pattern and are vibrating constantly. This substance can be in

(1) the solid phase only

(2) the liquid phase only

(3) either the liquid or the solid phase

(4) neither the liquid nor the solid phase

4 The graph below represents the uniform cooling of a substance, starting with the substance as a gas above its boiling point.

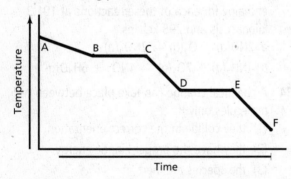

During which interval is the substance completely in the liquid phase?

(1) AB   (3) CD

(2) BC   (4) DE

5 When a substance melts, it undergoes the process called

(1) condensation   (3) sublimation

(2) fusion   (4) vaporization

6 As a nonvolatile solute is added to a solvent, what happens to the freezing point and the boiling point of the solution?

(1) The freezing point decreases and the boiling point decreases.

(2) The freezing point decreases and the boiling point increases.

(3) The freezing point increases and the boiling point decreases.

(4) The freezing point increases and the boiling point increases.

7 Which graph best shows the relationship between Kelvin temperature and average kinetic energy?

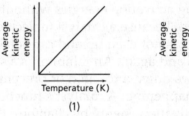
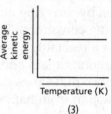

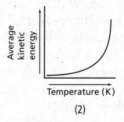
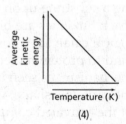

8 An assumption of the kinetic theory of gases is that the particles of a gas have

(1) little attraction for each other and a significant volume

(2) little attraction for each other and an insignificant volume

(3) strong attraction for each other and a significant volume

(4) strong attraction for each other and an insignificant volume

9 Which phase change is endothermic?

(1) gas $\rightarrow$ solid   (3) liquid $\rightarrow$ solid

(2) gas $\rightarrow$ liquid   (4) liquid $\rightarrow$ gas

10 Which statement correctly describes a sample of gas confined in a sealed container?

(1) It always has a definite volume, and it takes the shape of the container.

(2) It takes the shape and the volume of any container in which it is confined.

(3) It has a crystalline structure.

(4) It consists of particles arranged in a regular geometric pattern.

11 What will be the new volume of a 1.00-mole sample of a gas at STP if the pressure remains constant and the Kelvin temperature is halved?

(1) 11.2 L   (3) 33.6 L

(2) 22.4 L   (4) 44.8 L

12 Which change is exothermic?

(1) freezing of water

(2) melting of iron

(3) vaporization of ethanol

(4) sublimation of iodine

13 The forces between atoms that create chemical bonds are the result of interactions between

(1) nuclei

(2) electrons

(3) protons and electrons

(4) protons and nuclei

14 Two reactant particles collide with proper orientation. The collision will be effective if the particles have

(1) high activation energies

(2) high ionization energies

(3) sufficient kinetic energies

(4) sufficient potential energies

15 Which statement describes KCl(aq)?

(1) KCl is the solute in a homogeneous mixture.

(2) KCl is the solute in a heterogeneous mixture.

(3) KCl is the solvent in a homogeneous mixture.

(4) KCl is the solvent in a heterogeneous mixture.

Part B–1

16 What is the molarity of a solution that contains 40. grams of NaOH in 0.50 liter of solution?

(1) 1.0 M   (3) 0.50 M

(2) 2.0 M   (4) 0.25 M

17 A 20.-milliliter sample of 0.60 M HCl is diluted with water to a volume of 40. milliliters. What is the new concentration of the solution?

(1) 0.15 M   (3) 0.30 M

(2) 0.60 M   (4) 1.2 M

18 If 50.0 milliliters of 3.0 M HNO_3 completely neutralized 150.0 milliliters of KOH, what was the molarity of the KOH solution?

(1) 1.0 M   (3) 3.0 M

(2) 4.5 M   (4) 6.0 M

19 At STP, a 22.4-liter sample of $NH_3(g)$ contains the same number of molecules as

(1) 11.2 L of $H_2(g)$ (3) 33.6 L of $CH_4(g)$

(2) 22.4 L of $CO_2(g)$ (4) 44.8 L of $O_2(g)$

20 Refer to Table H in the Regents Reference Tables. Water boils at 90°C when the vapor pressure exerted on the liquid is equal to

(1) 150 kPa   (3) 40 kPa

(2) 101 kPa   (4) 68 kPa

21 At the same temperature and pressure, which sample contains the same number of moles of particles as 1 liter of $O_2(g)$?

(1) 1 L Ne(g)   (3) 0.5 L $SO_2(g)$

(2) 2 L $N_2(g)$ (4) 1 L $H_2O(l)$

22 Which substance can be decomposed by a chemical change?

(1) ammonia   (3) magnesium

(2) aluminum   (4) manganese

23 Given: 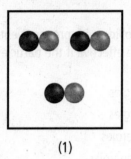 = particle X

         = particle Y

Which diagram represents a mixture?

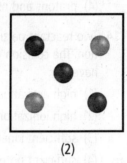 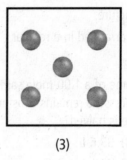 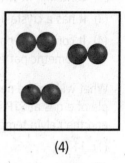

     (1)   (2)   (3)   (4)

24 What is the total number of moles of solute in 250 milliliters of a 1.0-M solution of NaCl?

25 How many milliliters of 0.20-M KOH are needed to completely neutralize 90.0 milliliters of 0.10-M HCl?

  (1) 25 mL   (3) 90. mL

  (2) 45 mL   (4) 180 mL

26 A gas has a volume of 1400 milliliters at a temperature of 20. K and a pressure of 1.0 atmosphere. What will be the new volume when the temperature is changed to 40. K and the pressure is changed to 0.50 atmospheres?

  (1) 350 mL   (3) 1400 mL

  (2) 750 mL   (4) 5600 mL

27 A gas sample has a volume of 25.0 milliliters at a pressure of 1.00 atmosphere. If the volume increases to 50.0 milliliters and the temperature remains constant, what will be the new pressure?

28 The pressure on a 200-milliliter sample of $CO_2(g)$ at constant temperature is increased from 0.79 atmospheres to 1.58 atmospheres. What is the new volume of the gas?

29 The pressure on a gas confined above a liquid increases. How does this affect the solubility of the gas in the liquid?

Part C

30 The temperature of a sample of nitrogen gas is a measure of what property of the nitrogen molecules in the sample?

31 Compared to the boiling point of H_2S, the boiling point of H_2O is relatively high. Which type of bonding causes this difference?

32 A 3.00-liter sample of gas is at 288 K and 2.00 atmospheres. If the pressure of the gas is increased to 3.00 atmospheres and its volume is decreased to 1.50 liters, what will be the Kelvin temperature of the sample?

33 The gas volume in the cylinder is 6.2 milliliters and its pressure is 1.4 atmospheres. The piston then is pushed in until the gas volume is 3.1 milliliters while the temperature remains constant.

Calculate the pressure, in atmospheres, after the change in volume. Show all work.

VOCABULARY

chemical equilibrium	homogeneous catalyst	reaction order
equilibrium constant	Le Châtelier's principle	reaction rate
free energy	phase diagram	reversible reaction
heterogeneous catalyst	rate law	

A reaction does not occur instantaneously; it takes time. Furthermore, different reactions usually do not proceed at the same rate. The oxidation of iron to form rust, for example, is a slow reaction compared to the combustion that occurs when hydrogen and oxygen combine explosively. To quantify the speed at which a reaction proceeds, chemists measure the reaction rate.

Rates of Reaction

Reaction rate is the change in concentration of a reactant or a product per unit time, generally expressed in moles per liter per second. The average rate can be determined from the concentration of a product at two different times as follows:

Reaction Rate

$$\text{Average Rate} = \frac{[\text{product}]_{t_2} - [\text{product}]_{t_1}}{t_2 - t_1}$$

What factors affect reaction rate? Recall that in collision theory, the reactants collide to create an unstable intermediate called the activated complex. The activated complex then forms the products.

The energy needed to form the activated complex is called the activation energy. Activation energy is represented by the hill in the energy diagram shown in Figure 7.1. This graph represents a reaction between CO and NO_2 to form CO_2 and NO. This reaction is exothermic because the energy of the products is less than the energy of the reactants.

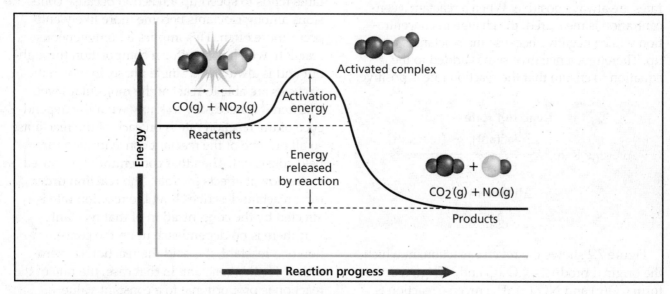

Figure 7.1 The graph shows energy changes for the reaction between CO(g) and NO_2(g). The size of the hill on the graph indicates how much energy is needed to cause the reaction to occur.

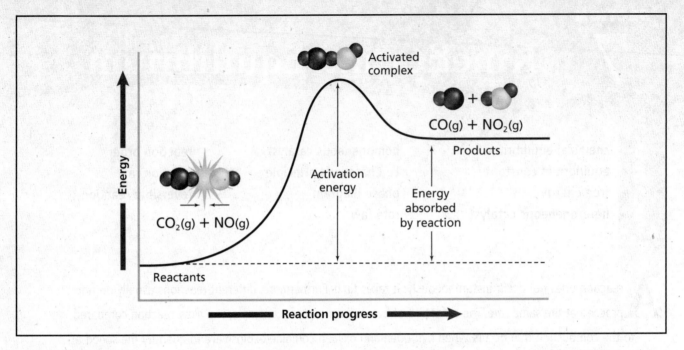

Figure 7.2 The graph shows a potential energy diagram for the reverse reaction: $CO_2(g) + NO(g)$. How does it differ from the forward reaction?

To understand activation energy, an analogy can be made with the first big hill of a roller-coaster ride. Energy is needed to raise the roller-coaster cars up to the top of the first hill. Once the initial energy has been supplied, the cars then can move down the track with no further energy input. In the same way, once the activated complex is formed, the reaction proceeds without any further input of energy.

As products form, reactants are used up. Therefore, reaction rates can be determined using the concentration of a reactant. Note that reaction rates are always positive. When a reactant's concentration is measured, the change in concentration will be negative because the reactant is used up. Therefore, a negative sign is added to the equation to ensure that the reaction rate is positive.

Reaction Rate

$$\text{Average Rate} = \frac{[\text{reactant}]_{t_2} - [\text{reactant}]_{t_1}}{t_2 - t_1}$$

$$= -\frac{\Delta[\text{reactant}]}{\Delta t}$$

Figure 7.2 shows the reverse reaction, in which the original products, $CO_2(g)$ and $NO(g)$, react to form $CO(g)$ and $NO_2(g)$. The reverse reaction is

endothermic. Notice that the activation energy is greater for the reverse reaction than it is for the forward reaction.

Several other factors affect the formation of the activated complex, and therefore affect the reaction rate. These factors include concentration of reactants and products, surface area, temperature, and the presence of a catalyst.

Effect of Concentration

Increasing the concentration of one or more reactants tends to speed up a reaction because collisions among reactants become more likely and occur more often. This implies a homogeneous reaction, which has uniform composition throughout and is always in a single phase, in which the particles are able to react at the molecular level.

Often it is necessary to know what the dependence of the reaction rate is on each of the reactants, so all but one of the reactant concentrations are held consistent. Then that concentration is varied to see how it affects the rate. The **reaction order** for a reactant describes how the reaction rate is affected by the concentration of that reactant.

If there is no dependence upon the concentration of a reactant, it is said the reaction is "zero-order" for that reactant. In that case, the rate of the reaction is proportional to a constant value, k, which is called the reaction constant. The value of k is particular to each different chemical reaction and always must be determined experimentally.

Consider a generic reaction, such as

$$A + 3B \rightarrow AB_3$$

If it is experimentally determined that doubling the concentration of reactant A doubles the reaction rate, it is said the reaction is "first-order" for reactant A. In this case, the average rate is proportional to $k[A]$.

If doubling the concentration of reactant B quadruples the reaction rate, it is said the reaction is "second-order" for reactant B. The average rate then is proportional to $k[B]^2$.

The mathematical relationship between the rate of a chemical reaction at a given temperature and the concentration of the reactants is the **rate law** for the reaction. For the generic reaction above, the rae law is as follows.

$$\text{Average rate} = k[A][B]^2$$

Note that the exponent in this equation is experimentally determined and has no relation to the coefficient of the balanced equation.

✓ **CHECK FOR UNDERSTANDING** Describe how doubling the concentration of a reactant affects the reaction rate if the reaction is first-order.

Effect of Temperature

Increasing temperature generally will speed up a reaction because the reactant particles on average have a higher kinetic energy, E_k. Therefore, more of the particles are likely to have the energy needed to form an activated complex upon collision. Also, there will be more collisions per unit of time because the particles are moving faster.

Figure 7.3(a) shows that there is a nonlinear relationship between reaction rate and temperature. It only takes a small increase in temperature (10 K) to double the reaction rate for this particular reaction. Figure 7.3(b) compares the particle energy at two temperatures. The number of particles that have energy greater than the activation energy, E_a, is indicated as the shaded area under the curve. At the higher temperature, many more of the particles have the activation energy needed to form an activated complex.

Effect of Surface Area

In a heterogeneous system, which does not have uniform composition and in which the individual substances remain distinct, the surface area of reactants becomes a factor. More surface area provides more opportunity for contact between reactant particles.

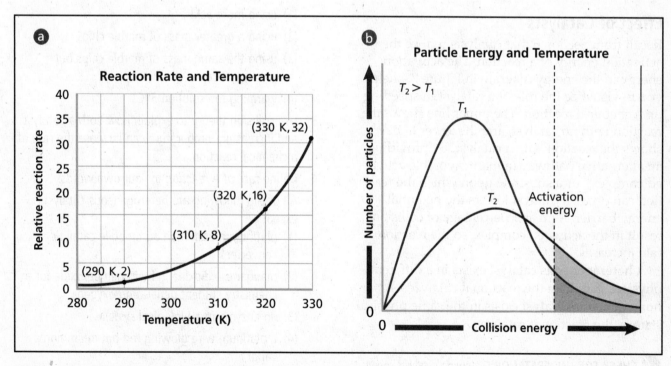

Figure 7.3 **(a)** As temperature increases, reaction rate can increase exponentially. **(b)** At higher temperatures, a much higher percentage of the reactants will have energy greater than the activation energy.

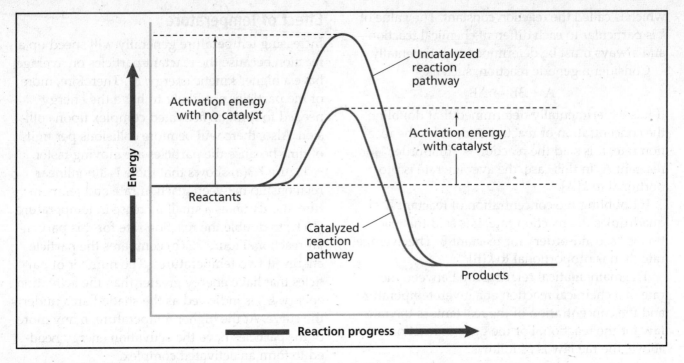

Figure 7.4 This graph shows that adding a catalyst reduces the activation energy.

Increasing the surface area of a reactant generally will increase the number of collisions per unit of time, so the reaction rate increases. Note that the concentration of a solid does not change when it is crushed or ground up, but more particles in the solid are available to react, so the reaction rate increases.

Effect of Catalysts

Recall from Section 6 that catalysts reduce the activation energy of a reaction. The activation energy in the energy diagram in Figure 7.4 helps you to visualize the role of a catalyst in speeding up a chemical reaction. The upper line shows the reaction with no catalyst, and the lower line shows the reaction with a catalyst. By providing an alternative pathway (a more favorable activated complex), or a substrate upon which the reaction can occur, a catalyst lowers the potential energy barrier. A greater percentage of collisions result in the activated complex, so the reaction rate increases.

A **heterogeneous catalyst** exists in a different physical state than the reaction it catalyzes. A **homogeneous catalyst** exists in the same physical state as the reaction it catalyzes.

✓ **CHECK FOR UNDERSTANDING** How do catalysts speed up reactions?

Quick Review

1 List four factors that can affect the rate of a chemical reaction.

2 Which of these actions would be least likely to increase the rate of the reaction of marble chips (CaCO_3) with hydrochloric acid (HCl)?
   (1) using more acid
   (2) using a greater mass of marble chips
   (3) using the same mass of marble chips but smaller pieces
   (4) warming the solution 5°C

3 Use collision theory to explain how both a catalyst and increasing temperature can increase the rate of a chemical reaction.

4 Define *rate of a reaction* in your own words.

5 All of the following are heterogeneous catalysts except
   (1) platinum metal in an automobile catalytic converter
   (2) manganese dioxide in hydrogen peroxide for a chemistry student generating oxygen
   (3) an enzyme in a biological system
   (4) a platinum wire glowing red-hot in ammonia vapor

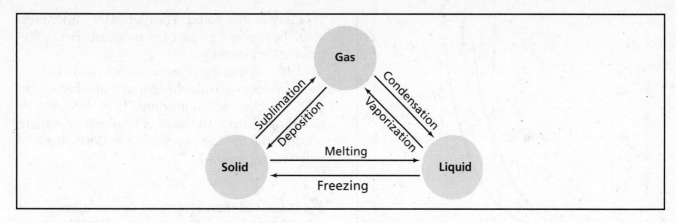

Figure 7.5 There are six possible processes that occur when a substance changes phase.

Equilibrium

As long as products are removed from a reaction system in some way, such as by formation of an insoluble solid, a gas, or by manually removing them, the reaction generates products until the limiting reagent is consumed. However, if the products build up in the system (if the system is closed), their particles also can collide to reform the activated complex and then change back into reactants.

Dynamic Equilibrium

In an equilibrium reaction, the rates of formation of reactants and products are equal in a closed reaction system. This is called *dynamic equilibrium* because, according to the kinetic-molecular theory, the particles are moving and they will be con-

stantly forming reactants and products simultaneously. Such reactions are indicated with a double arrow.

Physical changes also can be in equilibrium. At the temperature of its phase change, a substance will be in phase equilibrium as long as the system is closed and the temperature and pressure are not varied. Figure 7.5 shows the processes that occur as solids, liquids, or gases change phase. At equilibrium, the opposite processes occur at the same rate.

For instance, at 0°C in a closed system, ice and liquid water both will be present. At 100°C both liquid water and steam will be present. In fact, a liquid and its vapor will be in equilibrium at every temperature during the liquid phase in a closed system. Look at Figure 7.6.

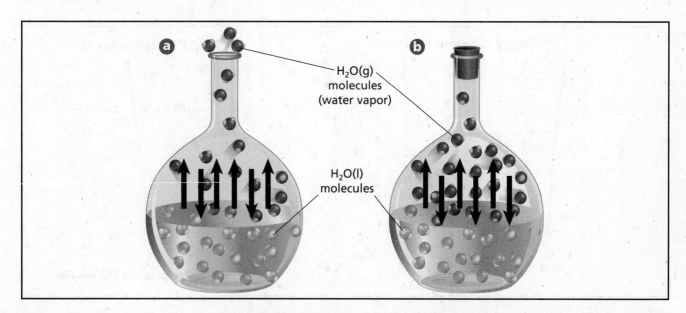

Figure 7.6 (a) In an open container, the rate at which water molecules enter the gas phase exceeds the rate at which they enter the liquid phase. **(b)** In a closed container, vapor pressure increases until equilibrium is reached.

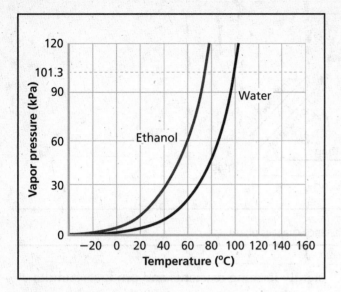

Figure 7.7 This graph compares vapor pressure versus temperature for ethanol and water.

At equilibrium at a given temperature and pressure, the rate of evaporation equals the rate of condensation. As the temperature is raised, the rate of evaporation increases until the boiling point is reached. At the boiling point, the vapor pressure within the liquid equals the external pressure above the liquid.

The vapor pressures of various liquids, and especially of solvents, are tabulated at selected temperatures and also can be read from printed vapor-pressure graphs at any desired temperature. Figure 7.7 shows vapor pressure curves for ethanol and for water. The vapor pressure of a liquid at room temperature is a measure of the volatility of that liquid. The higher the vapor pressure, the higher the rate of evaporation, hence the greater the volatility.

Note also that the phase change from liquid to gas is an endothermic change, so that when evaporation occurs, heat is absorbed from the surroundings. This is the basis of evaporative cooling, which is the cooling of a liquid's surroundings when it evaporates.

✔ **CHECK FOR UNDERSTANDING** Describe dynamic equilibrium.

Phase Diagrams

Chemists use a **phase diagram** to show all of the conditions of temperature and pressure under which the phases of a substance are at equilibrium. Figure 7.8 shows phase diagrams for water and for carbon dioxide.

On a phase diagram there are two important points, and an interesting region for each substance. The triple point gives the temperature and pressure under which all three phases are at equilibrium (can coexist). The critical point gives the critical temperature and critical pressure; above this temperature there is no possible pressure that can liquefy the gas. Below the triple point the liquid phase cannot exist, and a substance sublimes, going directly from the solid to the gaseous state. Iodine and dry ice (solid CO_2) both sublime at room temperature. Ice sublimes in the freezer compartment of a refrigerator.

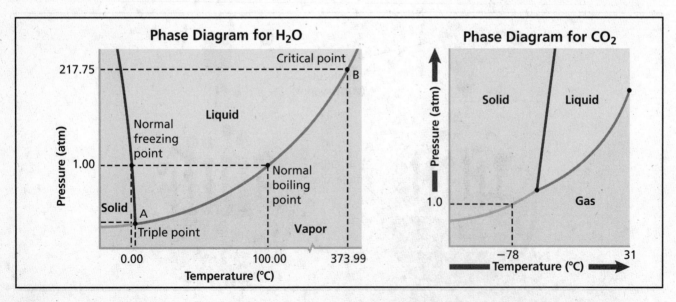

Figure 7.8 (a) The phase diagram for H_2O shows conditions of pressure and temperature for the solid, liquid, and gas phases. **(b)** The phase diagram for CO_2 has a large range of temperatures at which sublimation occurs (solid → gas).

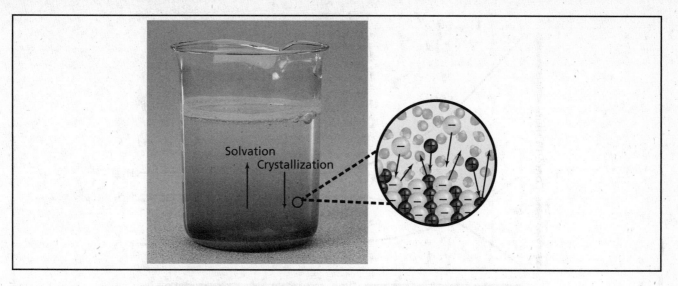

Figure 7.9 At equilibrium in a saturated solution, the rate of solvation equals the rate of crystallization.

Equilibrium in Solutions

When a solution is saturated, solution equilibrium is achieved. Figure 7.9 shows equilibrium of a solid solute in a liquid solvent. At equilibrium, there are equal rates of solvation and crystallization. Note that if the solvent is evaporating, this may affect the equilibrium, but this effect is negligible in short time intervals.

In a system of a gas solute in a liquid solvent, equilibrium can be reached when the system is closed so that the gaseous solute cannot escape, nor the solvent evaporate. At equilibrium, there are equal rates of evolution and dissolution of the gas.

✓ CHECK FOR UNDERSTANDING For a system to be at equilibrium, what must occur with the reaction rates?

Quick Review

6 A vapor-pressure curve for a liquid can show all of the following except
   (1) the rate at which evaporation occurs
   (2) the volatility of the liquid
   (3) the boiling point of the liquid at a given pressure
   (4) the vapor pressure at room temperature

7 Describe the relationship of a vapor-pressure curve to the phase-diagram for a given substance.

8 Is a saturated solution sitting in an open beaker an equilibrium system? Explain.

9 At equilibrium in a saturated solution of sodium chloride,
   (1) the salt crystal has stopped dissolving
   (2) the ions in solution have stopped crystallizing
   (3) the rate of solvation is greater than the rate of crystallization
   (4) the rate of solvation equals the rate of crystallization

10 Use the KMT and the concept of equilibrium to explain why it is better to cool a carbonated beverage before opening it and putting in ice cubes, rather than to use ice cubes to cool the room-temperature beverage after opening it.

11 Which is the most correct statement?
   (1) Heating a solution always increases the solubility of a salt.
   (2) Heating a solution always increases the solubility of a gas.
   (3) Cooling a solution decreases the solubility of a gas.
   (4) Cooling a solution can increase or decrease the solubility of a salt.

12 If you looked at a saturated solution in a closed reagent bottle, you would see the solute just sitting on the bottom. Draw a diagram to show what the ions and molecules are doing that illustrates the dynamic equilibrium that actually is occurring.

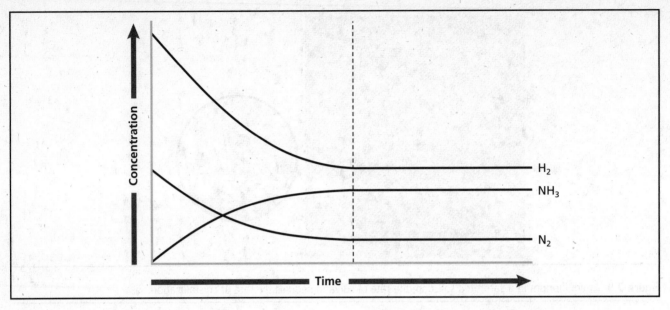

Figure 7.10 This graph shows how concentration changes as H_2 and N_2 react to produce NH_3. When equilibrium is reached (the dashed line), the concentrations remain constant.

Chemical Equilibrium

A **reversible reaction** is one that readily occurs in both the forward and reverse directions. Figure 7.10 shows a concentration graph for the reaction of hydrogen and nitrogen gas to produce ammonia. Initially, the concentration of the reactants decreases and the product's concentration increases. Because the reaction is reversible, the NH_3 can decompose to produce H_2 and N_2. When the forward and reverse reactions occur at equal rates, **chemical equilibrium** is reached, as shown in Figure 7.11.

In chemical reactions, the only reactants and products that are considered to be participating in the equilibrium are those that are homo-geneous and in intimate contact, such as gases, miscible liquids, and dissolved solids, ions, and molecules. These are the only situations in which a molarity expression can be written for the concentration of the substance.

Equilibrium Constants

A mass-action expression is used to tell if a chemical system is at equilibrium or not. In this expression, the molarity of each product is raised to the power of its coefficient in the balanced equation, and multiplied by each other. This mathematical product is placed over the mathematical product of the reactants treated in the same way. The quotient of this function

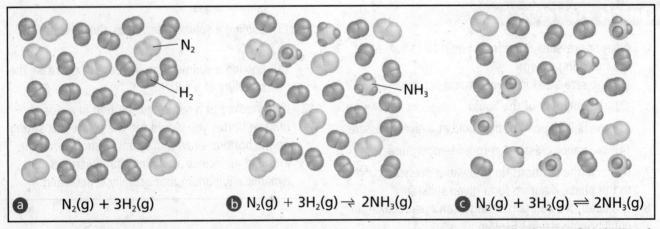

(a) $N_2(g) + 3H_2(g)$ (b) $N_2(g) + 3H_2(g) \rightleftharpoons 2NH_3(g)$ (c) $N_2(g) + 3H_2(g) \rightleftharpoons 2NH_3(g)$

Figure 7.11 **(a)** Initially, N_2 and H_2 molecules have not yet reacted, so no NH_3 molecules are present. **(b)** The rate of production of NH_3 is greater than the rate at which NH_3 decomposes to produce N_2 and H_2. **(c)** At equilibrium, the forward and reverse reaction rates are equal.

Table 7.1 • Three Experiments for an Equilibrium System

Trial	$[H_2]_0$ (M)	$[I_2]_0$ (M)	$[HI]_0$ (M)	$[H_2]_{eq}$ (M)	$[I_2]_{eq}$ (M)	$[HI]_{eq}$ (M)	$K_{eq} = \dfrac{[HI]^2}{[H_2][H_1]}$
1	1.0000	2.0000	0.0	0.06587	1.0659	1.8682	$\dfrac{(1.8682)^2}{(0.06587)(1.0659)} = 49.70$
2	0.0	0.0	5.0000	0.5525	0.5525	3.8950	$\dfrac{(3.8950)^2}{(0.5525)(0.5525)} = 49.70$
3	1.0000	1.0000	0.2485	0.2485	0.2485	1.7515	$\dfrac{(1.7515)^2}{(0.2485)(0.2485)} = 49.70$

is defined as Q, the reaction quotient, and it then is compared with K, the tabulated **equilibrium constant** for this particular reaction at standard state, or with K previously determined at the lab conditions at hand. Table 7.1 shows typical data used to determine K at a given temperature and pressure for the reaction between hydrogen and iodine.

$$H_2(g) + I_2(g) \rightleftharpoons 2HI(g)$$

If $Q > K$, the reaction will shift to the left; it will produce reactants until $Q = K$. If $Q < K$, the reaction will shift to the right; it will produce more products until $Q = K$. Note that if K is very large, this means that the reaction goes to completion. If K is much smaller than 1, the reaction does not proceed very far to the right, and the system consists mostly of reactants.

Typical equilibrium problems involve reactions with gases, with weak acids and weak bases, and with precipitation reactions. Various designations are K_a, K_b, K_i, K_h, and K_{sp}, for acid, base, ionization, hydrolysis, and solubility-product equilibrium constants, respectively.

Le Châtelier's Principle

Le Châtelier's principle, named after a French mining engineer, states that a system at equilibrium will shift to adjust to a stress put upon the system. Once again recall that an equilibrium system is, by definition, closed, so the various stresses could be:

1 a change in temperature,
2 a change in pressure (given a gaseous reactant and/or product),
3 a change in concentration of a reactant or product,
4 reactants or products are either added or removed.

✓ **CHECK FOR UNDERSTANDING** For what is the mass-action expression used?

Effect of Temperature

Changing the temperature changes the actual value of the equilibrium constant, so the equilibrium will shift to achieve this new value in the equilibrium expression. The other stresses will shift the equilibrium by forming reactants or products until the original value of K is re-obtained.

Look at Figure 7.12 on page 116. The Maxwell-Boltzmann distribution, which describes the distribution of molecular kinetic energies at a given temperature, can help show how raising the temperature shifts the equilibrium. It also explains why liquids evaporate, turning to gases, before the boiling point is attained.

✓ **CHECK FOR UNDERSTANDING** How does changing the temperature affect the value of the equilibrium constant?

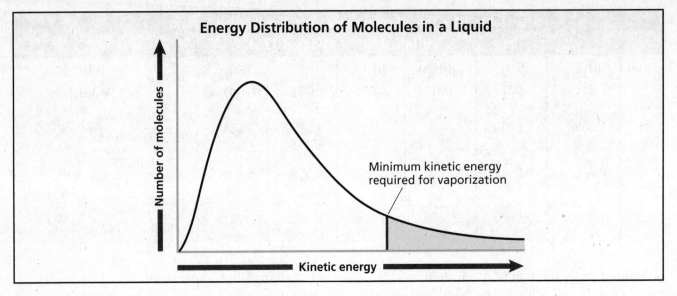

Energy Distribution of Molecules in a Liquid

Minimum kinetic energy required for vaporization

Number of molecules

Kinetic energy

Figure 7.12 This is a graph showing the energy distribution of molecules in a liquid at 25°C.

Effect of Pressure

If pressure increases, how is equilibrium affected? Look at 7.13, which shows the reaction of carbon monoxide and hydrogen:

$$CO(g) + 3H_2(g) \rightleftharpoons CH_4(g) + H_2O(g)$$

Notice that four gas particles on the left side react to produce two gas particles on the right side. In a confined space, two gas particles produce less pressure than four particles. According to Le Châtelier's principle, the direction that reduces pressure is favored. In this case, when pressure increases, the forward reaction to form products is favored.

Effect of Concentration

When the concentration of one or more reactants increases, equilibrium will tend to shift to the right, so that more products form. This again is in accordance with Le Châtelier's principle, which states that if stress is applied to a system, the system shifts to relieve the stress. When reactants are used up to form more product, the stress on the system is reduced.

Note that removing one of the products in a reaction would have the same effect, because the forward reaction rate increases to reduce the stress on the equilibrium.

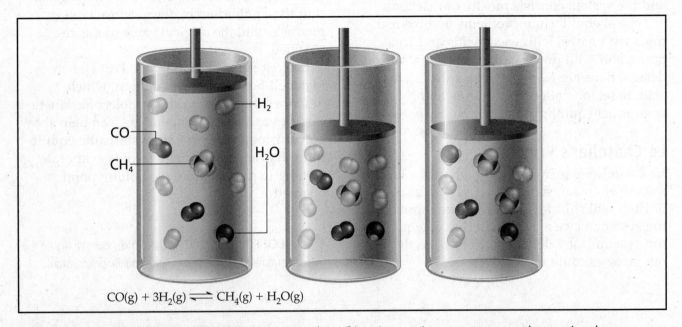

$$CO(g) + 3H_2(g) \rightleftharpoons CH_4(g) + H_2O(g)$$

Figure 7.13 **(a)** A reaction is at equilibrium between CO and H_2. **(b)** An increase in pressure causes a decrease in volume. **(c)** Due to higher pressure, more molecules of the products, $CH_4(g)$ and $H_2O(g)$, have formed.

Use Le Châtelier's principle to predict how decreasing the volume will affect the closed-system equilibrium in each case.

a $CH_4(g) + CO(g) \rightleftharpoons C_2H_4O(g)$

b $2SO_3(g) + CO_2(g) \rightleftharpoons CS_2(g) + 4O_2(g)$

c $H_2(g) + Br_2(g) \rightleftharpoons 2HBr(g)$

1 Analyze the Problem

Decreasing the volume will increase the pressure on the closed system. This will cause the reaction to do one of three things depending upon the number of moles on each side. It will shift to the left if the number of moles is greater on the right and likewise it will shift to the right if the number is greater on the left. The third option occurs when there are an equal number of moles on either side. This will result in no shift in the reaction.

2 Solve for the Unknown

Now the direction of the shift must be shown.

a $CH_4(g) + CO(g) \rightarrow C_2H_4O(g)$

This reaction shifts to the right because there are two moles on the left and one on the right.

b $2SO_3(g) + CO_2(g) \leftarrow CS_2(g) + 4O_2(g)$

This reaction shifts to the left because there are three moles on the left and five on the right.

c $H_2(g) + Br_2(g) \rightleftharpoons 2HBr(g)$

This reaction does not shift because the number of moles is two on each side.

3 Evaluate the Answer

• **Does the answer make sense?** The answer follows Le Châtelier's principle.

Quick Review

13 List the various kinds of stresses that can affect an equilibrium system.

14 Explain why an equilibrium system must be closed.

15 A chemistry student opens a bottle of saturated ammonium nitrate solution and adds 2.0 grams of the salt. Which statement best describes the result?
 (1) The rate of dissolution will increase.
 (2) The amount of salt dissolving will increase.
 (3) The rate of dissolution will stay the same.
 (4) An additional 1.0 g of ammonium nitrate will precipitate out.

16 Given the equilibrium reaction for the exothermic reaction

$$H_2(g) + Br_2(g) \rightleftharpoons 2HBr(g)$$

How could a chemist increase the yield of HBr?
 (1) Add more bromine.
 (2) Increase the size of the reaction vessel.
 (3) Decrease the pressure by removing bromine.
 (4) Increase the temperature.

Entropy, Enthalpy, and Free Energy

Look at Figure 7.14. The left side of the illustration shows samples of gas with the stopcock closed. When the stopcock is opened, after a short while, the gases are distributed uniformly throughout the containers. This change occurs spontaneously. Why? The answer has to do with entropy.

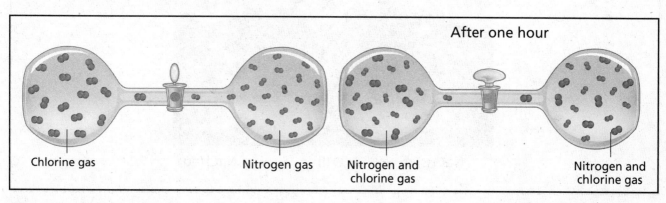

After one hour

Chlorine gas   Nitrogen gas   Nitrogen and chlorine gas   Nitrogen and chlorine gas

Figure 7.14 When chlorine and nitrogen gases are allowed to interact in a closed system, the gas molecules will distribute themselves randomly throughout the two bulbs.

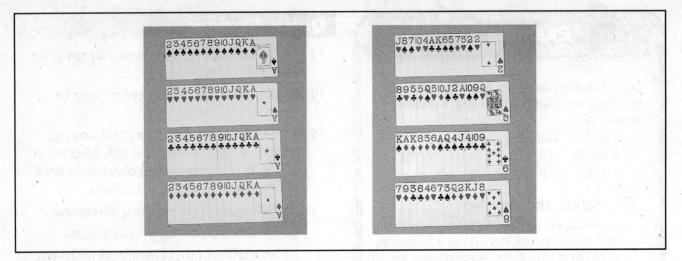

Figure 7.15 The illustration shows a change in entropy in a deck of cards.

Spontaneous Change and Entropy

When energy can be distributed among more microstates, one can say that the entropy of the system has increased. A microstate is the state defined by specifying in detail the location and momentum of each molecule and atom in a system. Entropy is defined as randomness or disorder.

Figure 7.15 shows an example with playing cards. On the left side, the cards are completely organized into suits (spades, hearts, clubs, and diamonds), and each card is in order within its suit. On the right side, you see what would be expected after shuffling the deck. It would be quite surprising if the results on the right were in the same order as the cards on the left. The chance of that happening is very slim. We could, of course, arrange the cards in order, as they are in the factory before the deck is sent to be sold. But in that case, the change would not be considered spontaneous. It takes energy to bring order to the cards.

A good example involves solutions. Figure 7.16 shows sodium chloride added to water to form a salt solution. In general, one can predict the change in entropy when a solid or a liquid solute

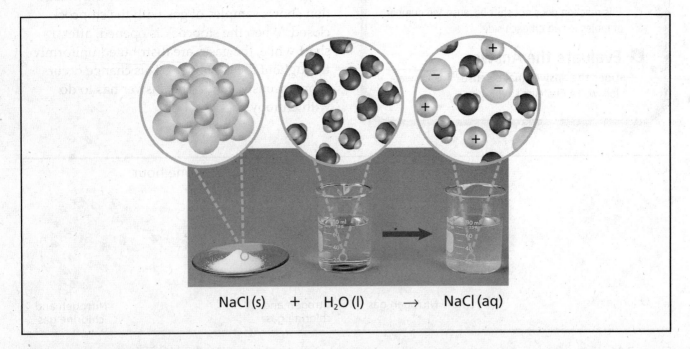

NaCl (s)   +   H₂O (l)   →   NaCl (aq)

Figure 7.16 The diagram shows how entropy changes when adding NaCl(s) to H₂O(l).

is mixed with a solvent. The solute particles, which are more ordered before dissolving, will disperse throughout the solvent. Once again, entropy increases in a spontaneous change.

Spontaneous Change and Free Energy

The second law of thermodynamics states that in any spontaneous process, there is always an increase in the entropy of the universe. This tendency can drive reactions and processes to occur.

You also know that as a whole, the universe tends toward lower potential energy in all of its processes and reactions. Therefore, to analyze any reaction as to whether or not it will occur spontaneously, you need to weigh both of these tendencies to see if they work together or oppose each other. You can define a new function, called the **free energy**, which chemists use for this purpose:

$$\Delta G = \Delta H - T\Delta S$$

For any reaction or process you can make a table to show how each term on the right contributes to ΔG. For a reaction to be spontaneous, ΔG must be negative. Therefore, you can see mathematically how varying conditions and values will affect the spontaneity.

Recall that ΔH is negative for exothermic reactions and positive for endothermic reactions. This means that, considering only enthalpy, ΔG is more likely to be negative if a reaction is exothermic.

Changes in entropy can be positive or negative, depending on whether the products inhabit more or fewer microstates. Note that increasing the temperature will always encourage spontaneity by increasing that term if ΔS is positive. If the enthalpy term is also negative (exothermic), then both terms drive spontaneity. But there can be endothermic reactions, that are spontaneous, or exothermic reactions, that are nonspontaneous. It depends on the relative combination of enthalpy and entropy. These relationships are summarized in Table 7.2.

REGENTS EXAM

Strategies for Success

STEP 1 READ the Regents Question . . .

Which process is accompanied by a decrease in entropy?

(1) boiling of water

(2) condensing of water vapor

(3) subliming of iodine

(4) melting of ice

STEP 2 ANALYZE each choice . . .

(1) Boiling of water is a system that is going from a liquid to a gas, which is an increase in entropy because the particles are less ordered in the gas state than in the liquid state.

(2) Condensation of water vapor is a system that is going from a liquid to a solid, which is a decrease in entropy because particles in the solid state are more ordered than in the liquid state.

(3) Subliming of iodine is a system that is going from a solid to a gas, which is an increase in entropy because the disorder increases.

(4) Melting of ice is a system that is going from a solid to a liquid, which is an increase in entropy because the disorder increases.

STEP 3 CHOOSE the best answer . . .

After considering all the options, the correct answer is number 2 because that is the only answer that is a decrease in entropy.

✓ CHECK FOR UNDERSTANDING What is the second law of thermodynamics?

Table 7.2 • ΔG_{system} and Reaction Spontaneity		
Type of Reaction or Process	ΔG_{system}	$\Delta S_{universe}$
Spontaneous	negative	positive
Nonspontaneous	positive	negative

17 The best definition of entropy would be
(1) a lot of heat energy
(2) a lot of particles
(3) a lot of ways particles could be arranged
(4) a lot of particles bouncing off the walls of a container

18 Which process tends to drive a reaction to occur?
(1) formation of a solid
(2) formation of a gas
(3) products with a higher potential energy
(4) all of the above

19 "Heating a reaction will always make it more likely to occur." Use your understanding of ΔG to explain why this is a false statement.

20 Write a brief essay explaining to another chemistry student the meaning of the words *system*, *surroundings*, and *universe*.

21 Define the meaning of a *spontaneous reaction*.

22 Choose the most correct statement about entropy.
(1) The entropy of a chemical system always is increasing.
(2) The entropy of a chemical system only increases when you heat it.
(3) The entropy of the universe always is increasing.
(4) The enthalpy of a system always increases when the entropy increases.

Part A

1 Which event must always occur for a chemical reaction to take place?

(1) formation of a precipitate

(2) formation of a gas

(3) effective collisions between reacting particles

(4) addition of a catalyst to the reaction system

2 An increase in the surface area of reactants in a heterogeneous reaction will result in

(1) a decrease in the rate of the reaction

(2) an increase in the rate of the reaction

(3) a decrease in the heat of reaction

(4) an increase in the heat of reaction

3 Given the reaction
$S(s) + O_2(g) \rightleftharpoons SO_3(g) + energy$,
which diagram best represents the potential energy changes for this reaction?

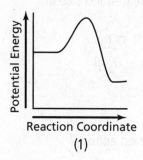

Reaction Coordinate

(1)

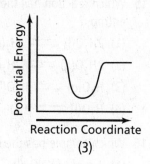

Reaction Coordinate

(3)

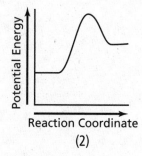

Reaction Coordinate

(2)

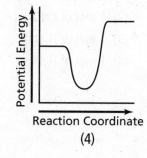

Reaction Coordinate

(4)

4 In a reversible reaction, chemical equilibrium is attained when the

(1) rate of the forward reaction is greater than the rate of the reverse reaction

(2) rate of the reverse reaction is greater than the rate of the forward reaction

(3) concentration of the reactants reaches zero

(4) concentration of the products remains constant

5 The heat energy, ΔH, absorbed or released during the formation of products is equal to

(1) $(H_{products}) - (H_{reactants})$

(2) $(H_{reactants}) - (H_{products})$

(3) $(H_{products})(H_{reactants})$

(4) $(H_{products})/(H_{reactants})$

6 Which statement best describes a chemical reaction in which energy is released?

(1) It is exothermic and has a negative ΔH.

(2) It is exothermic and has a positive ΔH.

(3) It is endothermic and has a negative ΔH.

(4) It is endothermic and has a positive ΔH.

7 Given the reaction
$H_2O(l) + 286 \text{ kJ} \rightleftharpoons H_2(g) + 1/2O_2(g)$
which statement describes the reverse reaction?

(1) It is endothermic and releases 286 kJ.

(2) It is endothermic and absorbs 286 kJ.

(3) It is exothermic and releases 286 kJ.

(4) It is exothermic and absorbs 286 kJ.

8 As carbon dioxide sublimes, its entropy

(1) decreases

(2) increases

(3) remains the same

9 Given the system at equilibrium
$$H_2(g) + F_2(g) \rightleftharpoons 2HF(g) + heat$$
which change will not shift the point of equilibrium?

(1) changing the pressure

(2) changing the temperature

(3) changing the concentration of $H_2(g)$

(4) changing the concentration of $HF(g)$

10 Given the closed system at equilibrium
$$CO_2(g) \rightleftharpoons CO_2(aq)$$
as the pressure on the system increases, the solubility of the $CO_2(g)$

(1) decreases

(2) increases

(3) remains the same

11 Given the solution at equilibrium:
$$CaSO_4(s) \rightleftharpoons Ca^{2+}(aq) + SO_4^{2-}(aq)$$
when Na_2SO_4 is added to the system, how will the equilibrium shift?

(1) The amount of $CaSO_4(s)$ will decrease, and the concentration of $Ca^{2+}(aq)$ will decrease.

(2) The amount of $CaSO_4(s)$ will decrease, and the concentration of $Ca^{2+}(aq)$ will increase.

(3) The amount of $CaSO_4(s)$ will increase, and the concentration of $Ca^{2+}(aq)$ will decrease.

(4) The amount of $CaSO_4(s)$ will increase, and the concentration of $Ca^{2+}(aq)$ will increase.

12 Adding a catalyst to a chemical reaction changes the rate of reaction by causing

(1) a decrease in the activation energy

(2) an increase in the activation energy

(3) a decrease in the heat of reaction

(4) an increase in the heat of reaction

13 Given the system at equilibrium
$$N_2O_4(g) + 58.1 \text{ kJ} \rightleftharpoons 2NO_2(g)$$
what will be the result of an increase in temperature at constant pressure?

(1) The equilibrium will shift to the left, and the concentration of $NO_2(g)$ will decrease.

(2) The equilibrium will shift to the left, and the concentration of $NO_2(g)$ will increase.

(3) The equilibrium will shift to the right, and the concentration of $NO_2(g)$ will decrease.

(4) The equilibrium will shift to the right, and the concentration of $NO_2(g)$ will increase.

14 Given the reaction at equilibrium
$$2SO_2(g) + O_2(g) \rightleftharpoons 2SO_3(g) + heat$$
which change will shift the equilibrium to the right?

(1) increasing the temperature

(2) increasing the pressure

(3) decreasing the amount of $SO_2(g)$

(4) decreasing the amount of $O_2(g)$

15 Which reaction has the greatest increase in entropy?

(1) $2H_2O(l) \rightleftharpoons 2H_2(g) + O_2(g)$

(2) $2H_2O(g) \rightleftharpoons 2H_2(g) + O_2(g)$

(3) $H_2O(g) \rightleftharpoons H_2O(l)$

(4) $H_2O(l) \rightleftharpoons H_2O(s)$

16 Which sample has the lowest entropy?

(1) 1 mol of $KNO_3(l)$

(2) 1 mol of $KNO_3(s)$

(3) 1 mol of $H_2O(l)$

(4) 1 mol of $H_2O(g)$

17 What is the change in the free energy of a reaction, ΔG, equal to?

18 Given the reaction for the Haber process
$$N_2(g) + 3H_2(g) \rightleftharpoons 2NH_3(g) + heat$$
if the temperature is 450°C, how will raising the temperature by 1000°C affect the reaction?

Base your answers to questions 19 and 20 on the following reaction.

$$A(g) + B(g) \rightleftharpoons 2C(g)$$

19 Write the correct equilibrium expression.

20 If you added more product so that the concentration of the product is doubled when a new equilibrium is reached, what will be the concentration of each reactant at the new equilibrium?

Base your answers to questions 21 and 22 on the following information.

A potential-energy diagram of an equilibrium reaction is shown below.

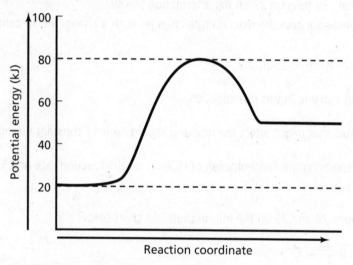

21 Why must energy be added to the reactants to start the reaction?

22 Describe two ways that you can increase the rate of the forward reaction.

Base your answer to question 23 on the following information.

Given the following reactions:

$$4Fe(s) + 3O_2(g) \rightarrow 2Fe_2O_3(s) + 1625 \text{ kJ}$$

$$27 \text{ kJ} + NH_4NO_3(s) \rightarrow NH_4^+(aq) + NO_3^-(aq)$$

23 Which of these reactions will have an equilibrium shift to the right if the temperature increases? Explain your answer.

An energy diagram is shown below.

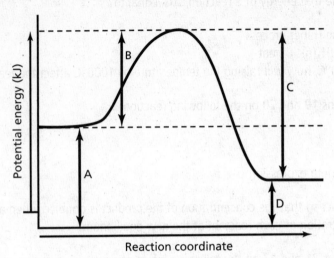

24 A catalyst is added, which increases the forward reaction rate. How will this effect the equilibrium constant?

Base your answers to questions 25 through 27 on the information below.
  A student wishes to investigate how the reaction rate changes with a change in concentration of HCl(aq).
  Given the reaction
      $Zn(s) + HCl(aq) \rightleftharpoons H_2(g) + ZnCl_2(aq)$

25 Identify the independent variable in this investigation.

26 Identify one other variable that might affect the rate and should be held constant during this investigation.

27 Describe the effect of increasing the concentration of HCl(aq) on the reaction rate and justify your response in terms of collision theory.

Base your answers to questions 28 and 29 on the information and chart below.

  Given the reaction $A + B \rightleftharpoons C$

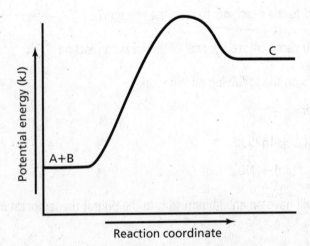

28 Does the diagram illustrate an exothermic or an endothermic reaction? State one reason, in terms of energy, to support your answer.

29 Draw a dashed line to indicate a potential-energy curve for the reaction if a catalyst is added.

8 Acids and Bases

VOCABULARY

acid-base indicator
conjugate acid
conjugate base
electrolyte
end point

equivalence point
net ionic equation
neutralization reaction
salt
strong acid

strong base
titration
weak acid
weak base

Acids and bases play an important role in our daily lives. They are used in industrial processes and agriculture, in batteries and household cleaners, and in cooking. In fact, you consume weak acids and bases every day in the foods you eat, and your stomach's contents are acidic to help various enzymes break down food. This section will investigate the chemistry of acids and bases.

Properties of Acids and Bases

Some of the most important industrial chemicals are acids and bases. In terms of total mass produced, the amount of sulfuric acid exceeds any other chemical in the United States. Sulfuric acid is used in manufacturing fertilizers, automobile batteries, metals, and in many industrial processes. Sodium hydroxide is the most commonly produced base, used in making soap, in textile production, and in manufacturing.

Acids and bases have many household applications. Acids such as acetic acid and citric acid give foods a sharp or sour taste. They also are used in household cleaners. Some metals react with certain acids to produce hydrogen gas.

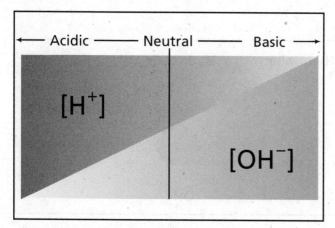

Figure 8.1 In an acid, [H$^+$] is higher than [OH$^-$] and in a base, [OH$^-$] is higher than [H$^+$].

The most familiar base in the kitchen is sodium hydrogen bicarbonate, also known as baking soda. Antacid tablets also contain bases to neutralize stomach acid. Bases generally have a bitter taste, feel slippery to the touch, and normally do not react with metals. Some bases, such as sodium hydroxide used in drain and oven cleaners, react with organic molecules in your skin and can cause severe burns on contact.

What gives acids and bases their properties? Pure water does not conduct an electric current, but all solutions of acids or bases in water are electrolytes. An **electrolyte** is a solution, containing ions, that conducts an electric current. The amount of current conducted depends on the concentration of ions in the solution. Acids dissolved in water are electrolytes. Because of this they must interact with water molecules to produce ions in solution.

Arrhenius Model of Acids and Bases

The first definition of an acid came from the Swedish chemist Svante Arrhenius in 1884. The Arrhenius theory of acidity defines an acid as a substance that produces hydrogen ions, H$^+$, in aqueous solution. The theory defines a base as a substance that produces hydroxide ions, OH$^-$, in solution. In an Arrhenius acid, the concentration of H$^+$ ions, written [H$^+$], is greater than the concentration of OH$^-$ ions, [OH$^-$]. In an Arrhenius base, [OH$^-$] is greater than [H$^+$], as shown in Figure 8.1.

An example of an Arrhenius acid is hydrochloric acid, a gas that ionizes in water to form hydrogen and chloride ions.

$$HCl(g) \rightarrow H^+(aq) + Cl^-(aq)$$

Sodium hydroxide, a white ionic solid, is an example of an Arrhenius base because it dissociates (the ions separate) in water to form sodium ions and hydroxide ions in solution.

$$NaOH \rightarrow Na^+(aq) + OH^-(aq)$$

✓ CHECK FOR UNDERSTANDING Describe the difference between Arrhenius acids and bases. How do they allow solutions to carry a current?

Hydronium Ions

Water ionizes, forming hydrogen ions and hydroxide ions. In pure water, or in a neutral solution—one which is neither acidic nor basic—there are equal numbers of the two kinds of ions.

$$H_2O(l) \rightleftharpoons H^+(aq) + OH^-(aq)$$

Because the concentration of the two ions is the same, pure water is a neutral substance, neither acidic nor basic.

The hydrogen ion does not really exist in solution. Water is a very polar molecule, with a partial negative charge on the oxygen atom due to two unshared pairs of electrons. A positively charged hydrogen ion, which is actually a proton in solution, is attracted to the polar water molecule and forms a new ion, the hydronium ion, H_3O^+. Figure 8.2 shows how two water

molecules combine to form a hydronium ion and a hydroxide ion. In practice, the symbols $H^+(aq)$ and H_3O^+ are used interchangeably and it is often more convenient to use the hydrogen ion when writing chemical equations involving acids. The hydroxide ion is solvated, which means that it is attracted to and surrounded by water molecules, but exists as a separate ion in solution.

✓ CHECK FOR UNDERSTANDING What do water molecules and hydrogen ions combine to form?

Brönsted-Lowry Model of Acids and Bases

Although the Arrhenius theory explains much about most acids and bases in water, other explanations have been developed. The Brönsted-Lowry model focuses solely on the hydrogen ion, defining an acid as a hydrogen ion donor (proton donor) and a base as a hydrogen ion acceptor (proton acceptor). For example, dissolving hydrogen chloride in water is an acid-base reaction.

$$HCl(g) + H_2O(l) \rightarrow H_3O^+(aq) + Cl^-(aq)$$

In this reaction, HCl is an acid because it donates the hydrogen ion and H_2O is a base because it accepts the hydrogen ion. Every Arrhenius acid or base is considered to be an acid or a base in the Brönsted-Lowry model. However, this more general model also explains the behavior of compounds that are basic but do not contain hydroxide ions. For example, ammonia, NH_3, has the properties of a base but does

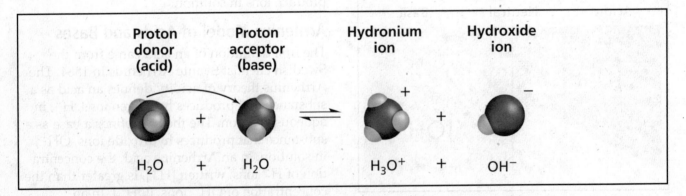

Proton donor (acid)	Proton acceptor (base)	Hydronium ion	Hydroxide ion
H_2O +	H_2O	H_3O^+ +	OH^-

Figure 8.2 In pure water, one molecule acts as an acid and donates a hydrogen ion to another molecule, which accepts the ion. This results in an equal number of hydronium ions (H_3O^+) and hydroxide ions (OH^-).

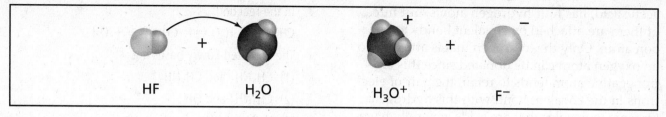

HF   +   H₂O   →   H₃O⁺   F⁻

Figure 8.3 Shown is the equation for the ionization of hydrogen fluoride in water.

not contain an OH⁻ ion. NH₃ is a Brönsted-Lowry base because it accepts a hydrogen ion.

$$NH_3(g) + H_2O(l) \rightleftharpoons NH_4^+(aq) + OH^-(aq)$$

In this reaction, water is considered to be an acid. Note that it is an equilibrium reaction because the reaction can proceed in both the forward and the reverse directions at the same time.

The example shown in Figure 8.3 is the equation for the ionization of hydrogen fluoride in water.

☑ **CHECK FOR UNDERSTANDING** In the Brönsted-Lowry model, how is a base defined?

Because the donation of a hydrogen ion is an equilibrium process, it is a reversible reaction. The reverse reaction also involves the donation of a proton, so there is an acid and a base on both sides of the equilibrium equation. Either direction involves the reaction of an acid and a base.

A **conjugate acid** is the species produced when a base accepts a hydrogen ion from an acid. The hydronium ion is a conjugate acid of the base in this reaction, water. A **conjugate base** is the species that results when an acid donates a proton to a base.

$$HX(g) + H_2O(l) \rightleftharpoons H_3O^+(aq) + X^-(aq)$$
acid   base   Conjugate   Conjugate
                             acid   base

In this reaction, X⁻, which can represent any singly-charged negative ion, is the conjugate base of the original acid.

Note that in the reverse reaction, the role of acid and base are reversed. Therefore, water is the conjugate base of the hydronium ion because it results from the donation of a hydrogen ion to the X⁻ ion.

In an equilibrium reaction involving Brönsted-Lowry acid-base pairs, it often is necessary to predict which way the reaction is favored to go. The rule is that the equilibrium favors the weaker conjugate acid-base pair.

In order to be acidic, a compound must be able to donate a hydrogen ion. Hydrogen ions are easily removed from many molecules that consist of hydrogen bonded to an electronegative element. Some acids can donate more than one hydrogen ion to solution. Examples include sulfuric acid, H_2SO_4, and phosphoric acid, H_3PO_4, which are able to donate more than one hydrogen ion.

A molecule does not necessarily donate every hydrogen atom to a base as a hydrogen ion. Look at Figure 8.4. Ethanoic acid, also known as

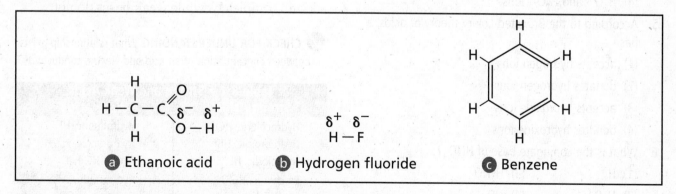

ⓐ Ethanoic acid   ⓑ Hydrogen fluoride   ⓒ Benzene

Figure 8.4 The O-H bond in ethanoic acid and the H-F bond in hydrogen fluoride are polar. In water, HF and ethanoic acid are acidic because the H⁺ ionizes. Because there are no polar bonds in the benzene molecule, benzene is not an acid.

acetic acid, has four hydrogen atoms, but three of them are attached by covalent bonds to a carbon atom. Only the hydrogen that is attached to an oxygen atom can be donated since this electronegative atom tends to retain the pair of electrons in the covalent bond with this hydrogen. Organic molecules that are acids generally have the structure R-COOH, in which R usually represents a hydrocarbon chain, a chain of hydrogen and carbon atoms. Benzene has six hydrogen atoms, but none of them can ionize, so benzene is not an acid.

☑ **CHECK FOR UNDERSTANDING** What must be true of a compound for it to be acidic?

Quick Review

1 Which of these compounds can be classified as an Arrhenius base?

  (1) HCl   (3) LiOH

  (2) CH_3OH (4) $MgCl_2$

2 An Arrhenius acid forms an excess of which ion(s) in aqueous solution?

  (1) H_3O^+ (3) H^+ and Cl^-

  (2) OH^- (4) OH^+

3 Arrhenius acids and bases are always

  (1) electrolytes

  (2) positively charged

  (3) proton acceptors

  (4) inorganic molecules

4 A sample of pure water contains

  (1) no ions

  (2) H^+ and OH^- ions

  (3) H_3O^+ and OH^- ions

  (4) H_2O^+ and H_2O^- ions

5 According to the Brönsted-Lowry theory of acids, a base

  (1) accepts hydrogen ions

  (2) donates hydrogen ions

  (3) accepts hydroxide ions

  (4) donates hydroxide ions

6 What is the conjugate base of HNO_3?

  (1) H^+ (3) H_2NO_3

  (2) H_3O^+ (4) NO_3^-

7 In the reaction:

$CH_3NH_2 + H_2O \rightleftharpoons CH_3NH_3^+ + OH^-$

The Brönsted-Lowry bases are

  (1) CH_3NH_2 and $CH_3NH_3^+$

  (2) CH_3NH_2 and OH^-

  (3) H_2O and OH^-

  (4) H_2O and $CH_3NH_3^+$

8 How many protons can propanoic acid, CH_3CH_2COOH, donate in an aqueous solution?

  (1) 0   (3) 3

  (2) 1   (4) 6

9 Which of these compounds is an Arrhenius base?

  (1) CH_3OH (3) NH_3

  (2) HOH   (4) $Ba(OH)_2$

10 Explain why ammonia is a Brönsted-Lowry base but not an Arrhenius base when it is dissolved in water.

The Strengths of Acids and Bases

In an electrolytic solution, ions conduct electric current. If you double the concentration of an acid, such as hydrochloric acid, the solution will conduct twice as much current. However, solutions of some acids have greater electric conductivity given the same concentration of acid than others. This is because some acids, such as HCl, ionize completely in water. These acids are known as **strong acids**. Examples of strong and weak acids are listed in Table 8.1.

A solution of acetic acid, on the other hand, contains a mixture of hydronium and acetate ions along with acetic acid molecules that have not ionized, as shown in Figure 8.5. Acids that do not ionize completely are weaker electrolytes and thus are **weak acids**. In the same way, **strong bases** ionize (or dissociate) completely, while **weak bases** do not.

☑ **CHECK FOR UNDERSTANDING** What relationship exists between concentration of an acid and electric conductivity?

Table 8.1 • Strong and Weak Acids	
Strong Acids	**Weak Acids**
Hydrochloric, HCl	Hydrofluoric, HF
Hydrobromic, HBr	Hydrocyanic, HCN
Hydroiodic, HI	Acetic, $HC_2H_3O_2$
Perchloric, $HClO_4$	Hydrosulfuric, H_2S
Nitric, HNO_3	Carbonic, H_2CO_3
Sulfuric, H_2SO_4	Hypochlorous, HClO

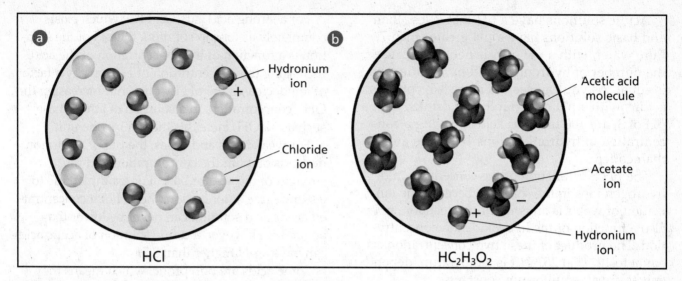

Figure 8.5 (a) In HCl, a strong acid, all of the HCl molecules have ionized to hydronium and chloride ions. **(b)** In HC$_2$H$_3$O$_2$, a weak acid, only one molecule has ionized to a hydronium ion and an acetate ion.

The pH Scale

In an aqueous solution, the concentration of the hydronium ions in a solution is directly related to its acidity, and this concentration is compared on a scale known as the pH scale. The pH scale is a logarithmic scale, which means that a change in one pH unit indicates a change of ten times the concentration of hydronium ions. This scale generally ranges from a value of 0, which is a very strong acid such as battery acid, to a value of 14, which is a very strong base such as oven cleaner in solution, as seen in Figure 8.6. The mathematical expression for pH can be written in either of two ways:

Calculating pH

$$pH = -\log [H^+], \text{ or } [H^+] = 10^{-pH}$$

Note that as the logarithm gets smaller, the concentration of acid gets greater, so it is an inverse relationship. It is also possible to have a pH of less than zero.

To calculate the pH of a solution based on the concentration of hydrogen ions:

1 Write the concentration in scientific notation.

   3.0×10^{-5} M

2 Calculate pH using the formula

   $pH = -\log[H^+]$
   $= -\log (3.0 \times 10^{-5})$
   $= -(\log (3.0) + \log (10^{-5}))$

3 Use a log table or calculator to substitute numbers for the log values.

   $pH = -(0.48 + (-5)) = -(-4.52)$
   $= 4.52$

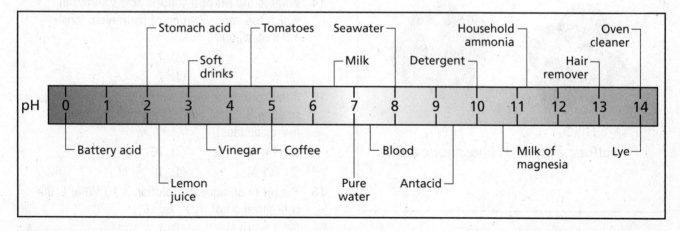

Figure 8.6 This shows pH values of common substances. Substances with pH values below 7 are acids and substances with pH values above 7 are bases. What substance has a pH of 7?

Acidic solutions have a pH that is less than 7 and basic solutions have a pH greater than 7. Pure water, with a pH of 7, is neutral because the number of hydronium and hydroxide ions is equal. As you can see in Figure 8.6, coffee is acidic, with a pH of about 5. Soft drinks, with a pH of 3, are 100 times as acidic, having a concentration of hydronium ions 100 times greater than coffee.

The pH is a function of the concentration of hydrogen ions in the solution. Because the ionization of water is an equilibrium reaction, pH is also a function of the hydroxide ion concentration. The product of these two concentrations is equal to 10^{-14} at 25°C (it is temperature dependent, as are all equilibrium constants).

$$[H^+][OH^-] = 1.0 \times 10^{-14} = K_w$$

This is the water equilibrium constant. When hydrogen ions or hydroxide ions are added to water, the equilibrium shifts to maintain the above relationship.

The pH value is defined as the negative logarithm of the hydrogen ion concentration. Therefore, if the concentration of hydrogen ions is 0.01 M or 10^{-2} M, the pH is 2, which is very acidic. If the concentration of hydrogen ions is 10^{-12} M (which means the concentration of OH^- ions is 10^{-2} M), the pH is 12, which is very basic.

✓ **CHECK FOR UNDERSTANDING** What is pH related to? Briefly explain the pH scale in your own words.

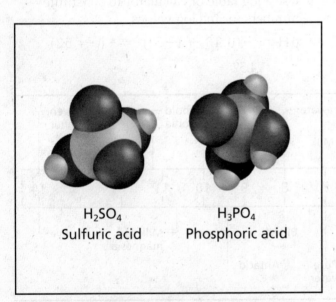

H₂SO₄
Sulfuric acid

H₃PO₄
Phosphoric acid

Figure 8.7 Both sulfuric acid and phosphoric acids are polyprotic, which means they can donate more than one proton.

For a strong acid, such as HCl, which exists completely as ions in solution, the pH of the solution is a function of the concentration of the acid. Increasing the concentration of H^+ ions by a factor of ten decreases the pH by one unit. Increasing the OH^- concentration, in a solution of strong base such as NaOH, increases the pH by one unit.

For weak acids and bases, the pH of a solution depends on both the concentration and the strength of the acid or base. For example, due to a lesser degree of ionization, the pH of a concentrated acetic acid solution can never be lower than about 3.5. However, a dilute solution of acetic acid can have a pH higher than 3.5.

Some acids are polyprotic, which means they can ionize more than once. H_2SO_4, for example, can ionize to produce HSO_4^-(aq), which then ionizes to produce SO_4^{-2}(aq). Two polyprotic acids are shown in Figure 8.7.

Quick Review

11 If the pH of an aqueous solution is 12, the solute could be
   (1) HCl   (3) LiOH
   (2) NaCl   (4) KMnO₄

12 The pH of a solution is a function of
   (1) the concentration of hydrogen ions
   (2) the degree of ionization of the acid
   (3) the concentration of hydroxide ions
   (4) the temperature of the solution

13 The pH of solution A is 9. The pH of solution B, which is 1000 times as acidic as solution A, is
   (1) 0   (3) 7
   (2) 6   (4) 12

14 What is the pH of a sulfuric acid solution in which the concentration of hydronium ions is 1.0 moles/liter?
   (1) 0   (3) 7
   (2) 6   (4) 2

15 If the concentration of hydrogen ions in an aqueous solution is 0.1 M, what is the concentration of hydroxide ions?
   (1) 1.0 M   (3) 10^{-7} M
   (2) 0.1 M   (4) 10^{-13} M

16 The pH of an aqueous solution is 10. What is the concentration of H_3O^+ ions?
   (1) 1×10^{-1} (3) 1×10^{-7}
   (2) 1×10^{-4} (4) 1×10^{-10}

17 The degree of ionization of a strong acid is

(1) more than that of a strong base

(2) more than that of a weak acid

(3) dependent on pH

(4) less than that of a weak base

Titration

When an Arrhenius acid and a base react, the anion of the acid combines with the cation of the base to form a **salt**. The other product of the reaction is water, HOH. (Note that if we write water like this, rather than as H_2O, we can more easily keep track of the hydroxide ions.) For example, the combination of hydrochloric acid (HCl) and sodium hydroxide (NaOH) forms common table salt (NaCl):

$$HCl(aq) + NaOH(aq) \rightarrow NaCl(aq) + HOH(l)$$

This is a **neutralization reaction**, a special kind of double-replacement reaction. As in any other reaction, the equation must be balanced.

For the neutralization of the base, calcium hydroxide, with the acid, hydrogen chloride (hydrochloric acid), the balanced equation is:

$$\underset{\text{acid}}{2HCl(aq)} + \underset{\text{base}}{Ca(OH)_2(aq)} \rightarrow \underset{\text{salt}}{CaCl_2(aq)} + \underset{\text{water}}{2HOH(l)}$$

For both of these neutralization reactions, you can write a **net ionic equation**, which is an equation that shows only the particles that participate in the reaction. The net ionic equation for a strong acid and a strong base, shown in Figure 8.8, is the same for all simple neutralization reactions.

✓ **CHECK FOR UNDERSTANDING** What two products result from the reaction of an acid and a base?

Because the neutralization reaction involves one hydrogen ion for each hydroxide ion, it can

STEP 1 **READ the Regents Question . . .**
Which of the following 0.1-M solutions has the lowest pH?
(1) 0.1 M NaOH   (3) 0.1 M NaCl
(2) 0.1 M CH₃OH   (4) 0.1 M HCl

STEP 2 **ANALYZE each choice . . .**

(1) Sodium hydroxide dissolves in water to from a basic solution. All basic solutions have a high pH, which is over 7.

(2) CH_3OH is not an acid. Therefore, a solution of it will not have a low pH.

(3) Sodium chloride will dissolve in water to form Na^+ and Cl^- ions. Neither of these ions will result in an increased H^+ concentration, so this solution will not have a low pH.

(4) Hydrogen chloride will completely dissociate and form H^+ and Cl^- in solution. The H^+ ions means the solution will be acidic and have a low pH.

STEP 3 **CHOOSE the best answer . . .**
Number 4 is the best choice. It is the only solution given that is acidic and therefore, has a low pH.

be used to determine the concentration of acid or a base in a solution. **Titration** is the laboratory process used to determine an unknown concentration. In effect, the titration is a controlled neutralization reaction. In a titration, the volume of a solution of known concentration necessary is reacted with a known volume of another solution of unknown concentration. For acids that donate a single proton and bases that accept a single proton, $M_aV_a = M_bV_b$, where M_a and M_b are the respective molarities of the acid and base, and V_a and V_{sb} are the volumes used to achieve neutralization.

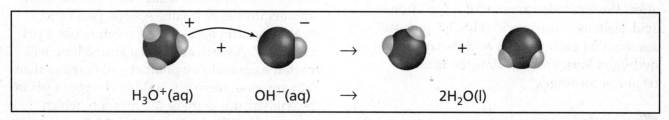

$$H_3O^+(aq) \qquad OH^-(aq) \qquad \rightarrow \qquad 2H_2O(l)$$

Figure 8.8 In the net ionic equation for a neutralization reaction between a strong acid and a strong base, a hydronium ion transfers a hydrogen ion to a hydroxide ion. The loss of the hydrogen ion by the H_3O^+ and the gain of the hydrogen ion by the OH^- results in two water molecules.

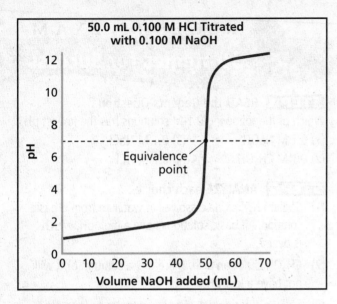

50.0 mL 0.100 M HCl Titrated with 0.100 M NaOH

Figure 8.9 The pH of the solution changes during the titration of 50.00 mL of 0.100 M HCl, with 0.100 M NaOH. The point at which the curve intersects the dashed line is the equivalence point of titration.

Equivalence Point

The **equivalence point** is the point at which equal numbers of moles of acid and base have reacted. The base is added slowly to the acid (or vice versa) while monitoring the pH. As base is added, the pH of the solution changes gradually, as shown in Figure 8.9. When nearly all of the H^+ ions have reacted, the pH increases at a greater rate. At the point where all of the acid is neutralized, there is a sudden increase in pH with the addition of a very small amount of base. This point, at which all of the hydrogen ions that will react have reacted, is called the equivalence point. There will always be an equal number of unreacted H^+ and OH^- ions. Using the concentration and volume of base needed to reach the equivalence point and the volume of the original acid solution, the concentration of the acid can be calculated as shown in Example Problem 1.

Note that if an acid is polyprotic, this will affect the equivalence point. If it is a strong acid, such as sulfuric acid (H_2SO_4), you can assume that each mole of acid donates 2 mol of hydrogen ions, and calculate the titration results accordingly.

✓ **CHECK FOR UNDERSTANDING** How is the pH of a solution affected when nearly all H^+ ions have reacted?

Example Problem 1

What is the concentration of a hydrochloric acid solution if 33.2 milliliters of 0.102 milliliters NaOH solution is needed to neutralize 20.0 M of the acid?

1 Analyze the Problem

Write the equation for the acid-base reaction:
$HCl(aq) + NaOH(aq) \rightarrow NaCl(aq) + H_2O(l)$

Known:	Unknown:
$M_{NaOH} = 0.102$ M	$M_{HCl} = ?$
$Vol_{NaOH} = 33.2$ mL	
$Vol_{HCl} = 20.0$ mL	

2 Solve for the Unknown

- Determine how many moles of NaOH neutralize 1 mole of HCl.
  From the equation, 1 mole of NaOH is needed for each mol of HCl
- Calculate the moles of NaOH used.
  33.2 mL × 0.102 mol/L × 1 L/1000 mL
  = 3.39×10^{-3} mol NaOH
- Determine the number of moles of HCl in the sample.
  1 mol HCl = 1 mol NaOH = 3.39×10^{-3} mol
- Determine the concentration of HCl.
  $$\frac{3.39 \times 10^{-3} \text{ mol HCl}/20.0 \text{ mL}}{\times 1000 \text{ mL}/1 \text{ L}} = 0.170 \text{ M HCl}$$

3 Evaluate the Answer

- **Are the units correct?** Concentration can be expressed as molarity as it is.
- **Does the answer make sense?** About 1.7 mL of base neutralizes 1 mL of acid, so it makes sense that the acid concentration is about 1.7 times as high as the base concentration.

Indicators

The equivalence point of the titration between a strong acid and a strong base is at pH 7, but other combinations of acids and bases have different equivalence points. A strong acid and a weak base form a salt whose solution has a pH less than 7. A weak acid and a strong base will reach the equivalence point at a pH greater than 7. In any case, there is a sudden change in pH at the equivalence point of the titration, which indicates that the hydrogen or hydroxide ions all have been neutralized.

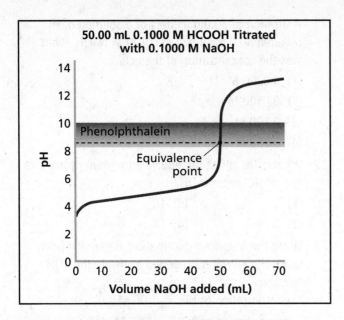

Figure 8.10 The equivalence point for the titration of methanoic acid (a weak acid) with sodium hydroxide (a strong base) lies between pH 8 and pH 9.

Titrations can be monitored with a pH meter, but chemists often use chemical dyes to detect the equivalence point. Dyes whose colors are affected by pH are called **acid-base indicators**, which were originally extracted from plants. One common indicator is phenolphthalein, which has a pink color in a basic solution, but is colorless in neutral or acidic solution. The color change occurs at a pH range between 8 and 10. As you can see from the

titration plot in Figure 8.10, a change in this pH range will occur very close to the equivalence point of a titration between a weak acid and a strong base. There are many other indicators, as shown on an indicator chart, that change colors at different places on the pH scale, depending upon the acid-base pair being titrated.

✓ **CHECK FOR UNDERSTANDING** Why is the equivalence point in an acid-base titration not always 7?

Titration End Point

If the indicator is correctly matched to the pH of the equivalence point, the indicator changes color at the **end point** of the titration. As shown previously in Figure 8.9, the titration of acetic acid with sodium hydroxide, phenolphthalein is a good indicator to choose. The equivalence point of this titration of a weak acid and a strong base is between pH 8 and pH 9. The end point can be detected by an indicator that changes color anywhere in the pH range from 6 to 10. Notice by looking at Figure 8.10 that there is another indicator which could be used for this titration, bromthymol blue, which changes color in the pH 6–8 range. Methyl orange, on the other hand, is not useful for this titration. Its color change at pH 3–4 does not fall into the range of the pH change of the neutralization. However, phenolphtalein is commonly used in titrations of

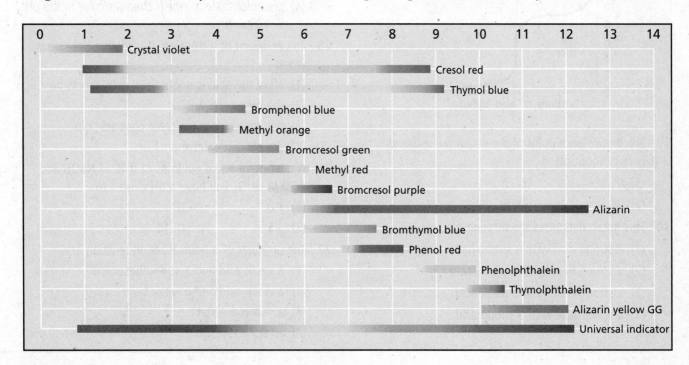

Figure 8.11 Shown is a pH scale illustrating the ranges of several common acid-base indicators.

strong acid-strong base. Although the endpoint and equivalence points are different, the difference is so small, it is negligible.

In addition to indicating a titration endpoint, indicators are useful in determining the approximate pH of a solution. Scientists often use paper strips incorporating a single indicator dye, or a mixture of indicators to estimate the pH of a solution. These latter change to different colors at a range of pHs. The most common indicator strip in use is litmus paper. There are two types of litmus paper, blue and red. Blue litmus paper turns pink in the presence of an acid and red litmus paper turns blue in the presence of a base. Other indicator strips can be chosen which change color above or below some other pH of interest.

✓ **CHECK FOR UNDERSTANDING** When would a chemist use indicator papers rather than drops of indicator?

Quick Review

18 Explain why phenolphthalein cannot be used as an indicator for every acid-base titration.

Use this graph to answer questions 19 and 20.

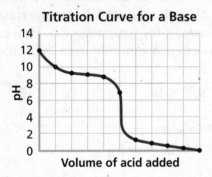

Titration Curve for a Base

19 The equivalence point of the titration illustrated here is about pH =
   (1) 9   (3) 7
   (2) 8   (4) 5

20 This graph illustrates the titration of
   (1) a strong acid with a strong base
   (2) a strong base with a strong acid
   (3) a strong base with a weak acid
   (4) a weak base with a strong acid

21 A titration of 20.0 milliliters of a solution of HCl required 40.0 milliliters of 0.100 M NaOH. What was the concentration of the acid?
   (1) 0.0200 M
   (3) 0.0500 M
   (3) 0.100 M
   (4) 0.200 M

22 What is the pH at the equivalence point of the titration of HCl with NaOH?
   (1) 1   (3) 10
   (2) 7   (4) 14

23 Using the following information, determine how much HBr solution is needed to titrate the KOH solution.
   concentration of HBr = 1.00 M
   concentration of KOH = 1.50 M
   volume of KOH = 15.0 mL
   (1) 10.0 mL   (3) 22.5 mL
   (2) 15.0 mL   (4) 30.0 mL

24 For the titration of a strong acid with a weak base, the best indicator would likely be
   (1) methyl orange, which changes color in the pH 3–4 range
   (2) bromthymol blue, which changes color in the pH 6–7.5 range
   (3) phenol red, which changes color in the pH 7–8 range
   (4) phenolphthalein, which changes color in the pH 8–10 range

25 The endpoint of a titration of acid with base occurs when
   (1) all of the acid is neutralized with excess base
   (2) the pH equals 7.0
   (3) the appropriate indicator changes color
   (4) the pH is greater than 7.0

26 A mixture of equal volumes of 0.10 M NaOH and 0.20 M HNO_3 will have a pH closest to
   (1) 1.0   (3) 7.0
   (2) 3.5   (4) 10.

27 The products of a neutralization reaction are
   (1) a weak acid and a strong base
   (2) a weak acid and a weak base
   (3) a salt and water
   (4) an acidic solution

Part A

1 According to the Arrhenius theory, which list of compounds includes only bases?

(1) KOH, $Ca(OH)_2$, and CH_3OH

(2) KOH, $NaOH$, and $LiOH$

(3) $LiOH$, $Ca(OH)_2$, and $C_2H_4(OH)_2$

(4) $NaOH$, $Ca(OH)_2$, and CH_3COOH

2 Which compound is an electrolyte?

(1) CH_3OH

(2) $Ca(OH)_2$

(3) $C_3H_5(OH)_3$

(4) $C_{12}H_{22}O_{11}$

3 An example of a nonelectrolyte is

(1) $C_6H_{12}O_6(aq)$

(2) $K_2SO_4(aq)$

(3) $NaCl(aq)$

(4) $HCl(aq)$

4 According to the Brönsted-Lowry theory, an acid is any species that

(1) releases hydroxide ions into a solution

(2) releases oxide ions into a solution

(3) donates H^+ ions to another species

(4) accepts H^+ ions from another species

5 An Arrhenius acid contains hydrogen and ionizes to produce

(1) only hydroxide ions in solution

(2) only hydrogen ions in solution

(3) hydrogen ions as the only positive ions in solution

(4) hydrogen ions as the only negative ions in solution

6 In which reaction is water acting only as a Brönsted-Lowry base?

(1) $H_2SO_4(aq) + H_2O(l) \rightleftharpoons$
$HSO_4^-(aq) + H_3O^+(aq)$

(2) $NH_3(g) + H_2O(l) \rightleftharpoons NH_4^+(aq) + OH^-(aq)$

(3) $CH_3COO^-(aq) + H_2O(l) \rightleftharpoons$
$CH_3COOH(aq) + OH^-(aq)$

(4) $H_2O(l) + H_2O(l) \rightleftharpoons H_3O^+(aq) + OH^-(aq)$

7 Both $HNO_3(aq)$ and $CH_3COOH(aq)$ can be classified as

(1) Arrhenius acids that turn blue litmus red

(2) Arrhenius bases that turn blue litmus red

(3) Arrhenius acids that turn red litmus blue

(4) Arrhenius bases that turn red litmus blue

Part B–1

8 If equal volumes of 0.1 M NaOH and 0.1 M HCl are mixed, the resulting solution will contain a salt and

(1) HCl

(2) NaOH

(3) H_2O

(4) NaCl

9 Given the neutralization reaction:
$H_2SO_4 + 2KOH \rightarrow K_2SO_4 + 2HOH$,
Which compound is a salt?

(1) KOH

(2) H_2SO_4

(3) K_2SO_4

(4) HOH

10 A solution with a pH of 11 is tested first with phenolphthalein and then with litmus. What is the color of each indicator in this solution?

(1) Phenolphthalein is colorless and litmus is blue.

(2) Phenolphthalein is colorless and litmus is red.

(3) Phenolphthalein is pink and litmus is blue.

(4) Phenolphthalein is pink and litmus is red.

11 Which relationship is present in a solution that has a pH of 7?

(1) $[H^+] = [OH^-]$

(3) $[H^+] < [OH^-]$

(2) $[H^+] > [OH^-]$

(4) $[H^+] + [OH^-] = K_w$

Part B–2

12 If lithium hydroxide were placed in an aqueous solution, would it act like an Arrhenius base or an Arrhenius acid and why?

13 Equal volumes of 0.1 M NaOH and 0.1 M HCl are thoroughly mixed. What is the pH of the resulting solution?

14 What is the pH of a 0.0001 M aqueous solution of HCl at 25°C?

Part C

15 Four flasks each contain 100 milliliters of aqueous solutions of equal concentrations at 25°C and 1 atmosphere.

KCl   CH₃OH   Ba(OH)₂   CH₃COOH

a Which solutions contain electrolytes?

b Which solution has the lowest pH?

c What causes some aqueous solutions to have a low pH?

d Which solution is most likely to react with an Arrhenius acid to form a salt and water?

Base your answers on questions 16 and 17 on the information below.

A truck carrying concentrated nitric acid overturns and spills its contents. The acid drains into a nearby pond. The pH of the pond water was 8.0 before the spill. After the spill, the pond water is 1000 times more acidic.

16 Name an ion in the pond water that has increased in concentration due to this spill.

17 What is the new pH of the pond water after the spill and what color would bromthymol blue be at this new pH? Use Regents Reference Table M.

18 A student recorded the following buret readings during a titration of a base with an acid:

	Standard 0.100 M HCl	Unknown KOH
Initial reading	9.08 mL	0.55 mL
Final reading	19.09 mL	5.56 mL

Calculate the molarity of the KOH, showing all work.

anode	electrolytic cell	redox reaction
battery	half-cells	reduction
cathode	half-reaction	salt bridge
electrochemical cell	oxidation	voltaic cell
electrolysis	oxidation-reduction reaction	

Just as acid-base reactions can be described as a transfer of protons, oxidation-reduction reactions are described as the transfer of electrons. One everyday application of these reactions is batteries. Stored chemical energy in a battery is released by oxidation-reduction reactions. The chemical energy becomes electric energy that drives electrons through wires to supply electricity when we need it.

Transferring Electrons

Many chemical reactions can be described as the transfer of electrons from one atom to another atom. A reaction in which electrons are transferred from one atom to another atom is called an **oxidation-reduction reaction**. Chemists also call this type of reaction a **redox reaction**. An example of a redox reaction is the combustion reaction that occurs when magnesium burns in air yielding magnesium oxide. The equation for this reaction is

$$2Mg(s) + O_2(g) \rightarrow 2MgO(s)$$

As shown in Figure 9.1, each magnesium atoms loses two electrons to become an Mg^{2+} ion and each oxygen atom gains two electrons to become an O^{2-} ion.

$$2Mg(s) + O_2(g) \rightarrow 2Mg^{2+} + 2O^{2-}$$

In redox reactions, the transfer of electrons is not necessarily from a metal to a nonmetal. When chlorine is added to a solution of potassium bromide, the colorless solution becomes very dark as bromine molecules are produced.

$$2KBr(aq) + Cl_2(aq) \rightarrow 2KCl(aq) + Br_2(aq)$$

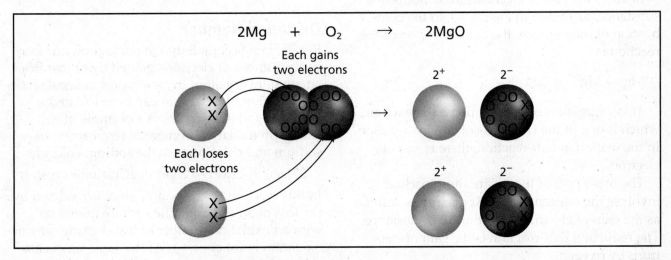

Figure 9.1 Shown is the redox reaction of magnesium and oxygen. In this process, each magnesium atom loses two electrons to an oxygen atom.

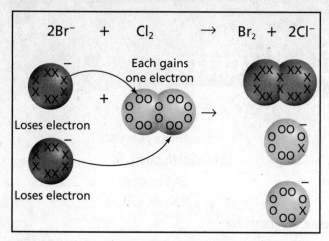

$$2Br^- + Cl_2 \rightarrow Br_2 + 2Cl^-$$

Each gains one electron

Loses electron

Loses electron

Figure 9.2 Shown is the redox reaction of chlorine and bromide. An electron from each bromide ion is being transferred to a chlorine atom. Which reactant is being reduced and which is being oxidized?

Notice that the potassium ions, K^+, do not change during the reaction, so the net reaction can be written as

$$2Br^- + Cl_2 \rightarrow Br_2 + 2Cl^-$$

Figure 9.2 shows the movement of electrons during this reaction. Each bromide ion transfers an electron to the chlorine molecule, which breaks apart to form two chloride ions. Because electrons are transferred, this is a redox reaction.

✔ **CHECK FOR UNDERSTANDING** Define *redox reaction*.

Half-Reactions

Despite the name, oxidation-reduction reactions do not necessarily involve oxygen. **Oxidation** is defined as the loss of electrons from atoms of a substance, as shown in Figure 9.3. In the combustion of magnesium, the oxidation part of the reaction is

$$Mg \rightarrow Mg^{2+} + 2e^-$$

This expression is an oxidation **half-reaction**, which is one of the two parts of a redox reaction. In the oxidation half-reaction, there is loss of electrons.

The other part of the magnesium reaction involves the oxygen atoms. **Reduction** is defined as the gain of electrons by atoms of a substance. The reduction half-reaction is the gain of electrons by oxygen.

$$O_2 + 4e^- \rightarrow 2O^{2-}$$

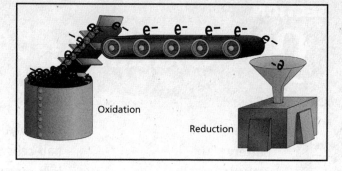

Oxidation

Reduction

Figure 9.3 Above is an illustration of an electron donor-acceptor machine to illustrate that electrons in a redox reaction can come from any source with electrons available and that the process also requires something to accept the electrons.

Oxidation and reduction are complementary processes, and neither can occur by itself. There is no oxidation reaction or reduction reaction, only oxidation-reduction. Notice that in the oxidation half-reaction, the expression might be changed to

$$2Mg \rightarrow 2Mg^{2+} + 4e^-$$

But this is not done because four electrons are needed for the reduction part of this particular redox reaction. The oxidation half reaction is changed to the "doubled" form, so that the number of electrons transferred are equal. As with any other reaction equation, redox equations must be written in a form that balances not only the atoms, but also the charges of the reaction. The number of electrons lost during oxidation is always exactly equal to the number of electrons gained during reduction.

✔ **CHECK FOR UNDERSTANDING** Why can there only be an oxidation-reduction reaction, and not just a reduction or an oxidation reaction?

Oxidation Number

Recall from Section 5 that the oxidation number is the number of electrons gained by or lost from an atom. Every atom in an ion or a molecule has an oxidation number that can be calculated using the following rules. An example of a change in oxidation number is the reaction of sodium and chlorine to make sodium chloride.

$$2Na(s) + Cl_2(g) \rightarrow 2Na^+ + 2Cl^- \text{ (ionic crystal)}$$

In this reaction, each sodium atom is oxidized by the loss of an electron. The sodium atom starts with an oxidation number of 0 and changes to an oxidation number of $+1$. At the same time, chlorine is reduced from an oxidation number of 0 to an oxidation number of -1.

Determining Oxidation Numbers

In order to understand and balance a redox reaction, chemists use a set of rules to determine the oxidation number of atoms and ions in the reaction.

1 The oxidation number of an uncombined atom is zero, including elements that exist as diatomic molecules. For example, Fe and H each have an oxidation number of zero in Fe and H_2).

2 The oxidation number of a monatomic ion is equal to the charge on the ion (oxidation number of the Na^+ ion is +1, and the oxidation number of the Ca^{2+} ion is +2.).

3 The oxidation number of the more electronegative atom in a molecule or polyatomic ion is the same as the charge it would have if it were an ion. For example, in a water molecule, H_2O, the oxidation number of oxygen is −2.

4 The most electronegative element, fluorine, always has an oxidation number of −1 when it is bonded to another element (oxidation number of fluorine is −1 in HF, but it is zero in F_2.

5 The oxidation number of oxygen in compounds is always −2, except in peroxides, where it is −1, or when it is bonded to fluorine, when it is +2. For example, in H_2O_2 (hydrogen peroxide), the oxidation number of O is −1.

6 The oxidation number of hydrogen in most compounds is +1. There is an exception when hydrogen is bonded to active metals to form hydrides, such as LiH. In this case, hydrogen has an oxidation number of −1.

7 The metals of groups 1 and 2 and aluminum form compounds in which the metal atom always has a positive oxidation number equal to its number of valence electrons. For example, the oxidation number of K is +1 and the oxidation number of Mg +2.

8 The sum of the oxidation numbers in a compound is zero. In CCl_4, for example, the oxidation number of Cl is −1. Therefore, the oxidation number of C must be +4.

9 The sum of the oxidation numbers of the atoms in a polyatomic ion is equal to the charge on the ion. For example, in the sulfate ion, SO_4^{2-}, the sum of oxidation numbers must be −2. Since O has an oxidation number of −2, the oxidation number of S must be +6.

Oxidation Number Assignment

Many elements, such as transition metals and metalloids, can have different oxidation numbers in different compounds. For example, in the compound Cu_2O, copper's oxidation number is +1 and oxygen is −2, but in the compound CuO, copper has an oxidation number of +2 and oxygen is −2.

✓ CHECK FOR UNDERSTANDING What is the oxidation number of an uncombined atom? Of a monatomic atom?

Table 9.1 shows how oxidation numbers can be determined and related to the atoms in the oxidation-reduction reaction:

$$2KBr(aq) + Cl_2(aq) \rightarrow 2KCl(aq) + Br_2(aq)$$

During the reaction, the oxidation number of Br changed from −1 to 0, the oxidation number of chlorine changed from 0 to −1, and the oxidation number of K remained at +1. That means that Cl is reduced, Br is oxidized, and K does not participate in the reaction.

Using the rules listed above, you also can determine the oxidation number of a particular atom in a molecule or polyatomic ion. For example, in the compound $KMnO_4$, the oxidation number of Mn can be determined as follows:

1 The compound is neutral so the overall oxidation number is 0. The oxidation number of K is +1 and the oxidation number of oxygen is −2. Therefore, the oxidation number of Mn is calculated as follows.

2 $\quad 0 \quad = 1 + ? + 4(-2)$
Total $\quad$ K $\quad$ Mn $\quad$ O_4

3 Oxidation number of Mn $= 0 - 1 - 4(-2)$
$$= -1 + 8$$
$$= +7$$

Table 9.1 • Oxidation Number Assignment		
Element	Oxidation Number	Rule
K in KBr	+1	7
Br in KBr	−1	7 and 8
Cl in Cl_2	0	1
K in KCl	+1	7
Cl in KCl	−1	7 and 8
Br in Br_2	0	1

Balancing Redox Equations

A redox reaction can include atoms, ions, molecules, or a combination of the three. Oxidation and reduction occur whenever a substance that can give up electrons comes in contact with one that can gain electrons. There are a number of different reactions that can oxidize or reduce any particular atom, molecule, or ion. For example, Table 9.2 shows a number of reactions that involve oxidation of iron, Fe. When iron rusts, it is oxidized by oxygen in the reaction.

$$4Fe + 3O_2 \rightarrow 2Fe_2O_3$$

In another reaction, iron is oxidized by a silver ion, Ag^+.

$Fe + AgNO_3 \rightarrow Ag + Fe(NO_3)_3$
(Note that this equation is *not* balanced.)

Look at the second column of the table and notice that the same oxidation half-reaction applies to each of the reactions of iron.

$$Fe \rightarrow Fe^{3+} + 3e^-$$

No matter what happens in the reduction side of the reaction, the oxidation is exactly the same because an iron atom is oxidized to an ion with a charge of 3+.

Separating the reaction into half-reactions helps to balance a redox equation. For example, if you place an iron nail in a solution of silver nitrate, silver metal will deposit on the nail as iron atoms are oxidized. The unbalanced equation is

$$Fe + AgNO_3 \rightarrow Ag + Fe(NO_3)_3$$

To balance this equation using half-reactions, follow these steps:

1 Write the net ionic equation, omitting ions that are not involved in the redox reaction.

$Fe + Ag^+ + NO_3^- \rightarrow Ag + Fe^{3+} + NO_3^-$
(Note that NO_3^- is not involved in oxidation or reduction)
$Fe + Ag^+ \rightarrow Ag + Fe^{3+}$

2 Write the oxidation and reduction half-reactions for the net ionic equation.

$Fe \rightarrow Fe^{3+} + e^-$
$Ag^+ + e^- \rightarrow Ag$

3 Balance the atoms and charges on each half-reaction.

$Fe \rightarrow Fe^{3+} + 3e^-$
$Ag^+ + e^- \rightarrow Ag$

4 Adjust the coefficients so that the number of electrons lost in oxidation equals the number of electrons gained in reduction.

$Fe \rightarrow Fe^{3+} + 3e^-$
$3Ag^+ + 3e^- \rightarrow 3Ag$

5 Add the balanced half-reactions and return the other ions.

$Fe + 3Ag^+ \rightarrow 3Ag + Fe^{3+}$
$Fe + 3AgNO_3 \rightarrow 3Ag + Fe(NO_3)_3$

The balanced equations tells us that each iron atom reduces three silver ions.

✓ **CHECK FOR UNDERSTANDING** When balancing redox equations, what must be balanced in each half-reaction?

Table 9.2 • Various Oxidation-Reduction Reactions in Which Iron Is Oxidized		
Overall Reaction (Unbalanced)	**Oxidation Half-Reaction**	**Reduction Half-Reaction**
$Fe + O_2 \rightarrow Fe_2O_3$	$Fe \rightarrow Fe^{3+} + 3e^-$	$O_2 + 4e^- \rightarrow 2O^{2-}$
$Fe + Cl_2 \rightarrow FeCl_3$	$Fe \rightarrow Fe^{3+} + 3e^-$	$Cl_2 + 2e^- \rightarrow 2Cl^-$
$Fe + F_2 \rightarrow FeF_3$	$Fe \rightarrow Fe^{3+} + 3e^-$	$F_2 + 2e^- \rightarrow 2F^-$
$Fe + HBr \rightarrow H_2 + FeBr_3$	$Fe \rightarrow Fe^{3+} + 3e^-$	$2H^+ + 2e^- \rightarrow H_2$
$Fe + AgNO_3 \rightarrow Ag + Fe(NO_3)_3$	$Fe \rightarrow Fe^{3+} + 3e^-$	$Ag^+ + e^- \rightarrow Ag$
$Fe + CuSO_4 \rightarrow Cu + Fe_2(SO_4)_3$	$Fe \rightarrow Fe^{3+} + 3e^-$	$Cu^{2+} + 2e^- \rightarrow Cu$

Example Problem 1

The addition of dichromate ions to an acidic aqueous solution containing iodide ions forms chromium(III) ions and elemental iodine, I_2. Using the overall reaction and the availability of water and hydrogen ions from the solution, balance the equation for the redox reaction.

$$Cr_2O_7^{2-}(aq) + I^-(aq) \rightarrow Cr^{3+}(aq) + I_2(s)$$

1 Analyze the Problem

- You have the skeleton reaction and the availability of hydrogen ions and water in an acidic solution. The overall reaction equation can be balanced by using redox half-reactions.

2 Solve for the Unknown

Write the net ionic equation for the reaction.

$$Cr_2O_7^{2-} + I^- \rightarrow Cr^{3+} + I_2$$

Write the oxidation and reduction half-reactions, including oxidation numbers.

$I^- \rightarrow I_2 + e^-$ (oxidation) $\qquad\qquad$ -1 $\qquad$ 0 (oxidation numbers)
$Cr_2O_7^{2-} + e^- \rightarrow Cr^{3+}$ (reduction) $\qquad$ $+6$ $\qquad$ $+3$ (oxidation numbers)

Using the oxidation numbers, balance the atoms and charges in the half-reactions.

$2I^- \rightarrow I_2 + 2e^-$ (oxidation)
$Cr_2O_7^{2-} + 6e^- + 14H^+ \rightarrow 2Cr^{3+} + 7H_2O$ (reduction) $\qquad$ Note: H^+ and H_2O are readily available in solution

Adjust the coefficients so that the number of electrons lost equals the number of electrons gained in reduction.

$6I^- \rightarrow 3I_2 + 6e^-$ (oxidation)
$Cr_2O_7^{2-} + 6e^- + 14H^+ \rightarrow 2Cr^{3+} + 7H_2O$ (reduction)

Add the half-reactions.
$$Cr_2O_7^{2-} + 14H^+ + 6I^- \rightarrow 2Cr^{3+} + 7H_2O + 3I_2$$

3 Evaluate the Answer

Does the answer make sense? The number of atoms of each element and the charges are balanced in the reaction, so the result is reasonable.

Quick Review

1 An oxidation-reduction reaction always involves
   (1) ionization of a compound
   (2) transfer of electrons
   (3) transfer of protons
   (4) molecular ions

2 What kind of process is represented by this reaction: $Na \rightarrow Na^+ + e^-$?
   (1) oxidation $\qquad$ (3) redox
   (2) reduction $\qquad$ (4) neutralization

3 Given the reaction $2HCl + Mg \rightarrow MgCl_2 + H_2$, what is the reduction half-reaction?
   (1) $Mg \rightarrow Mg^{2+} + 2e^-$
   (2) $Mg^{2+} + 2e^- \rightarrow Mg$
   (3) $2H^+ + 2e^- \rightarrow H_2$
   (4) $2H \rightarrow H_2$

4 What is the oxidation number for copper in the ion $Cu(NH_3)_4^{2+}$?
   (1) -2 $\qquad\qquad$ (3) $+2$
   (2) -3 $\qquad\qquad$ (4) $+3$

5 In the reaction $2Fe + 3CuSO_4 \rightarrow 3Cu + Fe_2(SO_4)_3$, which of the following occurs?

(1) Copper is oxidized.

(2) Iron is oxidized.

(3) Sulfate ions are oxidized.

(4) Sulfur is reduced.

6 In the unbalanced equation $Fe + O_2 \rightarrow Fe_2O_3$, what is the oxidation half-reaction?

7 In a redox reaction, the substance that undergoes oxidation will

(1) always bond with oxygen

(2) always break an oxygen bond

(3) lose electrons

(4) gain electrons

8 The oxidation number of an oxygen atom in O_2 is

(1) -2 (3) 0

(2) -1 (4) $+2$

9 Write the reduction half-reaction of this redox reaction: $Ni + Cl_2 \rightarrow NiCl_2$

10 Write this reaction as a balanced equation: $SO_2 + Cl_2 + H_2O \rightarrow HCl + H_2SO_4$

Electrochemical Cells

Oxidation-reduction reactions are a key part of electrochemistry, the study of the process by which chemical energy is converted to electric energy and vice versa. Because the reactions always involve a transfer of electrons, separating the two half-reactions can cause a flow of electrons.

Building a Cell

Figure 9.4 demonstrates one way to cause electrons to flow during an oxidation-reduction reaction. A half-reaction can occur in each beaker.

$$Zn \rightarrow Zn^{2+} + 2e^- \text{ (oxidation: loss of electrons)}$$
$$Cu^{2+} + 2e^- \rightarrow Cu \text{ (reduction: gain of electrons)}$$

Look at Figure 9.4(a). Can a redox reaction occur in these beakers? No, the half-reactions are completely separated. No reaction can occur because there is no way for zinc to transfer electrons to the copper(II) ions. Connecting the two metal strips with a copper wire, as shown in Figure 9.4(b), provides a pathway through which electrons can travel.

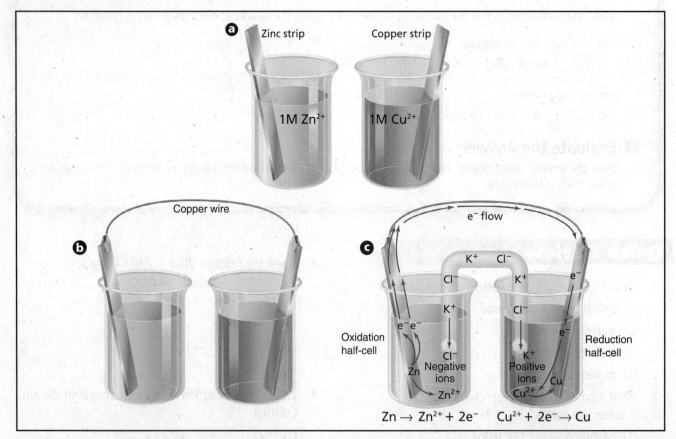

Figure 9.4 (a) The oxidation half-reaction is separated from the reduction half-reaction. **(b)** A copper wire connects the two half-reactions to conduct a flow of electrons. **(c)** A salt bridge allows electrons to be exchanged and the reaction to take place.

However, electrons do not flow due to a problem. As soon as the reaction starts, a positive charge builds in the zinc sulfate solution and a negative charge builds in the copper sulfate solution. These charges prevent oxidation of zinc atoms and reduction of copper ions. To fix this, a connection is inserted between the two solutions, as shown in Figure 9.4(c). This connection is called a **salt bridge**, which is a pathway constructed to allow the passage of ions from one solution to another. In this case, the salt bridge is a tube containing a solution of potassium chloride held in place by a permeable gel. Ions from the salt bridge can move through the gel, but the two solutions cannot mix.

When both connections—the wire and the salt bridge—are in place, electrons can flow through the wire, while ions move in the salt bridge to keep the charges balanced. The complete structure is an electrochemical cell. An **electrochemical cell** is an apparatus that uses a redox reaction to produce electric energy or uses electric energy to cause a chemical reaction. There are two types of electrochemical cells. A **voltaic cell** converts chemical energy to electric energy by a spontaneous redox reaction. The cell composed of zinc and copper strips in solution is a voltaic cell. An **electrolytic cell** uses electric energy to cause a chemical reaction.

Voltaic Cells

The oxidation and reduction reactions in an electrochemical cell occur in two parts of the cell, called **half-cells**. Each half-cell has an electrode, which carries electrons to and from a solution of ions. In Figure 9.4, each beaker of solution with a metal strip is a half-cell. The zinc and copper strips are the electrodes. Oxidation occurs in the beaker with the zinc strip as the strip gains electrons from the solution. The electrode where oxidation takes place is called the **anode** of the cell. Reduction occurs in the beaker with the copper strip as the copper loses electrons to the solution. The electrode where reduction takes place is the **cathode** of the cell.

If you think about it, the reverse reactions might occur:

$$Zn^{2+} + 2e^- \rightarrow Zn$$

$$Cu \rightarrow Cu^{2+} + 2e^-$$

Why don't these reactors occur instead? The reason that zinc is oxidized, rather than copper, is that zinc is more reactive than copper. An activity series like the one shown in Table 9.3 can be used to determine in which direction a reaction will occur spontaneously. To use this table with metals, for example, first determine which two metals may be oxidized or reduced. Then look up the metals in the table. The higher (more active) metal will be oxidized. The lower (less active) metal will be reduced.

✓ **CHECK FOR UNDERSTANDING** What does an electrode do?

Table 9.3 • Activity Series	
	Metals
Most active	Lithium
	Rubidium
	Potassium
	Cesium
	Barium
	Strontium
	Calcium
	Sodium
	Magnesium
	Aluminum
	Titanium
	Manganese
	Zinc
	Chromium
	Iron
	Cobalt
	Nickel
	Tin
	Lead
	Hydrogen**
	Copper
Least active	Silver
	Gold
	Nonmetals
Most active	Fluorine
	Chlorine
Least active	Bromine
	Iodine

** Activity series based on hydrogen standard.
Note: H_2 is *not* a metal.

Because voltaic cells cause a flow of electrons between the two half-reactions, they are useful as a source of electricity. Whenever you use a flashlight, a cell phone, or a portable CD player, you use voltaic cells. A **battery** is one or more electrochemical cells in a single package that generates electric current. An alkaline cell battery, contains zinc mixed in a paste with potassium hydroxide at the anode. The oxidation half-cell reaction is

$$Zn + 2OH^- \rightarrow ZnO + H_2O + 2e^-$$

Zinc metal is oxidized from an oxidation number of 0 to +2, losing two electrons. These electrons travel though your lightbulb or the motor of your CD player. The electrons return to the battery at the cathode, where the reduction half-cell reaction takes place.

$$MnO_2 + 2H_2O + 2e^- \rightarrow Mn(OH)_2 + 2OH^-$$

At the cathode, manganese (IV) oxide, which also is mixed with potassium hydroxide in a paste, is reduced. The oxidation number of manganese goes from +4 to +2. This reaction continues until one of the reactants has been consumed. At that point, the battery is useless and must be replaced. Other types of batteries use different half-reactions, but in every case electrons are lost at the anode and gained at the cathode.

✓ **CHECK FOR UNDERSTANDING** Which type of reaction occurs at the cathode?

Figure 9.5 shows a nickel-cadmium (NiCad) battery, which uses a different pair of half-reactions. Cordless tools, cell phones, and other devices that operate with rechargeable batteries use NiCad batteries. In NiCad batteries, the anode and cathode are long ribbons of material, separated by a layer that allows ions to pass.

The oxidation reaction at the anode is

$$Cd + 2OH^- \rightarrow Cd(OH)_2 + 2e^-$$

The two electrons lost during this reaction travel to the cathode where nickel oxide is reduced to nickel hydroxide.

$$NiO(OH) + H_2O + e^- \rightarrow Ni(OH)_2 + OH^-$$

NiCad batteries are rechargeable, meaning that the reactions at the anode and cathode can be reversed, storing energy that can be used again. There are many other combinations of half-reactions used in different types of batteries.

The choice of components is based on cost, how much electric current is needed, and whether recharging is desirable.

✓ **CHECK FOR UNDERSTANDING** Why do some devices use a NiCad battery?

Electrolytic Cells

Electrochemical cells also can convert electric energy into chemical energy. An electrolytic cell is a cell that uses redox reactions to convert electric energy into chemical energy. Essentially, an electrolytic cell is the reverse of a voltaic cell. The electrons flow in the opposite direction and the half-reactions are reversed. When you recharge a NiCad battery, it is acting as an electrolytic cell, reversing the chemical reactions that occur when you use the battery.

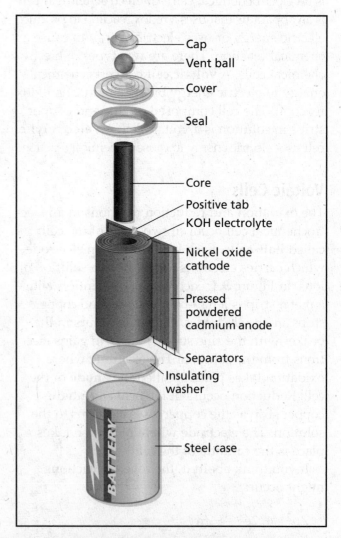

Figure 9.5 Shown here are the components of a rechargeable NiCad battery. What is the cathode and what is the anode?

Note that the reactions in an electrolytic cell are not spontaneous. The reaction only occurs when electric energy is provided from an external power source.

Figure 9.6 compares how a zinc-copper electrochemical cell functions both as a voltaic cell and as an electrolytic cell. If a lightbulb is attached to the wire of the zinc-copper electrochemical cell, it will use the energy of the electrons flowing from the zinc anode to the copper cathode. Notice in the illustration in Figure 9.6(a) that the zinc strip is shrinking and the copper strip is growing. Eventually there is either too little zinc metal or copper ions to continue the reaction and the electron flow stops. This is similar to what happens when a flashlight battery no longer works. The cell can be regenerated, though, if current is applied in the reverse direction using a power source such as a transformer plugged into a wall outlet. This is shown in Figure 9.6(b). Notice that the strips of metal now have reversed their functions. At the zinc strip, electrons now are being gained from the solution, so it becomes the cathode and the copper strip becomes the anode.

$Zn^{2+} + 2e^- \rightarrow Zn$
(reduction: gain of electrons)

$Cu \rightarrow Cu^{2+} + 2e^-$
(oxidation: loss of electrons)

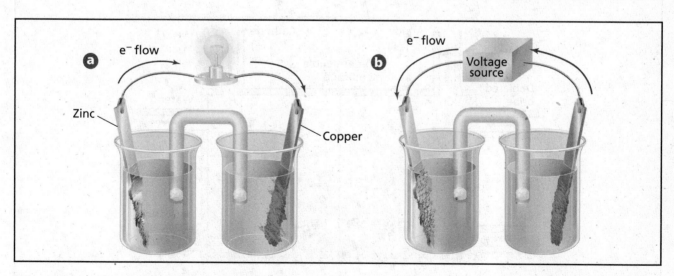

Figure 9.6 **(a)** A zinc-copper electrochemical cell powers a lightbulb by a spontaneous redox reaction. The electrons flow from the zinc to the copper. Over time the zinc is oxidized and the flow of electrons decreases. **(b)** The cell can be regenerated using a reverse current from a voltage source. The reverse reaction is nonspontaneous.

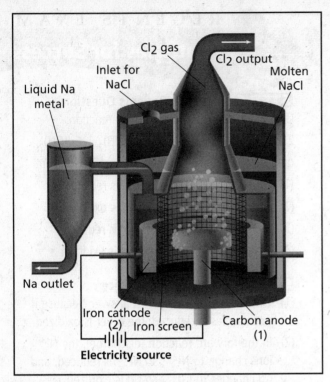

Figure 9.7 This is an example of a Down's cell, which is used to separate molten sodium chloride into sodium metal and chlorine gas.

Electrolysis

The use of electric energy to cause a chemical reaction is called **electrolysis**. Electrolysis is used in the chemical and metal industries to manufacture and purify chemicals. One common use of electrolysis is the production of sodium and chlorine from salt, as shown in Figure 9.7.

This is a Down's cell, which is an electrolytic cell that uses electric energy to obtain sodium metal. Inside the cell there is an iron cathode and a carbon anode. At the cathode, sodium ions gain electrons to become sodium metal, while chlorine is formed at the anode.

$$Na^+ + e^- \rightarrow Na \text{ (reduction: gain of electrons)}$$

$$2Cl^- \rightarrow Cl_2 + 2e^- \text{ (oxidation: loss of electrons)}$$

A similar process, decomposing sodium chloride in an aqueous solution, is shown in Figure 9.8. As in the Down's cell, the anode reaction produces chlorine gas. Two reactions occur at the cathode in this cell, the reduction of sodium ions and the reduction of hydrogen in water molecules.

$$Na^+ + e^- \rightarrow Na$$

$$H^+ + e^- \rightarrow H$$

Conditions favor the production of hydrogen, the sodium ions react with hydroxide ions to form NaOH, and the overall cell reaction is:

$$2H_2O + 2NaCl \rightarrow H_2 + Cl_2 + 2NaOH$$

This reaction is commercially important because all of its products—hydrogen gas, chlorine gas, and sodium hydroxide—are commercial materials used by industry.

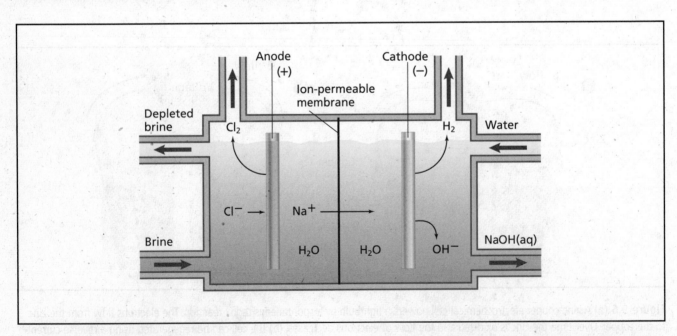

Figure 9.8 The electrolytic process of brine (NaCl solution) results in the products of hydrogen gas, chlorine gas, and sodium hydroxide.

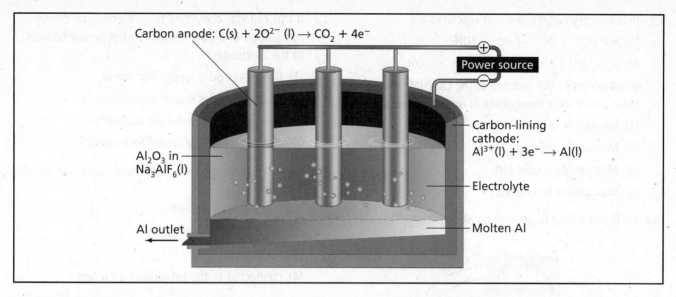

Figure 9.9 In the Hall-Héroult process, relatively pure aluminum is produced by electrolysis of aluminum oxide (obtained from bauxite ore).

In the Hall-Héroult process, shown in Figure 9.9, aluminum is produced by electrolysis of aluminum oxide. A large vat is lined with carbon, which serves as the cathode. Carbon rods are used as the anode. The vat contains molten aluminum oxide, Al_2O_3, in solution. At the cathode, Al^{3+} ions are reduced to Al. The molten aluminum is periodically removed to help the reaction proceed in the forward direction. At the anode, O^{2-} ions are oxidized to produce oxygen gas, which then reacts with carbon to produce carbon monoxide.

Figure 9.10 shows another way that electrolytic cells can be used. A metal object placed in a silver nitrate solution can be electroplated, meaning a thin layer of silver is added to its surface. In this case, the anode is a silver rod which is oxidized to form silver ions. The cathode is the object to be electroplated. As the electric current flows through the electrolytic cell, silver metal is oxidized at the anode, and silver ions are reduced at the cathode. As a result, the cathode is coated with silver.

✓ CHECK FOR UNDERSTANDING What is electrolysis used for?

Quick Review

11 The purpose of a salt bridge in an electrochemical cell is to
(1) transfer electrons
(2) transfer water
(3) transfer protons
(4) transfer positive and negative ions

12 The addition of energy is necessary to operate a(n)
(1) battery
(2) electrochemical cell
(3) electrolytic cell
(4) voltaic cell

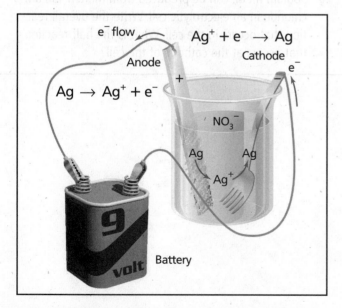

Figure 9.10 Shown is an electrolytic cell used for silver plating. Ions in the electrolyte solution are reduced to silver metal and deposit on the cathode.

13 In a mercury battery, the half-reactions are:

$$HgO + H_2O + 2e^- \rightarrow Hg + 2OH^-$$
$$MnO_2 + 2H_2O + 2e^- \rightarrow Mn(OH)_2 + 2OH^-$$

What occurs at the cathode of the cell? (Mercury is more active than manganese in an activity series.)

(1) Mercury is oxidized.

(2) Mercury is reduced.

(3) Manganese is oxidized.

(4) Manganese is reduced.

Use the figure below to answer questions 14 and 15.

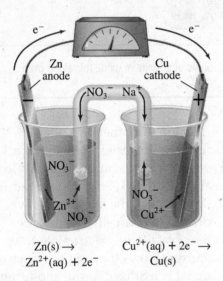

$$Zn(s) \rightarrow$$
$$Zn^{2+}(aq) + 2e^-$$

$$Cu^{2+}(aq) + 2e^- \rightarrow$$
$$Cu(s)$$

14 The oxidation half-reaction for this cell is

(1) $Zn \rightarrow Zn^{2+} + 2e^-$

(2) $Cu \rightarrow Cu^{2+} + 2e^-$

(3) $Zn^{2+} + 2e^- \rightarrow Zn$

(4) $Cu^{2+} + 2e^- \rightarrow Cu$

15 If this cell was converted to an electrolytic cell by application of a power source, what would happen to the electrodes?

(1) Both electrodes would add metal.

(2) Both electrodes would lose metal.

(3) The zinc electrode would add metal.

(4) The zinc electrode would lose metal.

16 When electroplating an object with silver, the object must be

(1) the anode of the cell

(2) the cathode of the cell

(3) made of iron

(4) connected to the cathode of a battery

17 A rechargeable battery acts as

(1) a voltaic cell only

(2) an electrolytic cell only

(3) either a voltaic or an electrolytic cell

(4) neither a voltaic nor an electrolytic cell

18 The final products of the electrolysis of water are

(1) hydrogen gas and hydroxide ions

(2) hydrogen gas and oxygen gas

(3) oxygen gas and hydrogen ions

(4) oxygen gas and hydroxide ions

19 What kind of energy is added to cause the reactions in an electrolytic cell?

20 Sodium metal can be produced from molten sodium chloride in an electrolytic cell. Write the overall reaction that occurs in the cell. What is the half-reaction that occurs at the cathode of the cell?

Part A

1 Which quantities are conserved in all oxidation-reduction reactions?

(1) charge only

(2) mass only

(3) both charge and mass

(4) neither charge nor mass

2 In any redox reaction, the substance that undergoes reduction will

(1) lose electrons and have a decrease in oxidation number

(2) lose electrons and have an increase in number

(3) gain electrons and have a decrease in oxidation number

(4) gain electrons and have an increase in oxidation number

3 An oxidation half-reaction always involves the

(1) gain of electrons and a decrease in the oxidation number

(2) gain of electrons and an increase in the oxidation number

(3) loss of electrons and a decrease in the oxidation number

(4) loss of electrons and an increase in the oxidation number

4 In any redox reaction, a reactant can undergo a decrease in oxidation number by

(1) losing electrons only

(2) gaining electrons only

(3) losing protons only

(4) gaining protons only

5 Which statement is true for any electrochemical cell?

(1) Oxidation occurs at the anode, only.

(2) Reduction occurs at the anode, only.

(3) Oxidation occurs at both the anode and the cathode.

(4) Reduction occurs at both the anode and the cathode.

6 In an electrolytic cell, the anode is always the

(1) negative electrode, where reduction occurs

(2) negative electrode, where oxidation occurs

(3) positive electrode, where reduction occurs

(4) positive electrode, where oxidation occurs

7 Which procedure requires the use of an external electric current to force a redox reaction to occur?

(1) polymerization

(2) distillation

(3) electrolysis

(4) saponification

Part B–1

8 Given the redox reaction:

$$Fe^{2+}(aq) + Zn(s) \rightarrow Zn^{2+}(aq) + Fe(s)$$

Which species is oxidized?

(1) Fe(s)

(2) $Fe^{2+}(aq)$

(3) Zn(s)

(4) $Zn^{2+}(aq)$

9 Given the reaction

$$3Sn^{4+}(aq) + 2Cr(s) \rightarrow 3Sn^{2+}(aq) + 2Cr^{3+}(aq)$$

Which half-reaction correctly represents the reduction that occurs?

(1) $Sn^{4+}(aq) + 2e^- \rightarrow Sn^{2+}(aq)$

(2) $Sn^{2+}(aq) \rightarrow Sn^{4+}(aq) + 2e^-$

(3) $Cr(s) \rightarrow Cr^{3+}(aq) + 3e^-$

(4) $Cr^{3+}(aq) + 3e^- \rightarrow Cr(s)$

10 Which expression correctly represents a balanced reduction half-reaction?

(1) $Na^+ + e^- \rightarrow Na$

(2) $Na \rightarrow Na^+ + e^-$

(3) $Cl_2 + 2e^- \rightarrow Cl^-$

(4) $2Cl^- \rightarrow Cl_2 + 2e^-$

11 Given the reaction:

$$2Li(s) + Cl_2(g) \rightarrow 2LiCl(s)$$

As the reaction takes place, the $Cl_2(g)$ will

(1) gain electrons

(2) lose electrons

(3) gain protons

(4) lose protons

12 Given the cell reaction:

$$Ca(s) + Mg^{2+}(aq) \rightarrow Ca^{2+}(aq) + Mg(s)$$

Which substance is oxidized?

(1) $Ca(s)$ (3) $Ca^{2+}(aq)$

(2) $Mg^{2+}(aq)$ (4) $Mg(s)$

13 Given the reaction:

$$Zn(s) + 2HCl(aq) \rightarrow ZnCl_2(aq) + H_2(g)$$

Which substance is reduced?

(1) $Zn(s)$ (3) $Cl^-(aq)$

(2) $HCl(aq)$ (4) $H^+(aq)$

14 Given the redox reaction:

$$Mg(s) + CuSO_4(aq) \rightarrow MgSO_4(aq) + Cu(s)$$

Which species is reduced?

(1) $Cu(s)$ (3) $Mg(s)$

(2) $Cu^{2+}(aq)$ (4) $Mg^{2+}(aq)$

15 Given the reaction:

$$Zn(s) + 2HCl(aq) \rightarrow ZnCl_2(aq) + H_2(g)$$

Which equation represents the correct oxidation half-reaction?

(1) $Zn(s) \rightarrow Zn^{2+} + 2e^-$

(2) $2H^+ + 2e^- \rightarrow H_2(g)$

(3) $Zn^{2+} + 2e^- \rightarrow Zn(s)$

(4) $2Cl^- \rightarrow Cl_2(g) + 2e^-$

16 Given the lead-acid battery reaction:

$$Pb + PbO_2 + 2H_2SO_4 \rightarrow 2PbSO_4 + 2H_2O$$

Which equation represents the half-reaction for the oxidation that occurs?

(1) $Pb \rightarrow Pb^{2+} + 2e^-$

(2) $Pb^{4+} + 4e^- \rightarrow Pb$

(3) $Pb^{2+} + 2e^- \rightarrow Pb$

(4) $Pb \rightarrow Pb^{4+} + 4e^-$

17 Which equation represents an oxidation-reduction reaction?

(1) $HCl + KOH \rightarrow KCl + H_2O$

(2) $4HCl + MnO_2 \rightarrow MnCl_2 + 2H_2O + Cl_2$

(3) $2HCl + CaCO_3 \rightarrow CaCl_2 + H_2O + CO_2$

(4) $2HCl + FeS \rightarrow FeCl_2 + H_2S$

18 Which simple oxidation-reduction reaction is not correctly balanced?

(1) $Sn(s) + Cu^{2+}(aq) \rightarrow Cu(s) + Sn^{2+}(aq)$

(2) $Ni(s) + Sn^{2+}(aq) \rightarrow Sn(s) + Ni^{2+}(aq)$

(3) $2I^-(aq) + Fe^{3+}(aq) \rightarrow Fe^{2+}(aq) + I_2(s)$

(4) $2I^-(aq) + Hg^{2+}(aq) \rightarrow Hg(l) + I_2(s)$

19 What is the oxidation number of carbon in $NaHCO_3$?

(1) -2 (3) -4

(2) $+2$ (4) $+4$

20 Given the redox reaction:

$$2NaCl(l) \rightarrow 2Na(l) + Cl_2(g)$$

As the Cl^- is oxidized, the oxidation number of chlorine will

(1) decrease

(2) increase

(3) remain the same

21 The oxidation number of nitrogen in N_2 is

(1) $+1$ (3) $+3$

(2) 0 (4) -3

22 The oxidation number of a species that is oxidized can change from

(1) -1 to -3 (3) 3 to -1

(2) -2 to -1 (4) 4 to -3

23 What will happen when the switch is closed and the salt bridge is removed?

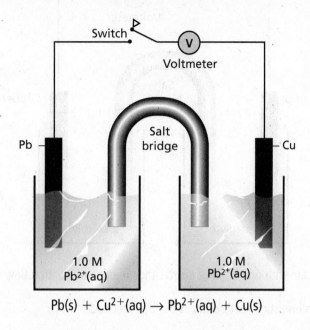

$$Pb(s) + Cu^{2+}(aq) \rightarrow Pb^{2+}(aq) + Cu(s)$$

24 The apparatus shown below is used to electroplate a metal key. The half-reaction at the key is
$$Ag^+ + e^- \rightarrow Ag(s)$$
Is the key an anode or cathode? Explain your answer.

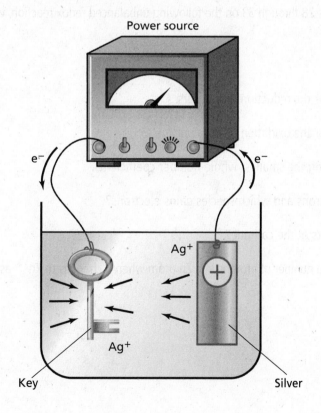

Base your answers to questions 25 through 27 on the diagram of a voltaic cell below and on your knowledge of chemistry.

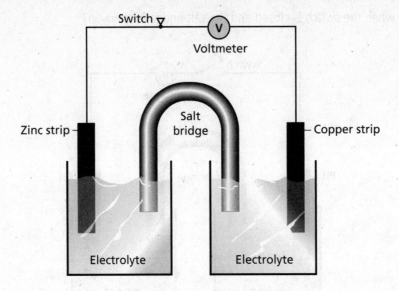

25 On the diagram above, indicate with one or more arrows the direction of electron flow through the wire.

26 Write an equation for the half-reaction that occurs at the zinc electrode.

27 Explain the function of the salt bridge.

Part C

Base your answers to questions 28 through 33 on the following unbalanced redox reaction, which occurs spontaneously in an electrochemical cell.

$$Zn + Cr^{3+} \rightarrow Zn^{2+} + Cr$$

28 Write the half-reaction for the reduction that occurs.

29 Write the half-reaction for the oxidation that occurs.

30 Balance the equation using the smallest whole-number coefficients.

31 Which species loses electrons and which species gains electrons?

32 Which half-reaction occurs at the cathode?

33 State what happens to the number of protons in a Zn atom when it changes to Zn^{2+} as the redox reaction occurs.

Organic chemistry is the chemistry of carbon compounds. The term **organic compound** applies to compounds containing carbon, with the exception of carbon oxides, carbides, and carbonates. In the early part of the nineteenth century, chemists could only synthesize organic compounds from plant and animal materials. Although this limitation no longer exists, the name applied during that time still remains.

Carbon Compounds

Why is there an entire field of chemistry based on one element? Carbon compounds have unique features, based on the way carbon forms chemical bonds with other atoms. Carbon has four valence electrons, which almost always form covalent bonds. This means that every carbon atom can form bonds with as many as four other atoms, most frequently with nonmetal elements, including other carbon atoms. Carbon atoms in organic molecules can be arranged in chains ranging from two carbon atoms to many thousands of carbon atoms. Because there are so many organic compounds, and their structures can be so complex, naming them is a complicated process. The International Union of Pure and Applied Chemistry (IUPAC) has established a system of rules to assign names to organic compounds based on the number and type of atoms in the molecule and how they are arranged.

Hydrocarbons

Most organic compounds include hydrogen, which forms one covalent bond. The simplest organic compounds, containing only the elements carbon and hydrogen, are called **hydrocarbons**. Figure 10.1 shows four different ways

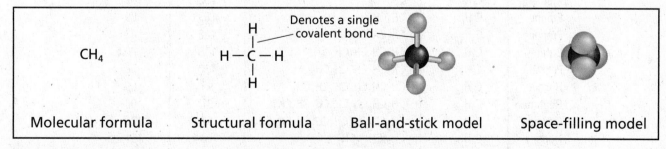

CH_4 — Molecular formula

Denotes a single covalent bond — Structural formula

Ball-and-stick model

Space-filling model

Figure 10.1 Here are four ways to depict a methane (CH_4) molecule, which consists of one carbon atom and four hydrogen atoms.

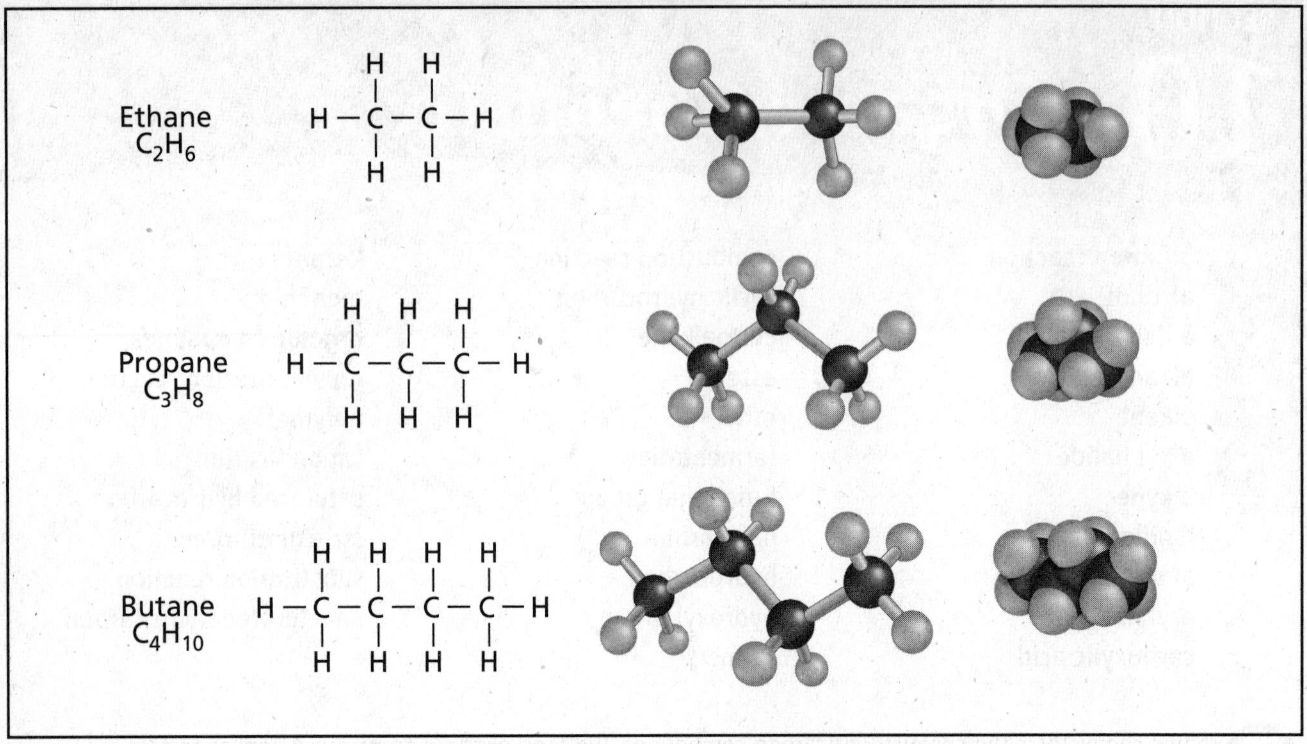

Ethane
C_2H_6

Propane
C_3H_8

Butane
C_4H_{10}

Figure 10.2 Here are four ways to model three straight-chain alkanes—ethane, propane, and butane. From right to left, they are the molecular formula, the structural formula, the ball-and-stick model, and the space-filling model.

to model methane, a simple hydrocarbon. The second model shows a **structural formula**, which designates atoms by their symbols and shows the chemical bonds. Structural formulas are useful in understanding the arrangement of atoms in organic molecules, because they indicate a spatial relationship.

Saturated Hydrocarbons

Hydrocarbons that have only single bonds are called **saturated hydrocarbons**. An **alkane** is a saturated hydrocarbon with no double or triple bonds. In an alkane, each carbon forms four sin-

gle bonds. Each bond is with another carbon atom or a hydrogen atom. The simplest alkane is methane, which has one carbon atom that forms bonds to four hydrogen atoms.

Because the carbon atoms can be arranged in complex chains in a variety of lengths, there are thousands of hydrocarbon molecules. Larger straight-chain alkanes consist of two or more carbons linked together by single bonds, each carbon atom bonded to two other carbon atoms, except for the carbons at the ends of the chain. End carbons are attached by covalent bonds to three hydrogen atoms, while the carbons inside

Table 10.1 • First Ten of the Alkane Series				
Name	**Molecular Formula**	**Condensed Structural Formula**	**Melting Point (°C)**	**Boiling Point (°C)**
Methane	CH_4	CH_4	−182	−162
Ethane	C_2H_6	CH_3CH_3	−183	−89
Propane	C_3H_8	$CH_3CH_2CH_3$	−188	−42
Butane	C_4H_{10}	$CH_3CH_2CH_2CH_3$	−138	−0.5
Pentane	C_5H_{12}	$CH_3CH_2CH_2CH_2CH_3$	−130	36
Hexane	C_6H_{14}	$CH_3CH_2CH_2CH_2CH_2CH_3$	−95	69
Heptane	C_7H_{16}	$CH_3CH_2CH_2CH_2CH_2CH_2CH_3$	−91	98
Octane	C_8H_{18}	$CH_3CH_2CH_2CH_2CH_2CH_2CH_2CH_3$	−57	126
Nonane	C_9H_{20}	$CH_3(CH_2)_7CH_3$	−54	151
Decane	$C_{10}H_{22}$	$CH_3(CH_2)_8CH_3$	−29	174

the chain are attached to two hydrogen atoms. Therefore, the formula for a straight-chain alkane is $C_nH_{(2n+2)}$, where n represents any integer. Figure 10.2 shows four different ways to model the first three straight chain alkanes, ethane, propane, and butane. Table 10.1 lists the first ten straight-chain alkanes along with their melting and boiling points. Beginning with pentane, alkanes are named, under IUPAC conventions, by a prefix indicating the number of carbons followed by the suffix *-ane*. Because the alkanes smaller than pentane were named before their structures were known, the prefixes *meth-*, *eth-*, *prop-*, and *but-* are not numerical.

Alkanes have equal charge distribution and tend to be symmetrical, so alkanes are nonpolar molecules. Compare the melting and boiling points of methane to that of water, a molecule with a similar size. Unlike water, which experiences strong intermolecular forces due to its polarity, methane molecules have very little interaction. Because of the difference in polarity, water and alkanes do not mix with one another. Alkanes do undergo combustion with oxygen and they are the main components of fuels, such as gasoline and diesel fuel.

✓ **CHECK FOR UNDERSTANDING** Why do water and alkanes not mix with one another?

Branched-Chain Alkanes

Look at the two molecules shown in Figure 10.3. Notice that both compounds have the same formula, C_4H_{10}, but the atoms are arranged differently. Because of the difference in arrangement of the atoms, the two compounds have different properties. The second compound, methylpropane, is a branched-chain alkane, a hydrocarbon in which all the carbon atoms form single bonds, but at least one of the carbon atoms is attached to three or four other carbon atoms. Like straight-chain alkanes, branched-chain alkanes have a formula that can be written as $C_nH_{(2n+2)}$.

Because more than one carbon atom can be a point of branching, a number of compounds can have the same molecular formula but have different molecular structures. These are called **isomers**. The IUPAC designates a unique name for each of these isomers based on the following rules.

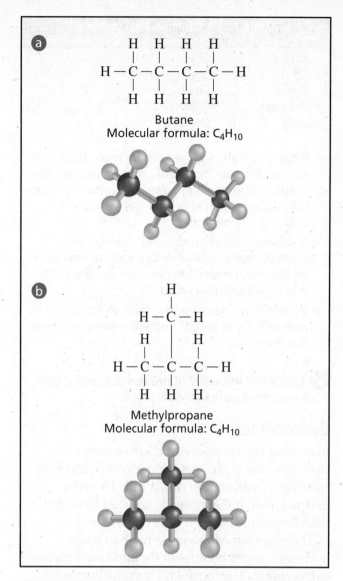

Figure 10.3 Butane and methylpropane have the same molecular formula, C_4H_{10}, but have different structural formulas. **(a)** Butane is a straight-chain alkane. **(b)** Methylpropane is a branched-chain alkane.

1 Count the number of carbon atoms in the longest continuous chain, called the parent chain. The parent chain is named for the straight-chain alkane with that number of carbons.

2 Number each carbon in the parent chain. First locate the end carbon closest to the substituent group, which is the side group that extends from the parent chain. Label that carbon *position one*.

3 Name each alkyl group substituent and place it before the name of the parent group. Names of common alkyl groups are given in Table 10.2 on page 156.

Table 10.2 • Common Alkyl Groups	
Name	Condensed Structural Formula
Methyl	CH_3-
Ethyl	CH_3CH_2-
Propyl	$CH_3CH_2CH_2-$
Isopropyl	$CH_3 CHCH_3$
Butyl	$CH_3CH_2CH_2-$

4 If the same alkyl group occurs more than once, use a prefix (*di-, tri-, tetra-, etc.*) to indicate the number of times it appears. Then use the number of the carbon to which it is attached to indicate its position.

5 If different alkyl groups are attached to the same parent structure, place their names in alphabetical order. Do not consider the prefix when determining order.

6 Write the name using hyphens to separate numbers from words and commas to separate numbers.

✓ **CHECK FOR UNDERSTANDING** How do branched-chain alkanes differ from straight-chain alkanes?

Cycloalkanes

In another type of alkane, a chain of carbons is closed to form a ring. An organic compound that contains a hydrocarbon ring is called a **cyclic hydrocarbon**. If the molecule does not have any double or triple bonds it is a **cycloalkane**.

The ring-shaped molecule has two fewer hydrogen atoms because of the additional carbon-carbon bond. The formulas for cycloalkanes follow the pattern C_nH_{2n}. Cycloalkanes are named by adding the prefix *cyclo-* to the name of the alkane. Figure 10.4 shows three different ways to show the structure of cyclohexane, the cycloalkane with a six carbon ring. Just as with alkanes, cycloalkanes can have branched structures.

✓ **CHECK FOR UNDERSTANDING** What is the formula for a cycloalkane?

Example Problem 1

Name the following alkane.

$$CH_3 \quad CH_3$$
$$CH_3CHCH_2CHCH_2CH_3$$

1 Analyze the Problem

- You are given the condensed structural formula for a branched-chain alkane.
- Use the IUPAC rules to determine the name of the parent chain and the names and locations of the substituent groups.

2 Solve for the Unknown

First, identify the longest chain and count the number of carbons. In this case, there are six carbons in the longest chain, so the parent chain is named hexane.

Next, determine the way to number the chain.

> Numbering from the left puts the alkyl groups at positions 2 and 4. Numbering from the right puts the alkyl groups at positions 3 and 5. Since 2 and 4 give the lowest position number, they will be used in the name.

Next, name the alkyl groups by counting the number of carbons.

> The two alkyl groups are methyl groups and are positioned at 2 and 4.

Count the alkyl groups that occur more than once and determine the prefix.

> Since there are two methyl groups, use the prefix –di, and indicate the position of each group.

Complete the name of the structure using hyphens and commas.

> The name of this structure is 2,4-dimethylhexane.

3 Evaluate the Answer

- **Does the answer make sense?** The longest carbon chain has been identified, named, and numbered correctly. The alkyl groups have been correctly named and designated with the correct prefix and location. Punctuation is also correct.

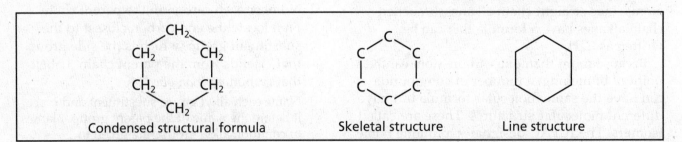

Condensed structural formula   Skeletal structure   Line structure

Figure 10.4 Here are three ways to represent cyclohexane, C_6H_{12}.

Table 10.3 • Examples of Alkenes and Alkynes					
Name	Molecular Formula	Structural Formula	Condensed Structural Formula	Melting Point (°C)	Boling Point (°C)
Ethene	C_2H_4		$CH_2{=}CH_2$	−169	−104
Propene	C_3H_6		$CH_3CH{=}CH_2$	−185	−48
1-Butene	C_4H_8		$CH_2{=}CHCH_2CH_3$	−185	−6
2-Butene	C_4H_8		$CH_3CH{=}CHCH_3$	−106	0.8
Ethyne	C_3H_4		$CH_3C{\equiv}CH$	−103	−23
1-Butyne	C_4H_6		$CH{\equiv}CCH_2CH_3$	−126	8

Unsaturated Hydrocarbons

In addition to sharing one pair of electrons, carbon atoms are able to form double or triple bonds with one another, sharing two or three pairs of electrons. Hydrocarbons that contain at least one double or triple bond between carbon atoms are called **unsaturated hydrocarbons**. Hydrocarbons with one or more double covalent bonds between carbon atoms in a chain are called **alkenes**. Unsaturated hydrocarbons that contain one or more triple bonds between carbon atoms in a chain are called **alkynes**. Table 10.3 summarizes the names and formulas for alkenes and alkynes, and gives their melting and boiling points. An alkene is named using the same prefix as for the corresponding alkane, but substituting –*ene* as the suffix.

It is also necessary to identify the position of the double bond for alkenes with more than four carbons. Begin by numbering the carbons of the parent chain starting with the carbon that will give the first carbon in the double bond the lowest number, and attach this number to the beginning of the alkene. Notice in Table 10.3, that the double bond in 1-butene is between the first and second carbons, and the double bond in 2-butene is between the second and third carbons. Naming branched-chain alkenes is the same as naming branched-chain alkanes except that the parent chain is always the longest carbon chain containing the double bond, and the position of the double determines how the chain is numbered. The general formula for alkenes is C_nH_{2n}. In alkynes, the triple bond means that the two atoms share three pairs of electrons. Naming of straight-chain and branched-chain alkynes is the same as naming alkenes except the name of the parent chain ends in –*yne* instead of –*ene*. For example, $CH_3-CH \equiv CH$ is named propyne. The general formula for alkynes is C_nH_{2n-2}

The physical properties of alkenes and alkynes are similar to those of alkanes. The melting and boiling points of an alkene, however, are higher than those of the corresponding alkane and lower than the corresponding alkyne. Chemically, unsaturated hydrocarbons are much more reactive because the increased electron density at the multiple bond makes it easier for other atoms to pull an electron away from the molecule.

✔ **CHECK FOR UNDERSTANDING** How do alkanes, alkenes, and alkynes differ and how are they alike?

Aromatic Hydrocarbons

In addition to single, double and triple covalent bonds, there is a fourth kind of chemical bond that can form in organic compounds. The hydrocarbon benzene, has a formula C_6H_6 and is not

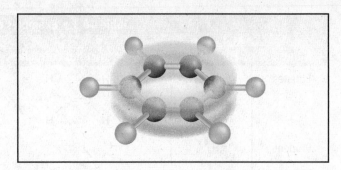

Figure 10.5 Benzene's bonding electrons do not associate with individual atoms, but rather, spread out evenly around the ring, making the molecule chemically stable.

very reactive. Although the structural formula for benzene often shows it as having alternating double and single bonds, its bonds actually are neither. In benzene, the electrons are actually not located between specific carbon atoms. Instead they are shared among all the carbons of the ring, as shown in Figure 10.5. The result is a chemically stable molecule from which the electrons are difficult to remove. To indicate that this is a different type of bond, structural diagrams often use the symbol of a circle inside a hexagon to represent a benzene ring.

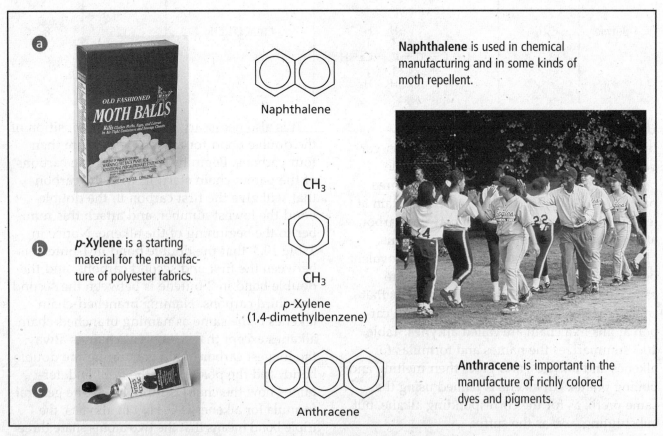

ⓐ

Naphthalene is used in chemical manufacturing and in some kinds of moth repellent.

Naphthalene

ⓑ **p-Xylene** is a starting material for the manufacture of polyester fabrics.

CH_3

CH_3

p-Xylene
(1,4-dimethylbenzene)

ⓒ

Anthracene is important in the manufacture of richly colored dyes and pigments.

Anthracene

Figure 10.6 Here are the structures and practical uses of three aromatic organic compounds.

Organic compounds that contain benzene rings as part of their structures are called aromatic compounds, while those without benzene rings are called aliphatic compounds. This term originated from the observation that aromatic compounds often are part of pleasant smelling oils. As with other hydrocarbons, carbon chains can be substituted for one or more of the hydrogen atoms. In another substitution, two or more rings can be fused together so that more than six carbon atoms jointly share electrons. The simplest example of this is naphthalene in which the electrons are shared by ten carbon atoms in a fused ring structure. Like benzene, naphthalene is a very stable molecule. The rings do not break easily in a chemical reaction. The structures and practical uses of three aromatic compounds, including naphthalene, are shown in Figure 10.6

✔ **CHECK FOR UNDERSTANDING** What is the major difference between aromatic compounds and aliphatic compounds?

Quick Review

1 Every organic compound includes at least one atom of which elements
   (1) carbon
   (2) hydrogen
   (3) both carbon and hydrogen
   (4) oxygen

2 The compound with the formula C_2H_2 is a(n)
   (1) saturated hydrocarbon
   (2) alkane
   (3) alkene
   (4) alkyne

3 This structural formula represents the compound

$$H-\underset{\underset{H}{|}}{\overset{\overset{H}{|}}{C}}-\underset{\underset{H}{|}}{\overset{\overset{H}{|}}{C}}-\underset{\underset{H}{|}}{\overset{\overset{H}{|}}{C}}-\underset{\underset{H}{|}}{\overset{\overset{H}{|}}{C}}-H$$

   (1) butane
   (2) butene
   (3) isobutane
   (4) propane

4 Which of these structural diagrams represents an unsaturated hydrocarbon?

(1) $H-\underset{\underset{H}{|}}{\overset{\overset{H}{|}}{C}}-\underset{\underset{H}{|}}{\overset{\overset{H}{|}}{C}}-H$

(3) $\underset{H}{\overset{H}{>}}C=C\underset{H}{\overset{H}{<}}$

(2) $Cl-\underset{\underset{H}{|}}{\overset{\overset{H}{|}}{C}}-\underset{\underset{H}{|}}{\overset{\overset{H}{|}}{C}}-Cl$

(4) $\underset{H}{\overset{Cl}{>}}C=C\underset{Cl}{\overset{H}{<}}$

5 The carbon atoms in a benzene ring are joined by
   (1) single bonds
   (2) double bonds
   (3) alternating single and double bonds
   (4) bonds that are neither single bonds nor double bonds

6 The generic formula for a saturated hydrocarbon can be written as
   (1) C_nH_{2n-2} (3) C_nH_{2n+2}
   (2) C_nH_{2n} (4) $C_{2n}H_{2n-2}$

7 Aromatic compounds are those that include
   (1) more than one double bond
   (2) only single bonds in a ring shape
   (3) a benzene ring
   (4) only double bonds

8 Which formula represents a hydrocarbon with exactly one double bond between carbon atoms?
   (1) C_4H_6 (3) C_4H_{10}
   (2) C_4H_8 (4) C_4H_{12}

9 Draw the structural diagram of the compound *n*-pentane.

10 What is the total number of covalent bonds in the compound ethane, C_2H_6?
   (1) 2   (3) 7
   (2) 6   (4) 8

Table 10.4 • Some Organic Compounds and Their Functional Groups

Compound Type	General Formula	Functional Group
Halocarbon	R–X (X = F, Cl, Br, I)	Halogen
Ketone	$$R-\overset{\displaystyle \overset{O}{\|\|}}{C}-R'$$	Carbonyl
Carboxylic acid	$$*-\overset{\displaystyle \overset{O}{\|\|}}{C}-OH$$	Carboxyl
Ester	$$*-\overset{\displaystyle \overset{O}{\|\|}}{C}-O-R$$	Ester
Amide	$$*-\overset{\displaystyle \overset{O}{\|\|}}{C}-\overset{\displaystyle \overset{H}{\|}}{N}-R$$	Amido

Substituted Hydrocarbons

Thousands of molecules exist that are composed of only carbon and hydrogen, but carbon also can form strong covalent bonds with other atoms. The most common elements found in organic molecules, along with carbon and hydrogen, are oxygen, nitrogen, fluorine, chlorine, bromine, iodine, sulfur, and phosphorus.

Functional Groups

Atoms other than carbon and hydrogen occur in organic molecules as **functional groups**, which are atoms or groups of atoms in an organic molecule that always act the same way. The physical and chemical properties of organic molecules with functional groups are always different from those of the parent hydrocarbon. Table 10.3 summarizes the names and structures of several important organic compounds and their functional groups. The symbols R and R' represent a hydrocarbon chain or ring attached to the group and the symbol * represents a hydrocarbon chain or ring, or a hydrogen atom.

Halocarbons

In the simplest form of functional group, a single halogen atom is substituted for one of the hydrogen atoms of a hydrocarbon. Any organic compound that contains a halogen substituent

is called a **halocarbon**. If the hydrogen of an alkane is replaced by a halogen, the halocarbon is known as an **alkyl halide**. If the halogen atom is attached to benzene or another aromatic ring, the compound is called an **aryl halide**.

The name of an organic compound with a functional group is based on the hydrocarbon structure. For halocarbons, the halogen is indicated by a prefix that changes the *-ine* at the end of the name to *-o*.

Using this format, the name for an ethane molecule with one hydrogen replaced by a fluorine is fluoroethane. If the molecule has two or more identical halogens, a prefix is used, as well as a number to indicate which carbon in the chain is bonded to each halogen. 1,3-difluoropropane and 1,2-difluoropropane are different compounds and have different properties. If two or more different halogens are present, the atoms are listed alphabetically, again with a number to indicate position, as in 1-bromo-3-chloro-2-fluorobutane.

Because the bond between carbon and halogen is more polar than that between carbon and hydrogen, halocarbon molecules are more polar than hydrocarbons. They are not sufficiently polar, however, to dissolve in water, so halocarbons are often used as solvents for nonpolar compounds. The boiling points of alkyl halides are higher than the corresponding alkane, increasing with the size of the halogen. Halocarbons are also much more reactive than hydrocarbons.

Alcohols

Many organic compounds include one or more oxygen atoms. Because oxygen has six valence electrons, it tends to form two covalent bonds. One of these bonds can be with a hydrogen atom, forming a functional group called a

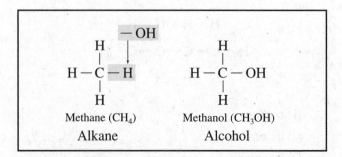

Figure 10.7 Shown is the relationship between the alkane methane and the alcohol methanol. In an alcohol, a hydroxyl group bonds with a carbon atom.

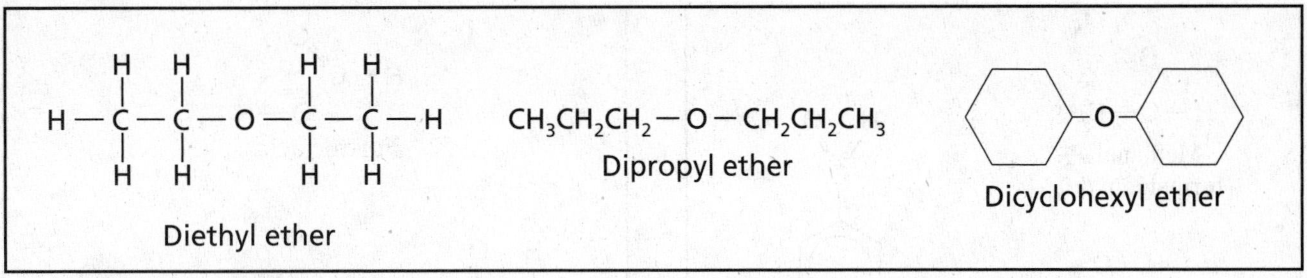

Figure 10.8 Shown are three examples of ethers. What is the common feature of these three structural formulas?

Diethyl ether

Dipropyl ether

Dicyclohexyl ether

hydroxyl group (–OH). An organic compound in which a hydroxyl group replaces a hydrogen atom of a hydrocarbon is called an **alcohol**. Alcohols are named by using the suffix -*ol* with the root name of the hydrocarbon, for example methanol, ethanol, and propanol. Figure 10.7 on page 160 illustrates the relationship of the alkane methane to the alcohol methanol. Because the hydroxyl group is very polar, and the molecules can undergo hydrogen bonding, the melting and boiling points of alcohols are much higher than those of the hydrocarbon. Alcohols with less than five carbon atoms are completely soluble in water, but the hydrocarbon part of the molecule is nonpolar enough to make alcohol useful as a solvent for other organic molecules, particularly those with some polarity.

Ethers

An **ether** is an organic compound containing an oxygen atom bonded to two carbon atoms. Figure 10.8 shows three examples of ethers. If the two hydrocarbon groups are identical, the ether is named by naming the parent group and then adding *ether*, as in *diethyl ether*. If the hydrocarbons are different, the groups are listed in

alphabetical order, as in *butylethyl ether*. Because ethers have no hydrogen atoms involved in a polar hydrogen-oxygen bond, they cannot form hydrogen bonds. Their melting and boiling points are lower than alcohols of similar size and they are much less soluble in water. Because of the oxygen atom, however, they are significantly more polar than hydrocarbons.

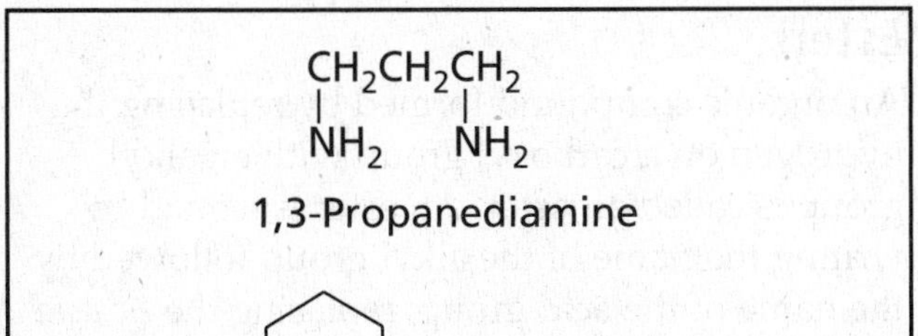

Amines

Another element that is fairly common in organic molecules is nitrogen. **Amines** contain nitrogen atoms bonded to carbon atoms in organic molecules and have the general formula RNH_2. Three amines are shown in Figure 10.9. The amines are named with the suffix -*amine*, as in ethylamine. Amines are more polar than ethers and less polar than alcohols. One characteristic of amines is a strong, often offensive odor.

✓ **CHECK FOR UNDERSTANDING** In which organic compound does a hydroxyl group replace a hydrogen atom?

Carbonyl Compounds

Because oxygen forms two covalent bonds, it can be attached to two other atoms, as in alcohols and ethers. Oxygen also can bond in another way in organic compounds. The arrangement in which an oxygen atom is double-bonded to a carbon atom is called a carbonyl group.

Aldehydes

Figure 10.10 on page 162 illustrates three examples of aldehydes. An **aldehyde** is an organic compound in which a carbonyl group, located at the end of a carbon chain, is bonded to a carbon atom on one side and a hydrogen atom on the other. Aldehydes are named by using the suffix -*al*. The aldehyde structure is polar and fairly

$CH_2CH_2CH_2$
NH_2 NH_2
1,3-Propanediamine

NH_2
Cyclohexylamine

CH_3CH_2
NH_2
Ethylamine

Figure 10.9 Amines are readily recognized because they contain an amino group ($-NH_2$).

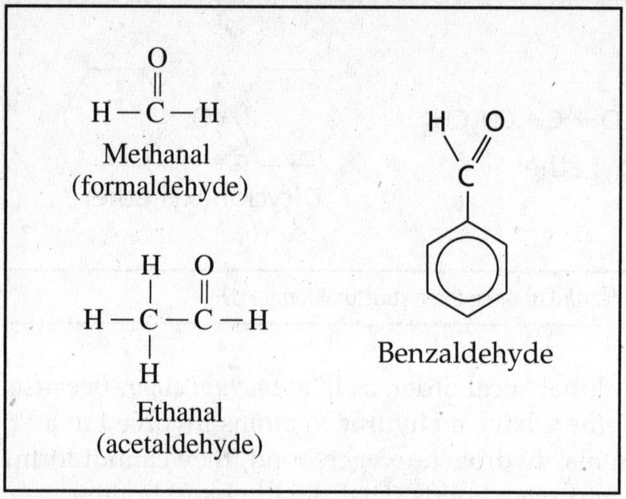

Figure 10.10 Aldehydes have a carbonyl group located at the end of the carbon chain that is bonded to a carbon atom on one side and a hydrogen atom on the other.

reactive because of the oxygen atom, but like ethers, aldehydes cannot form hydrogen bonds with themselves because there is no hydroxyl group. They are more soluble in water than hydrocarbons, but not as soluble as alcohols or amines.

Ketones

A **ketone** is an organic compound in which the carbon of the carbonyl group is bonded to two other carbon atoms. This means the carbonyl group is in the middle of the chain rather than at the end, as in an aldehyde. Figure 10.11 shows two ketones. Ketones are named by using the suffix -*one*, along with a number to indicate the position on the chain where the oxygen is located. Ketones are similar to aldehydes in their chemical and physical properties, but ketones are less reactive. Ketones often are used as solvents for other substances that are somewhat polar.

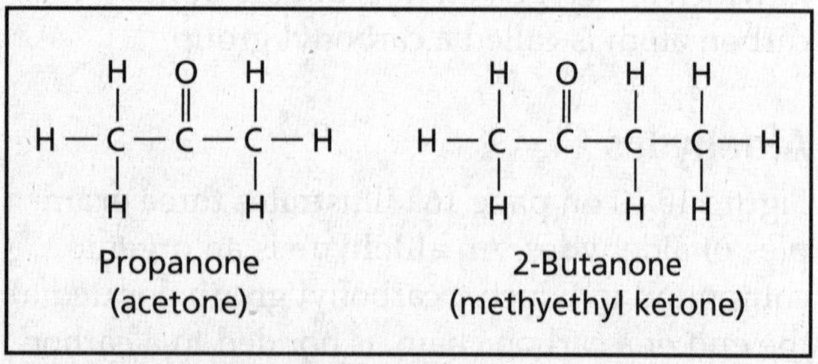

Figure 10.11 Ketones, like propanone and 2-butanone, have a carbonyl group located within a carbon chain and the carbon is bonded to two other carbon atoms.

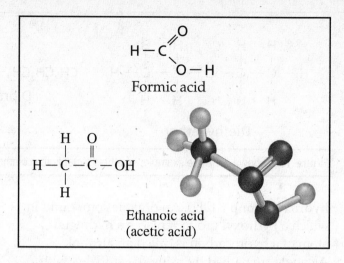

Figure 10.12 Carboxylic acids are organic compounds that have a carboxyl group.

Carboxylic Acids

If the carbonyl carbon is bonded to a hydroxyl group, it forms a carboxyl group. An organic molecule that has a carboxyl group is called a **carboxylic acid**. Many carboxylic acids have well-known common names, but the formal name uses the suffix -*anoic acid*, such as ethanoic acid. Carboxyl groups can be represented in formulas as —COOH, so that propanoic acid is written as CH_3CH_2COOH. Figure 10.12 shows two examples of carboxylic acids.

Because the two oxygen atoms are very electronegative, carboxylic acids are the most polar organic molecules. In an aqueous solution, the molecule can ionize to form a hydronium ion and an anion. Carboxylic acids have a sour taste characteristic of all acids. Many foods, including citrus fruits, contain carboxylic acids, which give them a sour flavor.

Esters

An organic compound formed by replacing the hydrogen on a carboxyl group with an alkyl group is called an **ester**. An ester is named by writing the name of the alkyl group followed by the name of the acid group, replacing the -*ic acid* suffix with -*ate*, as shown in Figure 10.13 for propyl ethanoate.

Esters are polar molecules, although not as polar as the acids from which they are derived. One property of esters is a strong, sweet odor, often the key components of flower and fruit fragrances, including apples, pineapples, and bananas.

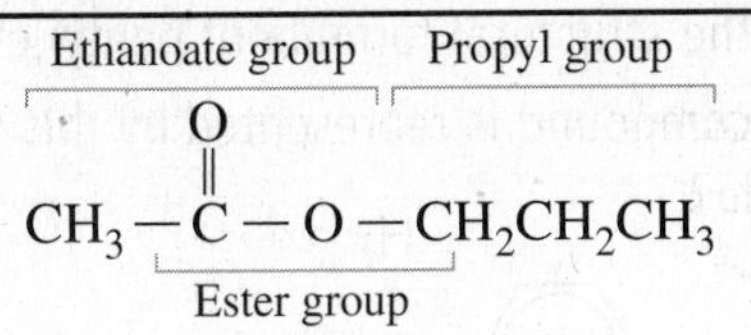

Ethanoate group   Propyl group

$$CH_3 - \overset{\displaystyle \overset{O}{\|}}{C} - O - CH_2CH_2CH_3$$

Ester group

Propyl ethanoate
(propyl acetate)

Figure 10.13 The name of an ester is formed by writing the name of the alkyl group followed by the name of the acid with the *–ic* acid ending replaced by *–ate*.

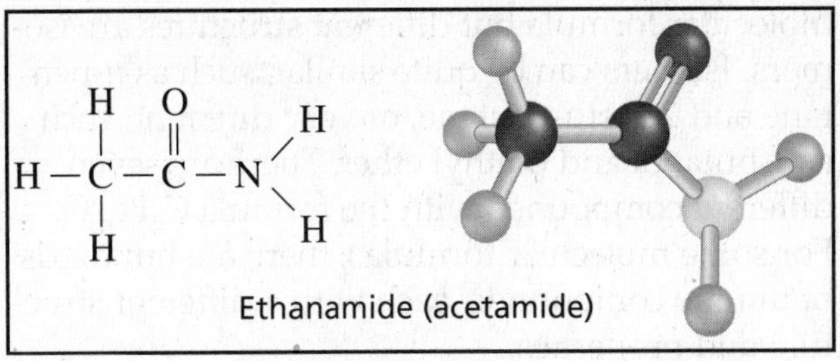

Ethanamide (acetamide)

Figure 10.14 Amides, like ethanamide, are organic compounds that contain an amide group. Which part of the structural formula represents the amino group?

When the hydroxyl group of a carboxylic acid is replaced by a nitrogen atom, bonded to other atoms, the resulting compound is called an **amide**. Amides are named based on the number of carbons, including the carbonyl carbon, with the suffix *-amide*. Figure 10.14 shows the structural formula for ethanamide.

Amino Acids

Amino acids are organic compounds that have an amino group, an acidic carboxylic group. Amino acids have a central carbon atom with four groups arranged around it. The four groups are an amino group, a carboxyl group, a hydrogen atom, and a variable side chain. Figure 10.15 shows the different side groups of several amino acids. Notice that

the side chains vary from a single hydrogen atom to a complex ring structure. The variety of side chains gives the different amino acids a large range of physical and chemical properties and the ability to carry out many different functions.

Isomers of Organic Molecules

If you examine the drawings of various organic compounds, it is clear that the structural formulas contain more information than the molecular formulas. For example, 1-butanol and ethyl ether both have the molecular formula $C_4H_{10}O$. If you look at the structural formulas, you can see that they are very different compounds, with different functional groups and very different properties. As you recall, compounds that have the same

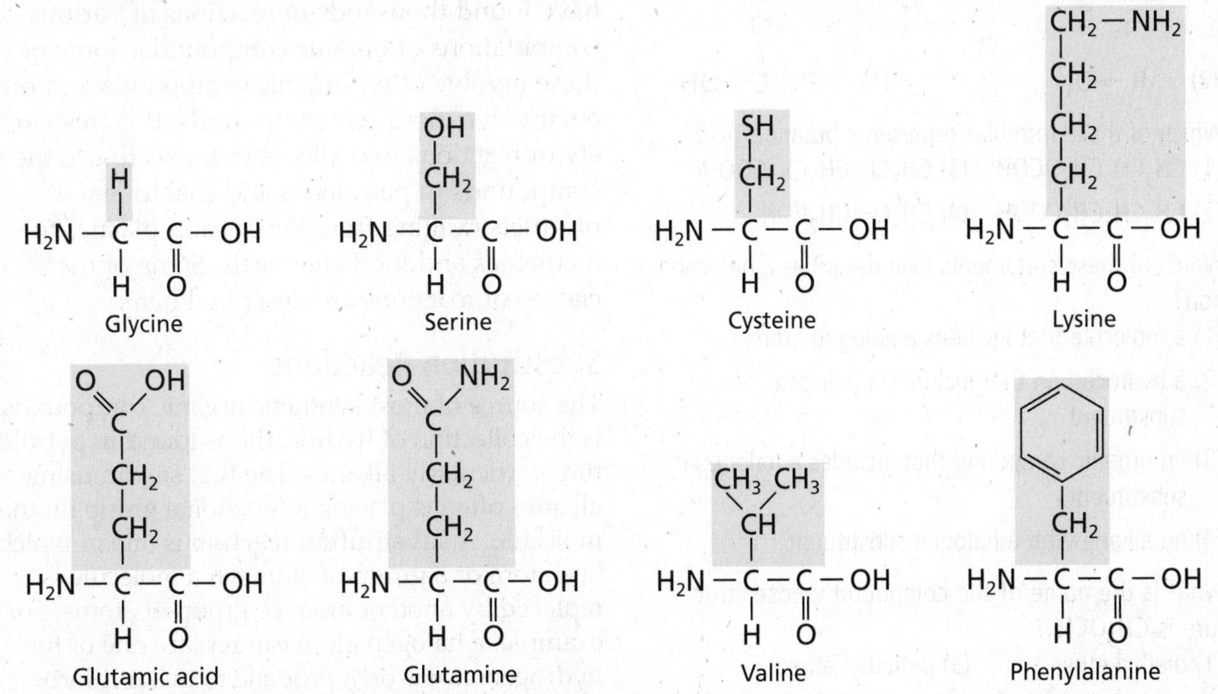

Figure 10.15 The structures of several amino acids are shown with their variable side chains highlighted.

molecular formula but different structures are isomers. Isomers can be quite similar, such as *n*-pentane and 2-methylbutane, or very different, such as 1-butanol and diethyl ether. There are seven different compounds with the formula $C_4H_{10}O$. For some molecular formulas, there are hundreds of unique compounds, each with a different structure and properties.

Quick Review

11 Any functional group on an organic compound includes
   (1) carbon
   (2) hydrogen
   (3) oxygen
   (4) at least one atom that is not carbon or hydrogen

12 Which of these general structures represents an alcohol?

   (1) $R_1 - O - R_2$ (3) $R - \overset{\overset{\displaystyle O}{\|}}{C} - H$

   (2) $R - OH$ (4) $R - \overset{\overset{\displaystyle O}{\|}}{C} - OH$

13 Which of these structures represents an organic acid?

   (1) $R_1 - O - R_2$ (3) $R - \overset{\overset{\displaystyle O}{\|}}{C} - H$

   (2) $R - OH$ (4) $R - \overset{\overset{\displaystyle O}{\|}}{C} - OH$

14 Which of these formulas represents butanoic acid?
   (1) $CH_3CH_2CH_2OCOH$ (3) $CH_3CH_2CH_2CH_2COOH$
   (2) $CH_3CH_2CH_2COOH$ (4) $CH_3CH_2CH_2COH$

15 Which of these statements best describes a halocarbon?
   (1) a molecule that includes a halogen atom
   (2) a hydrocarbon that includes a halogen substituent
   (3) an organic compound that includes a halogen substituent
   (4) an alkane with a halogen substituent

16 What is the name of the compound whose structure is CH_3OCH_3?
   (1) diethyl ether   (3) dimethyl ether
   (2) methyl alcohol   (4) methyl ketone

17 Draw the structural formula of pentyl ethanoate.

18 What compound is represented by this structural formula?

   (1) benzaldehyde   (3) benzoic acid
   (2) benzyl alcohol   (4) cyclohexyl aldehyde

19 The correct order of polarity, from least polar to most polar, for molecules of similar size is
   (1) ether, amine, acid, alcohol
   (2) ether, amine, alcohol, acid
   (3) amine, alcohol, ether, acid
   (4) alcohol, ether, amine, acid

20 The correct name for this compound is

   (1) 1-butanol   (3) 1-propanol
   (2) propane   (4) propanaldehyde

Reactions of Organic Compounds

Because of the large number of classes of compounds and functional groups, organic chemists have found thousands of reactions of various combinations of organic compounds. Some of these involve other organic compounds and others involve inorganic compounds. It is this variety of reactions that allows chemists to use the compounds in petroleum and coal to make products ranging from fabrics and plastics to medicines and food chemicals. Some of the classes of reactions are described here.

Substitution Reactions

The source of most synthetic organic compounds is the collection of hydrocarbons found in petroleum, particularly alkanes. The first step in using alkanes often is placing a functional group on the molecule. A **substitution reaction** is one in which one atom or a group of atoms in a molecule is replaced by another atom or group of atoms. For example, a halogen atom can replace one of the hydrogen atoms on a propane to make chloropropane.

$$CH_3CH_2CH_3 + Cl_2 \rightarrow CH_3CH_2CH_2Cl + HCl$$

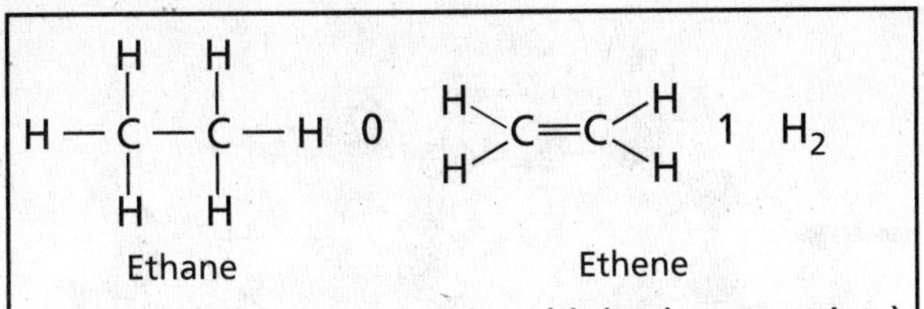

An elimination reaction (dehydrogenation)

Figure 10.16 During the elimination reaction, H_2 is removed from the alkane ethane, introducing a double bond, and the alkene ethene is produced.

After the halogen has been substituted for a hydrogen, a second substitution reaction, with the –OH group of an inorganic base, can be used to make an alcohol.

$$CH_3CH_2CH_2Cl + OH^- \rightarrow CH_3CH_2CH_2OH + Cl^-$$

Elimination Reactions

Another way to convert an alkane into a substance that is more reactive, is to introduce a double bond, converting it into an alkene. This is a type of elimination reaction, which is a reaction in which a combination of atoms is removed from two adjacent carbon atoms, forming an additional bond between the carbon atoms, shown in Figure 10.16. In addition to the elimination of hydrogen from an alkane, elimination reactions remove water from an alcohol or hydrogen chloride from an alkyl halide.

Addition Reactions

An **addition reaction** results when other atoms bond to each of the two atoms bonded by double or triple covalent bonds. Essentially, addition is the reverse of the elimination reaction. Addition reactions usually involve the double-bounded carbon atoms in alkenes or the triple bonded carbons in alkynes because of the high concentration of electrons in the double and tripple bonds. Addition reactions tend to occur with small molecules that use some of the electrons available in the double or triple bond, such as water or a halogen. Figure 10.17 illustrates several different types of addition reactions carried out with alkenes.

CHECK FOR UNDERSTANDING An addition reaction is the reverse of which type of reaction? Which types of molecules tend to participate in addition reactions?

Esterification Reactions

In an esterification reaction, an organic acid and an alcohol combine to form an ester and water. An example of this type of reaction is the synthesis of 3-methylbutyl ethanoate from ethanoic acid and 3-methylbutanol.

$$(CH_3)_2CH_2COO\,H + CH_3CH_2OH \rightarrow (CH_3)_2CH_2COOCH_2CH_3 + H_2O$$

Addition Reactions with Alkenes

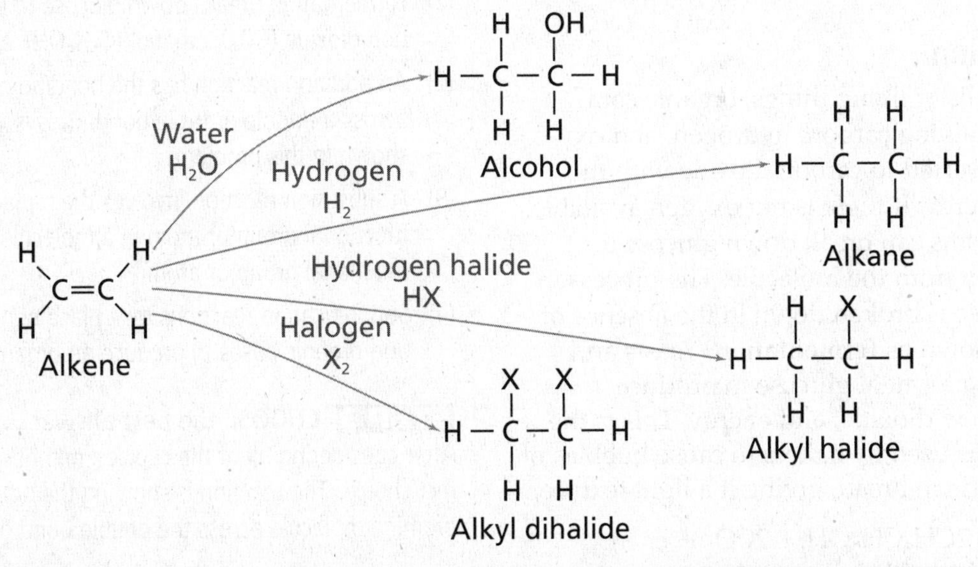

Figure 10.17 Many addition reactions are carried out with alkenes. Some common reactions are illustrated here.

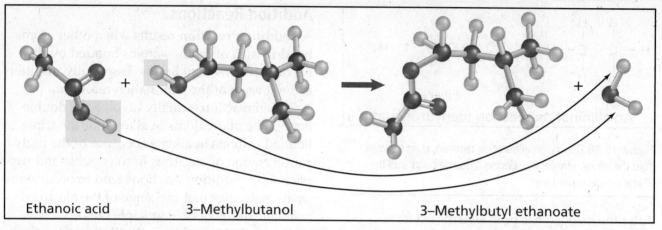

Ethanoic acid   3–Methylbutanol   3–Methylbutyl ethanoate

Figure 10.18 In a condensation reaction, two smaller organic molecules combine to form a more complex molecule and lose a smaller molecule such as water.

As shown in Figure 10.18, the water molecule is made from the –OH group of the acid and the hydrogen from the alcohol. The remaining parts of the two smaller organic molecules combine to form a larger molecule.

Combustion

Fossil fuels, which contain a variety of hydrocarbon molecules, are used to generate heat. In a **combustion reaction**, oxygen combines with the hydrocarbon, releasing energy in the form of heat and light. For example, octane C_8H_{18} reacts with oxygen in a car engine to produce carbon dioxide, water, and the energy to move the vehicle.

$$2C_8H_{18} + 25O_2 \rightarrow 16CO_2 + 18H_2O + \text{energy}$$

Although the combustion of hydrocarbons is the most common combustion reaction, most organic molecules combust with oxygen.

Fermentation

Inside the cells of living things, organic compounds containing carbon, hydrogen, and oxygen, are converted to carbon dioxide with the release of energy. If there is not oxygen available, some organisms can break down glucose to obtain energy from the molecule. The process in which glucose is broken down in the absence of oxygen is known as **fermentation**. Yeasts and some bacteria ferment glucose to produce ethanol, carbon dioxide, and energy. This is the process that is used by bakers to cause bubbles of carbon dioxide in bread, giving it a light texture.

$$\underset{\text{Glucose}}{C_6H_{12}O_6} \rightarrow \underset{\text{Ethanol}}{2CH_3CH_2OH} + \underset{\substack{\text{Carbon}\\\text{dioxide}}}{2CO_2} + \text{energy}$$

STEP 1 READ the Regents Question . . .

Given the organic reaction:

This reaction is an example of
(1) fermentation   (3) substitution
(2) addition   (4) saponification

STEP 2 ANALYZE each choice . . .
(1) Fermentation breaks down glucose to produce carbon dioxide (CO_2), ethanol (C_2H_5OH), and energy.
(2) An addition reaction has the bonding of atoms across a double or triple bond. This is what is shown in this problem.
(3) A substition reaction involves the replacement of a functional group or atom in a molecule by another functional group or atom.
(4) Saponification reactions take place between fats and organic bases to produce an organic salt.

STEP 3 CHOOSE the best answer . . .
After considering all of the choices, number 2 is the correct choice. The reaction is showing the addition of a bromine molecule across the double bond of propene.

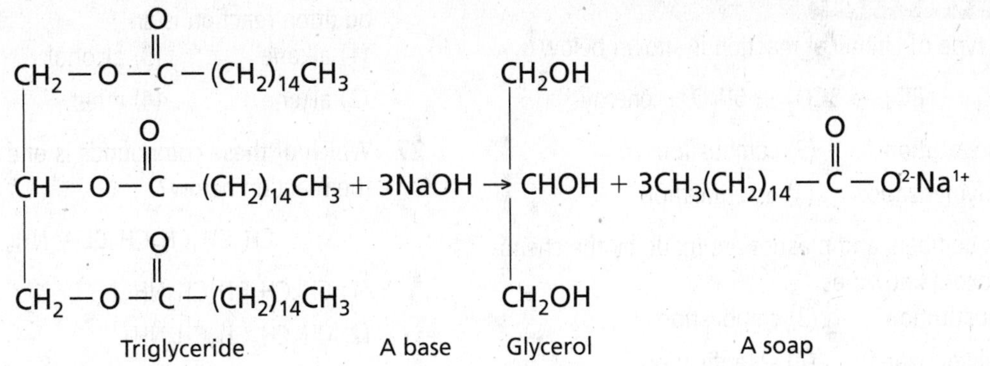

Figure 10.19 During a saponification reaction, a soap is produced.

Saponification

Soap is a product of a reaction of fats from animal or plant sources with an inorganic base. As shown in the Figure 10.19, these fats are esters of an alcohol, glycerol, that has three hydroxyl functional groups. The reaction of a triglyceride, which is a triple ester, with a base to form glycerol and the salts of the organic acid, is called **saponification**. The product of the reaction, the organic salt, is soap.

✓ **CHECK FOR UNDERSTANDING** Describe the process of saponification. What are the reactants? What are the products?

Polymerization

Plastics, synthetic fibers, and rubber are all examples of **polymers**, which are very large organic chains or networks based on bonds between carbons. Polymers consist of smaller molecules bonded together by a series of chemical reactions, such as addition or esterification. The reaction in which small organic units, known as **monomers**, are bonded together into a very large molecule is called a **polymerization reaction**. Polymerization is actually a series of hundreds or thousands of individual chemical reactions. Table 10.5 shows two familiar polymers and the monomers that bind together in a polymerization reaction.

Table 10.5 • Monomers and Polymers

Monomer(s)	Structural Unit of Polymer	Application
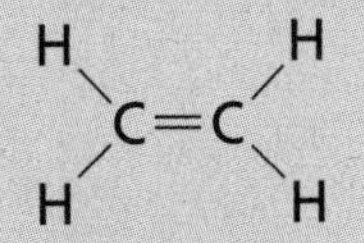 Ethene (ethylene)	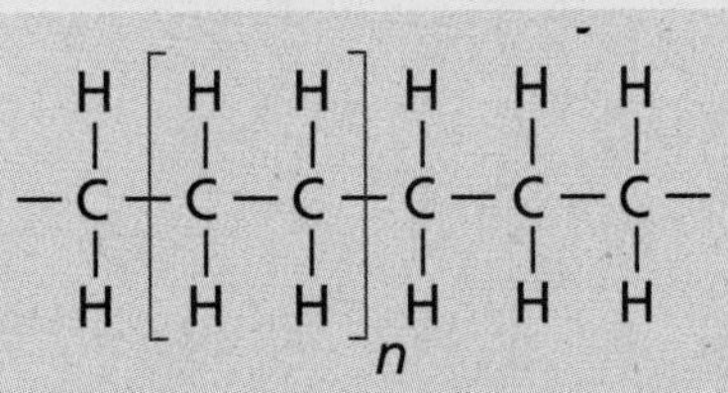 Polyethylene	Plastic bags, children's toys, food containers
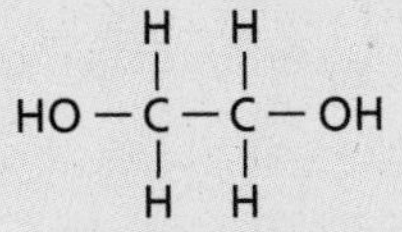 1,2-Ethanediol (ethylene glycol) 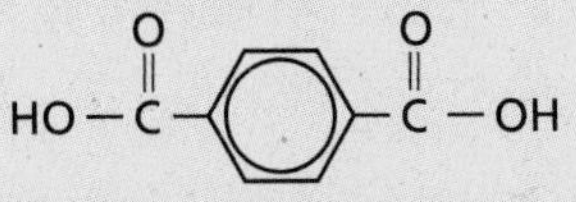 Terephthalic acid	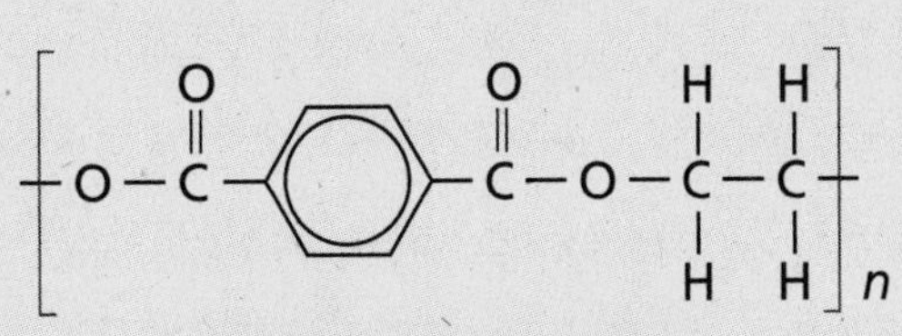 Polyethylene terephthalate (Dacron in fiber form) (Mylar in film form)	Soft drink bottles, tire cord, clothing, recording tape

Quick Review

21 What type of chemical reaction is shown below?

$$C_5H_{12} + 8O_2 \rightarrow 5CO_2 + 6H_2O + energy$$

(1) substitution   (3) combustion

(2) polymerization   (4) esterification

22 Synthetic fibers and plastics are made by the chemical process known as

(1) substitution   (3) combustion

(2) polymerization   (4) esterification

23 What is the product of the following elimination reaction?

$$CH_3CH_2CH_2CH_2OH \rightarrow H_2O + ?$$

(1) propene   (3) butene

(2) butane   (4) butanal

24 One of the products of a fermentation reaction is
(1) an alcohol

(2) an organic acid

(3) a ketone

(4) an unsaturated hydrocarbon

25 The reaction

$$CH_2CHCH_2CH_3 + Cl_2 \rightarrow CH_2ClCHClCH_2CH_3$$

is an example of

(1) addition   (3) combustion

(2) substitution   (4) fermentation

26 Of these, the most likely starting compound for an addition reaction is an

(1) alkane   (3) alcohol

(2) alkene   (4) ether

27 Which of these compounds is one of the products of the reaction below?

$$CH_3CH_2CH_2CH_2Cl + NH_3 \rightarrow ?$$

(1) $CH_3CH_2CH_2CH_2NHCl$

(2) $CH_3CH_2CH_2CH_2NH$

(3) $CH_3CH_2CH_2CH_2NH_2$

(4) $CH_3CH_2CH_2CH_2NH_3$

28 The reaction between the functional groups on an organic acid and an alcohol is known as

(1) substitution   (3) combustion

(2) polymerization   (4) esterification

29 The source of most organic compounds used in industry is

(1) alkanes in petroleum

(2) alkenes in petroleum

(3) ethanol from fermentation

(4) halocarbons

30 Write the substitution reaction between ethyl chloride and KOH(aq). What type of compound is the organic product of the reaction?

Part A

1 Which element is present in all organic compounds?

(1) hydrogen   (3) carbon

(2) helium   (4) calcium

2 When hydrocarbons burn completely in an excess of oxygen, the products are

(1) carbon monoxide and water

(2) carbon dioxide and water

(3) carbon monoxide and carbon dioxide

(4) carbon dioxide and carbon

3 An organic compound containing one or more –OH groups as the only functional group is classified as an

(1) aldehyde   (3) ester

(2) alcohol   (4) ether

4 Which formula represents an ether?

(1) $CH_3 - \overset{\overset{\displaystyle O}{\|}}{C} - O - CH_3$

(2) $CH_3 - \overset{\overset{\displaystyle O}{\|}}{C} - OH$

(3) $CH_3 - O - CH_3$

(4) $CH_3 - OH$

5 The principal products of saponification, a reaction between a fat and a base, are soap and

(1) water

(2) glycerol

(3) carbon dioxide

(4) ethyl alcohol

6 The products of the fermentation of a sugar are ethanol and

(1) water

(2) oxygen

(3) carbon dioxide

(4) sulfur dioxide

7 A hydrocarbon molecule is considered to be saturated if the molecule contains

(1) single covalent bonds, only

(2) a double covalent bond, only

(3) a triple covalent bond

(4) single and double covalent bonds

8 What is the name of the compound with the following formula?

$$H - \overset{\overset{\displaystyle H}{|}}{\underset{\underset{\displaystyle H}{|}}{C}} - \overset{\overset{\displaystyle O}{\|}}{C} - \overset{\overset{\displaystyle H}{|}}{\underset{\underset{\displaystyle H}{|}}{C}} - H$$

(1) propanone

(2) propanol

(3) propanal

(4) propanoic acid

9 Which hydrocarbon has more than one possible structural formula?

(1) CH_4

(2) C_2H_6

(3) C_3H_8

(4) C_4H_{10}

10 Which structural formula represents an unsaturated hydrocarbon?

(1)
$$H - \underset{\underset{H}{|}}{\overset{\overset{H}{|}}{C}} - H$$

(3)
$$\underset{H}{\overset{H}{>}} C = C \overset{H}{\underset{H}{<}}$$

(2)
$$H - \underset{\underset{H}{|}}{\overset{}{C}} - \overset{\overset{O}{||}}{C} - CH$$

(4)
$$H - \underset{\underset{H}{|}}{\overset{}{C}} - \overset{\overset{O}{||}}{C} - \underset{\underset{H}{|}}{\overset{\overset{H}{|}}{C}} - H$$

11 Which compound is an alcohol?

(1) propanal

(2) ethyne

(3) butane

(4) methanol

12 Given the compound below,

$$H - \underset{\underset{H}{|}}{\overset{\overset{H}{|}}{C}} - \underset{\underset{H}{|}}{\overset{\overset{H}{|}}{C}} - \underset{\underset{H}{|}}{\overset{\overset{H}{|}}{C}} - C \overset{\nearrow O}{\underset{\searrow H}{}}$$

which structural formula represents an isomer?

(1)
$$H - \underset{\underset{H}{|}}{\overset{\overset{H}{|}}{C}} - \underset{\underset{H}{|}}{\overset{\overset{H}{|}}{C}} - \underset{\underset{H}{|}}{\overset{\overset{H}{|}}{C}} - \underset{\underset{H}{|}}{\overset{\overset{H}{|}}{C}} - OH$$

(2)
$$H - \underset{\underset{H}{|}}{\overset{\overset{H}{|}}{C}} - \underset{\underset{H}{|}}{\overset{\overset{H}{|}}{C}} - \underset{\underset{H}{|}}{\overset{\overset{H}{|}}{C}} - C \overset{\nearrow O}{\underset{\searrow OH}{}}$$

(3)
$$H - \underset{\underset{H}{|}}{\overset{\overset{H}{|}}{C}} - \underset{\underset{H}{|}}{\overset{\overset{H}{|}}{C}} - O - \underset{\underset{H}{|}}{\overset{\overset{H}{|}}{C}} - \underset{\underset{H}{|}}{\overset{\overset{H}{|}}{C}} - H$$

(4)
$$H - \underset{\underset{H}{|}}{\overset{\overset{H}{|}}{C}} - \overset{\overset{O}{||}}{C} - \underset{\underset{H}{|}}{\overset{\overset{H}{|}}{C}} - \underset{\underset{H}{|}}{\overset{\overset{H}{|}}{C}} - H$$

13 The formula for a saturated hydrocarbon is

(1) C_6H_6 (3) C_6H_{12}

(2) C_6H_{10} (4) C_6H_{14}

14 Which structural formula represents an isomer of 1-propanol?

(1)
$$H - \underset{\underset{H}{|}}{\overset{\overset{H}{|}}{C}} - \underset{\underset{H}{|}}{\overset{\overset{H}{|}}{C}} - \overset{\overset{O}{||}}{C} - H$$

(2)
$$H - \underset{\underset{H}{|}}{\overset{\overset{H}{|}}{C}} - \underset{\underset{H}{|}}{\overset{\overset{H}{|}}{C}} - \overset{\overset{O}{||}}{C} - OH$$

(3)
$$H - \underset{\underset{H}{|}}{\overset{\overset{H}{|}}{C}} - \overset{\overset{O}{||}}{C} - \underset{\underset{H}{|}}{\overset{\overset{H}{|}}{C}} - H$$

(4)
$$H - \underset{\underset{H}{|}}{\overset{\overset{H}{|}}{C}} - \underset{\underset{OH}{|}}{\overset{\overset{H}{|}}{C}} - \underset{\underset{H}{|}}{\overset{\overset{H}{|}}{C}} - H$$

15 Given the compound:

$$H - \underset{\underset{H}{|}}{\overset{\overset{H}{|}}{C}} - \underset{\underset{H}{|}}{\overset{\overset{H}{|}}{C}} - \underset{\underset{Cl}{|}}{\overset{\overset{H}{|}}{C}} - Cl$$

Which structural formula represents an isomer?

(1)
$$H - \underset{\underset{H}{|}}{\overset{\overset{H}{|}}{C}} - \underset{\underset{H}{|}}{\overset{\overset{H}{|}}{C}} - \underset{\underset{H}{|}}{\overset{\overset{H}{|}}{C}} - \underset{\underset{Cl}{|}}{\overset{\overset{H}{|}}{C}} - Cl$$

(2)
$$Cl - \underset{\underset{H}{|}}{\overset{\overset{H}{|}}{C}} - \underset{\underset{Cl}{|}}{\overset{}{C}} - \underset{\underset{H}{|}}{\overset{\overset{H}{|}}{C}} - H$$

(3)
$$H - \underset{\underset{H}{|}}{\overset{\overset{H}{|}}{C}} - \underset{\underset{H}{|}}{\overset{\overset{H}{|}}{C}} - \underset{\underset{H}{|}}{\overset{\overset{H}{|}}{C}} - Cl$$

(4)
$$Cl - \underset{\underset{H}{|}}{\overset{\overset{H}{|}}{C}} - \underset{\underset{H}{|}}{\overset{\overset{H}{|}}{C}} - \underset{\underset{H}{|}}{\overset{\overset{H}{|}}{C}} - \underset{\underset{Cl}{|}}{\overset{\overset{H}{|}}{C}} - Cl$$

16 Given the structural formula for ethyne:

H — C ≡ C — H

what is the total number of electrons shared between the carbon atoms?

17 The reaction $CH_2CH_2 + H_2 \rightarrow CH_3CH_3$ is an example of what process?

18 Given the equation:

$CH_4 + Br_2 \rightarrow CH_3Br + HBr$

Which type of reaction does this equation represent?

19 How is the bonding between carbon atoms different in unsaturated hydrocarbons and saturated hydrocarbons?

Part C

20 Given the formulas of four organic compounds, which pair below contains an alcohol and an acid?

21 Draw the structural formula for diethyl ether.

22 Draw a structural formula for an alcohol that is an isomer of diethyl ether.

23 To what class of organic compounds does reactant 2 belong?

Reactant 1   Reactant 2

24 Draw the structural formula of an isomer of reactant 2.

25 Which type of reaction is represented by the equation below?
Note: n and n are very large numbers equal to about 2000.

alpha particle

band of stability

beta particle

critical mass

gamma rays

half-life

ionizing radiation

nuclear fission

nuclear fusion

nucleons

radiation

radioactive decay series

radioactivity

radiochemical dating

radioisotopes

radiotracer

strong nuclear force

transmutation

Nuclear chemistry is the study of the structure of the nucleus and changes in the nucleus. The nuclei of some elements undergo changes that affect their stability, but these are not chemical changes because new compounds do not form as a result of atoms rearranging. For this reason, nuclear chemistry usually is treated as a separate unit at the end of a chemistry course.

Nuclear Radiation

The first indication that the nucleus of an atom may be unstable came late in the nineteenth century when Henri Becquerel discovered that uranium ore emits rays that can darken a photographic plate. Marie and Pierre Curie determined that the rays came from radium atoms. They named the process of spontaneously emitting rays and particles from an atom **radioactivity**. The particles and rays that come from radioactive material are called **radiation**. Becquerel and the Curies received the Nobel prize for this work and went on to discover other elements that are radioactive.

Unstable Nuclei

The radiation that they observed was not a chemical reaction, but rather a reaction involving the nucleus of the atom. Table 11.1 compares some of the characteristics of chemical and nuclear reactions. As you can see, they are very different phenomena. The nucleus consists of protons and neutrons bound together by strong forces. Many elements have more than one isotope, whose masses vary based on the number of neutrons. Although the most abundant nuclei of elements you encounter in daily life are stable and unlikely to change, other nuclei are unstable and emit radiation. Isotopes of atoms with unstable nuclei are called **radioisotopes**.

The instability of radioisotopes is a characteristic of the ratio of protons and neutrons, both of which are known as **nucleons**, in the nucleus. Protons tend to push away from each other due to electrostatic repulsion because they have positive charges. To overcome this repulsion, the nucleons are held together by the **strong nuclear force**, an attractive force which acts only on subatomic particles that are extremely close together. Because the strong nuclear force acts on neutrons that are neutral and do not experience electrostatic repulsion, the presence of neutrons stabilizes the nucleus. As the total number of

Table 11.1 • Characteristics of Chemical and Nuclear Reactions	
Chemical Reactions	**Nuclear Reactions**
1 Occur when bonds are broken and formed.	1 Occur when nuclei emit particles and/or rays.
2 Atoms do not change into atoms of another element.	2 Atoms are often converted into atoms of another element.
3 Involve only valence electrons.	3 May involve protons, neutrons, and electrons.
4 Associated with small energy changes.	4 Associated with large energy changes.
5 Reaction rate is influenced by temperature, pressure, concentration, and catalysts.	5 Reaction rate is not normally affected by temperature, pressure, or catalysts.

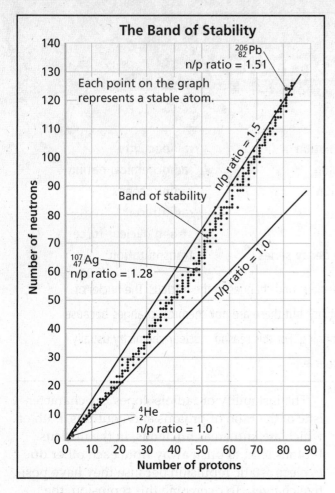

The Band of Stability

$^{206}_{82}$Pb
n/p ratio = 1.51

Each point on the graph represents a stable atom.

n/p ratio = 1.5

Band of stability

$^{107}_{47}$Ag
n/p ratio = 1.28

n/p ratio = 1.0

$^{4}_{2}$He
n/p ratio = 1.0

Number of neutrons

Number of protons

Figure 11.1 This graph shows the band of stability occupied by elements in nature.

nucleons increases, however, the strong nuclear force, which acts only at very short distances, is not enough to keep the nucleus stable. As shown in Figure 11.1, stability generally is related to the ratio of neutrons and protons. The area on the graph in which all stable nuclei are found is known as the **band of stability**. The band of stability generally includes nuclei in which the ratio of neutrons to protons is between 1:1 and 1.5:1. Nuclei outside this band are unstable and

radioactive. In addition, all elements with atomic numbers greater than 83 are unstable at any ratio of neutrons and protons.

✓ **CHECK FOR UNDERSTANDING** What is the ratio that characterizes the instability of radioisotopes?

Radioactive Decay

During radioactive decay, unstable nuclei lose energy, emitting one or more types of radiation. This emission of radiation by unstable nuclei is called spontaneous decay of the nucleus. The three most common types of nuclear radiation emitted during spontaneous decay are alpha particles, beta particles, and gamma rays, which are compared in Table 11.2. As shown on the table, the three types of radiation have very different properties.

Alpha Particles

An **alpha particle** consists of two protons and two neutrons, held together by nuclear forces. Because of their masses, alpha particles are slow moving compared to the other types of radiation and do not penetrate matter very far. Alpha particles can be stopped by a sheet of paper. When a nucleus emits an alpha particle, it loses two protons, so it becomes a different element, with a decrease of two in atomic number and four in mass number. For example, the emission of an alpha particle by radium-226 (atomic number 88) creates an atom of radon-222 (atomic number 86), as seen in Figure 11.2.

Beta Particles

A **beta particle** is an electron that is emitted at very high energy from a nucleus. Beta particles are much smaller and move much faster than alpha particles, so they can penetrate farther into

Table 11.2 • Properties of Alpha, Beta, and Gamma Radiation			
Property	**Alpha (α)**	**Beta (β)**	**Gamma (γ)**
Composition	Alpha particles	Beta particles	High-energy electromagnetic radiation
Description of radiation	Helium nuclei, $^{4}_{2}$He	Electrons, $^{0}_{-1}\beta$	photons, $^{0}_{0}\gamma$
Charge	2+	1−	0
Mass	6.64×10^{-24} kg	9.11×10^{-28} kg	0
Approximate energy*	5 MeV	0.05 to 1 MeV	1 MeV
Relative penetrating power	Blocked by paper	Blocked by metal foil	Not completely blocked by lead or concrete

*(1 MeV = 1.60×10^{-13} J)

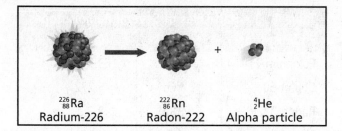

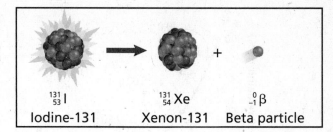

Figure 11.2 Alpha decay of radium-226 produces radon-222 and an alpha particle.

Figure 11.3 Beta decay of iodine-131 produces xenon-131 and a beta particle.

matter than alpha particles. Generally they can pass through a sheet of paper, but will be stopped by a piece of metal foil, which is much denser. As you can see from the decay of iodine-131, shown in Figure 11.3, the positive charge of the nucleus is increased by one, but the atomic mass is unchanged. This means that one of the neutrons has become a proton, with the loss of an electron from the nucleus. In this case, an atom of iodine-131 (atomic number 53) becomes an atom of xenon-131 (atomic number 54).

Gamma Rays

Gamma rays are a form of electromagnetic radiation, related to X rays and light, so they have neither mass nor charge. The emission of a gamma ray does not change the identity of the element, although they generally accompany either alpha or beta decay of the nucleus.

Gamma rays are very high-energy radiation and can easily pass through matter. It takes several centimeters of lead or several meters of concrete to stop gamma rays. Because they are so energetic, gamma rays can be very dangerous. They are able to pass completely through the human body, but they can cause damage to molecules inside the body as they do so.

Radioactive Decay Series

The type of radioactive decay that a nucleus undergoes is a characteristic of the particular combination of protons and neutrons. After the decay process, the new nucleus may be stable. If not, it will undergo further nuclear decay until a stable nucleus is formed. This process may take several steps. Figure 11.4 shows the series of nuclear reactions that occur during the conversion of uranium-238 to lead-206. A

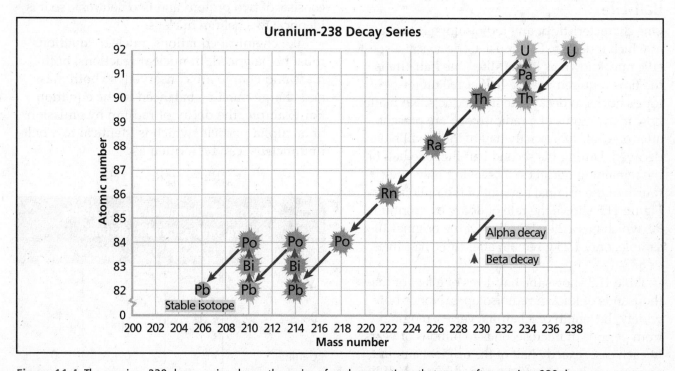

Figure 11.4 The uranium-238 decay series shows the series of nuclear reactions that occur after uranium-238 decays.

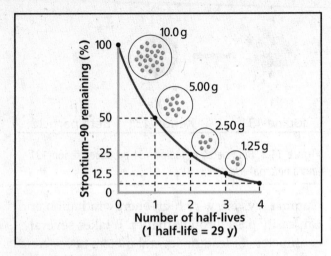

Figure 11.5 This graph shows the exponential decrease of 10.0 g of strontium-90 in terms of half-lives.

series of nuclear reactions that begins with an unstable nucleus and results in the formation of a stable nucleus is called a **radioactive decay series**. Remember that beta decay causes an increase in atomic number, so the third step of the uranium-238 decay series converts the nucleus back to uranium, but it is a smaller isotope of uranium. Atomic mass never increases during a radioactive decay series.

 CHECK FOR UNDERSTANDING Define the three most common types of radiation.

Half-Life

One characteristic of any radioisotope is the rate at which it decays. Each nucleus decays at a specific rate, known as its half-life. One **half-life** is the time required for one-half of the radioisotope's nuclei to decay into its products. No matter how many atoms of a radioisotope are present, after one half-life, exactly half of them will have decayed. During the second half-life, one-half of the remaining nuclei decay, leaving only one-fourth of the original amount of the radioisotope. Figure 11.5 shows the rate of decay of strontium-90, which has a 29-y half-life. Of the original 10-g sample, only 1.25 g remain after three half-lives, or 87 y.

Table 11.3 shows the half-lives of a few of the thousands of known radioisotopes. Notice how widely the length of a half-life varies, ranging from periods of microseconds to billions of years. In each case, exactly half of the original amount remains unchanged after a period of one half-life.

Table 11.3 • Half-Lives of Several Radioisotopes		
Radioisotope	Symbol	Half-Life
Polonium-214	$^{214}_{84}$Po	163.7 μs
Cobalt-60	$^{60}_{27}$Co	5.272 y
Radon-222	$^{222}_{86}$Ra	3.8 d
Phosphorous-32	$^{32}_{15}$P	14.28 d
Tritium	$^{3}_{1}$H	12.32 y
Carbon-14	$^{14}_{6}$C	5730 y
Uranium-238	$^{238}_{92}$U	4.46×10^9 y

Writing Nuclear Equations

Like chemical reactions, nuclear reactions can be expressed as written equations. Nuclear equations use symbols to identify the atomic nuclei and radiation involved. These symbols include the identity of the nucleus or particle, its mass, and its charge. For example, iodine-131 has 53 protons and 78 neutrons, making its mass number 131. The nuclear symbol for iodine-131 is $^{131}_{53}$I.

The charge on the nucleus (number of protons) is indicated as a subscript before the symbol and the mass (total number of nucleons) is indicated as a superscript. In addition to a symbol for atomic nuclei, there are symbols for particles and radiation, shown in Table 11.4. Notice that the symbol for an alpha particle uses He because the particle consists of two protons and two neutrons, so it is identical to a helium nucleus.

Like chemical equations, nuclear equations must be balanced. In nuclear reactions, both mass and charge are conserved, so both mass and charge must be balanced in the equation. For example, the decay of radium by emission of an alpha particle, which is identical to a helium nucleus, can be written as

$$^{226}_{88}\text{Ra} \rightarrow {}^{222}_{86}\text{Rn} + {}^{4}_{2}\text{He}$$

Table 11.4 • Characteristics of Alpha, Beta, and Gamma Radiation			
Radiation Type	Symbol	Mass (amu)	Charge
Alpha	$^{4}_{2}$He	4	2+
Beta	$^{0}_{-1}$β	$\frac{1}{1840}$	1−
Gamma	$^{0}_{0}$γ	0	0

The mass is balanced—222 for radon plus 4 for helium accounts for the original mass of 226; and charge is balanced—86 positive charges for the radon nucleus and 2 for the alpha particle. In a nuclear equation, beta particles are indicated by the symbol $_{-1}^{0}\beta$. The beta decay of iodine-131 is written as

$$_{53}^{131}I \rightarrow {}_{54}^{131}Xe + {}_{-1}^{0}\beta$$

Again, the mass is balanced—131 nucleons on each side of the equation and charge is balanced because $53 = 54 + (-1)$. Although gamma rays do not contribute mass or charge to the equation, their emission is indicated in nuclear equations, such as the decay of uranium-238

$$_{92}^{238}U \rightarrow {}_{90}^{234}Th + {}_{2}^{4}He + {}_{0}^{0}\gamma$$

✓ CHECK FOR UNDERSTANDING What does each number represent in the nuclear formula $_{2}^{4}He$?

Causing Nuclear Reactions

The conversion of an atom of one element to an atom of another element is called transmutation. Spontaneous decay is not the only process that causes **transmutation** of an atom. In 1919, Ernest Rutherford succeeded in converting one element into another by striking nitrogen-14 nuclei with high-energy alpha particles. The resulting nuclear reaction is shown in Figure 11.6. In this reaction the nitrogen atom is converted into fluorine-18, an unstable isotope that decays by emitting a proton to become oxygen-17. None of the elements larger than uranium exist naturally. They are produced by bombarding the nuclei of smaller atoms with high-energy particles, causing a

Example Problem 1

Write a balanced nuclear equation for the alpha decay of radon-222.

1 Analyze the Problem

- Given that radon undergoes alpha decay, one of the reaction products is an alpha particle.
- Spontaneous decay occurs within the nucleus, so radon-222 is the only starting material. From the periodic table, the atomic number of radon is 86.
- The reaction can be summarized as

$$_{86}^{222}Rn \rightarrow {}_{2}^{4}He + {}_{charge}^{mass} X$$

2 Solve for the Unknown

Using the mass number for each particle, and the fact that mass is conserved, balance the mass numbers on both sides of the reaction.

$222 = 4 +$ mass of X
mass of $X = 222 - 4 = 218$

Using the atomic number for each particle, and the fact that charge is conserved, balance the atomic numbers on both sides of the reaction.

$86 = 2 +$ charge of X
charge of $X = 86 - 2 = 84$

Identify the element from the periodic table and substitute its symbol.

The element with the atomic number 84 is polonium.

Write the balanced equation.

$$_{86}^{222}Rn \rightarrow {}_{2}^{4}He + {}_{84}^{218}Po$$

3 Evaluate the Answer

- **Does the answer make sense?** The sums of the superscripts and the subscripts are equal on both sides of the equation, so it is balanced.

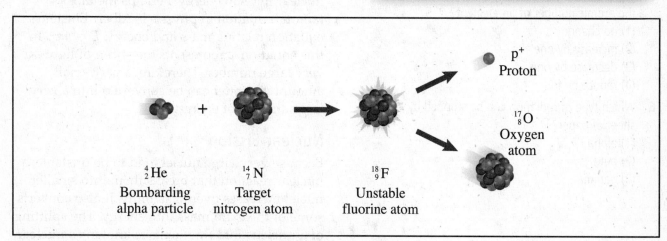

$_{2}^{4}He$
Bombarding alpha particle

$_{7}^{14}N$
Target nitrogen atom

$_{9}^{18}F$
Unstable fluorine atom

p^{+}
Proton

$_{8}^{17}O$
Oxygen atom

Figure 11.6 Rutherford's experiment demonstrated that nuclear reactions can be induced.

nuclear reaction that causes a transmutation to occur. The first such artificial transmutation occurred in 1940 when uranium-238 was placed in a stream of high-energy neutrons, leading to a radioactive decay series that produced the new elements neptunium and plutonium.

✓ CHECK FOR UNDERSTANDING How does artificial transmutation take place?

Quick Review

1 The nucleus of an atom is held together primarily by
(1) the strong nuclear force
(2) the weak nuclear force
(3) electromagnetic attraction
(4) gravity

2 Given the equation:

$$^{232}_{90}Th \rightarrow - \,^{228}_{88}Ra + \,^{4}_{2}He$$

What kind of process is represented by this reaction?

(1) alpha decay   (3) gamma radiation
(2) beta decay   (4) nuclear fission

3 What type of radiation completes this equation?

$$^{14}_{6}C \rightarrow \,^{14}_{7}N + ?$$

(1) alpha particle   (3) gamma ray
(2) beta particle   (4) neutron

4 All of the elements larger than uranium are made by
(1) nuclear fusion
(2) beta decay
(3) artificial transmutation
(4) natural transmutation

5 What is the effect of emission of a beta particle on the atomic number of an element?
(1) no change
(2) increase by one
(3) decrease by one
(4) reduce by four

6 Which type of radiation can be stopped by a thick sheet of paper?
(1) alpha
(2) beta
(3) gamma

7 The half-life of a radioisotope is 3.1 hours. How much of a 10.0-gram sample will remain unchanged after 9.3 hours?
(1) 5.00 g   (3) 1.25 g
(2) 2.50 g   (4) 1.00 g

8 After a period of 1000 years, only 62.5 grams of an original 1-kilogram sample of a radioisotope remains unchanged. What is the half-life of the radioisotope?
(1) 62.5 y   (3) 250 y
(2) 100 y   (4) 500 y

9 A radioactive decay series is the term used to describe
(1) the effect of a high-energy neutron on a nucleus
(2) the emission of more than one type of radiation
(3) the change in the atomic mass when a particle is emitted
(4) a sequence of emissions of particles leading to a stable isotope

10 Explain how a nuclear reaction differs from a chemical reaction.

Nuclear Fission and Nuclear Fusion

In addition to natural and artificial transmutations, there are nuclear reactions that cause transmutation of elements with the release of a large amount of energy. These reactions are the source of electric energy at nuclear power plants and the immense amount of energy from the Sun and other stars. The source of this energy is the conversion of matter to energy. The mass of a nucleus is not exactly equal to the sum of the masses of its nucleons. This difference in mass means that transmutation converts some of the nuclear mass to energy. Perhaps the most famous equation in physics is Albert Einstein's equation relating mass and energy, $E = mc^2$. In this equation, c represents the speed of light—a very large number. Therefore, a very small amount of matter can be converted into a very large amount of energy.

Nuclear Fission

Because very large nuclei tend to be unstable, a nuclear reaction that breaks them into smaller nuclei increases overall stability. It also converts some of the extra mass into energy. The splitting of a nucleus into fragments is known as **nuclear fission**. The first nuclear-fission reaction that

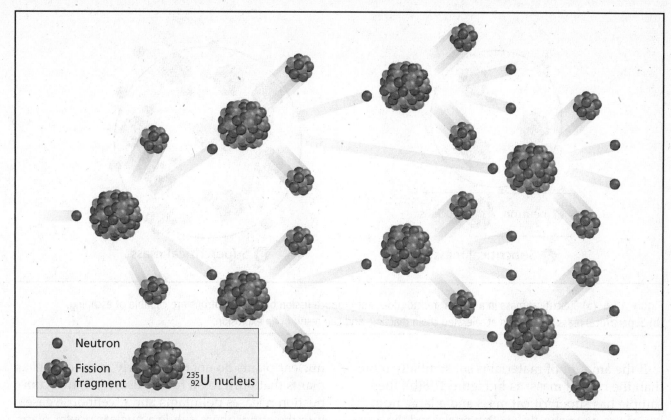

Figure 11.7 A fission chain reaction occurs when some of the emitted neutrons start new reactions.

was discovered, which is still the source of electricity in many nuclear power plants, is the fission of uranium-235. As shown in Figure 11.7, when a neutron strikes a uranium-235 nucleus it can cause the nucleus to break apart into smaller nuclei. There are many possible products of this reaction, including krypton-92 and barium-141. Notice that the nuclear-fission reaction also produces, in addition to energy, neutrons. If these neutrons strike another uranium-235 nucleus, they can cause that nucleus to break apart as well, releasing more neutrons that can strike more nuclei. The result is a self-sustaining process in which one reaction initiates the next, called a nuclear chain reaction. Figure 11.7 illustrates this process. Remember that each link in the chain reaction also releases a large amount of energy. This energy is much greater than the energy released by chemical reactions.

For a chain reaction to begin, there must be a minimum mass of fissionable material present. Otherwise, the neutrons escape the material without continuing the chain, as shown in Figure 11.8(a) on page 180. A sample that is massive enough to sustain a chain reaction has **critical mass**.

REGENTS EXAM
Strategies for Success

STEP 1 READ the Regents Questions ...
Which statement best describes what happens in a fission reaction?

(1) Heavy nuclei split into lighter nuclei.
(2) Light nuclei form into heavier nuclei.
(3) Energy is released and less stable elements form.
(4) Energy is absorbed and more stable elements form.

STEP 2 ANALYZE each choice ...

(1) This answer generalizes the splitting of uranium into barium and krypton, which occurs in fission.
(2) This answer does not conform to fission because heavy nuclei are split in fission.
(3) This is incorrect because, in fission, lower mass elements are formed, which are more stable.
(4) This statement is false because large amounts of energy are released in fission.

STEP 3 CHOOSE the best answer ...
Number 1 is correct, because it describes the process of nuclear fission.

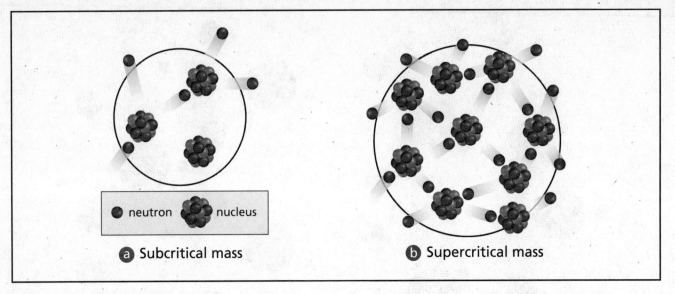

Figure 11.8 **(a)** Subcritical mass in a nuclear reactor does not produce fission because neutrons are capable of escaping. **(b)** Supercritical mass leads to an accelerated chain reaction, and can result in an explosion.

If the amount of material is substantially more than the critical mass, as in Figure 11.8(b), the sample has supercritical mass and a large number of the neutrons strike other nuclei and the chain reaction accelerates rapidly. The result is a violent nuclear explosion.

✓ **CHECK FOR UNDERSTANDING** Why does overall stability increase when fission occurs?

Nuclear Power

When the chain reaction is controlled, the energy created by nuclear fission can be captured and converted to electricity. In a nuclear power plant, rods of fissionable material are placed in a reactor, where the nuclear reactions generate heat. A liquid coolant pumped through the reactor carries heat to a water supply, which generates steam. The steam runs a turbine connected to an electric generator to produce electricity, as shown in Figure 11.9 on page 181. Inside the reactor, rods of cadmium or boron control the fission reaction by absorbing any neutrons beyond those needed to produce the required amount of heat. If the reactor must be shut down, these control rods are moved into a position where they absorb almost all of the neutrons produced in the fission reaction.

Compared to conventional power plants, nuclear power plants have advantages as well as disadvantages. The amount of heat generated by a small amount of fissionable material means that nuclear plants do not need nearly as much fuel as plants that burn fossil fuels. Also, fossil fuel combustion releases pollutants and greenhouse gases into the atmosphere, while a nuclear power plant that is operating correctly has no emissions. On the other hand, when the fuel rods are depleted, the waste material is extremely radioactive. Disposal of nuclear waste is one of the biggest problems for the nuclear power industry because the radioactivity remains at dangerous levels for many thousands of years. Another limitation of nuclear power plants, shared with fossil fuel plants, is that they must have a reliable supply of fuel to continue operating.

✓ **CHECK FOR UNDERSTANDING** Name one advantage and one disadvantage of using nuclear power.

Nuclear Fusion

In another form of nuclear reaction, nuclei of small atoms join together to form larger nuclei. The combining of atomic nuclei to form a large, more stable nucleus, is called **nuclear fusion**. Like fission, nuclear fusion is a nuclear reaction that converts matter into very large amounts of energy. The most familiar nuclear fusion reaction is occurring constantly in the Sun. The source of solar energy is a series of fusion reactions. The following is a net reaction for one of the pathways by which hydrogen is converted into helium in the Sun.

$$4\,^{1}_{1}\text{H} \rightarrow\,^{4}_{2}\text{He} + 2\,^{0}_{1}\beta + \text{energy}$$

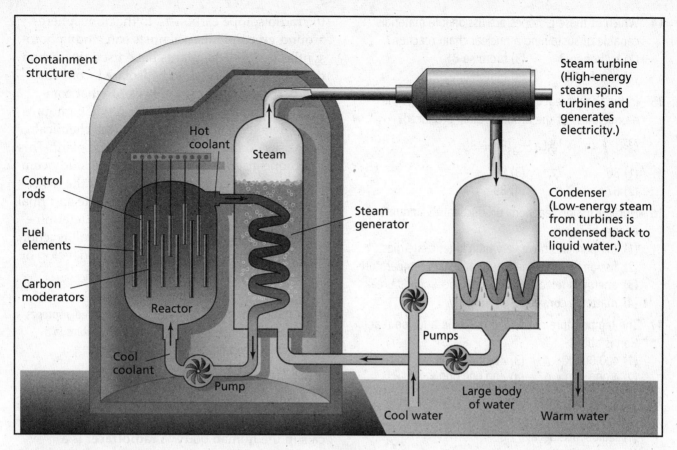

Figure 11.9 In a nuclear reactor, there must be systems for controlling the nuclear reactions and for utilizing thermal energy released by the reactions. What is the function of the steam turbine?

Scientists are studying nuclear fusion as a possible source of energy for production of electricity. The advantage of nuclear fusion is that it produces an enormous amount of energy, while consuming only a small amount of very abundant fuel. The major disadvantage is that the lowest temperature capable of producing the fusion reaction is about 40,000,000 K. Because of the technological problems of producing and controlling that high temperature and because there are no materials that can withstand that heat, nuclear fusion as a source of electric energy is unlikely in the near future.

✓ **CHECK FOR UNDERSTANDING** What is the most familiar source of a nuclear fusion reaction?

Quick Review

11 The purpose of a control rod in a nuclear fission reactor is to
(1) produce neutrons at a controlled rate
(2) slow the reaction by absorbing neutrons
(3) cool the reactor core
(4) slow the reaction by absorbing gamma rays

12 Starting a nuclear chain reaction requires
(1) an energy input
(2) very high temperature
(3) critical mass of fissionable material
(4) ionizing radiation

13 This nuclear equation represents the process of

$$^{2}_{1}H + ^{3}_{1}H \rightarrow ^{4}_{2}He + ^{1}_{0}n + energy$$

(1) nuclear fission
(2) nuclear fusion
(3) alpha decay
(4) hydrogen bonding

14 Which of these isotopes are fissionable materials capable of sustaining a nuclear chain reaction?
   (1) hydrogen-2   (3) bromine-81
   (2) carbon-14   (4) plutonium-239

15 In the fission reaction shown below, what is the atomic mass of the bromine atom produced?

$$^{235}_{92}U + ^{1}_{0}n \rightarrow ^{146}_{57}La + ^{?}_{35}Br + 3^{1}_{0}n$$

   (1) 86   (3) 88
   (2) 87   (4) 89

16 Nuclear fission reactions produce large amounts of energy because
   (1) the particles have very high kinetic energies
   (2) fissionable materials burn at a high temperature
   (3) energy is released as the chemical bonds break
   (4) matter is converted into energy

17 The temperature needed to maintain a fusion reaction is about
   (1) 400,000 K   (3) 40,000,000 K
   (2) 4,000,000 K   (4) 400,000,000 K

18 The source of the energy of the Sun and other stars is
   (1) radioactive decay
   (2) nuclear fission
   (3) nuclear fusion
   (4) artificial transmutation

19 What is the main problem with using nuclear fission as a source of electric power?

Using Radioisotopes

Besides generating electric energy, there are many other applications of radioactivity. Since its discovery over 100 years ago, radioactivity has been useful to scientific researchers, doctors, and manufacturers. The key to many uses of radioisotopes is that they react in exactly the same way as nonradioactive isotopes of the same element in chemical reactions.

Tracking Atoms

Because isotopes of the same element are chemically identical, radioisotopes can be used to monitor what happens to atoms in a chemical reaction. Radiation detectors are very sensitive, so only a small amount of the radioisotope needs to be added to the study sample. For example, by adding carbon dioxide containing the radioisotope carbon-14 to the atmosphere around green plants, scientists can study photosynthesis. After the plants have used the carbon dioxide, compounds can be isolated from various parts of the plant. Analysis of what compounds contain carbon-14 and in what amounts gives detailed information about the chemical processes occurring in the cells of the plant. This technique also is used by chemists to study complex chemical reactions. By following the distribution of radioisotopes in intermediate and final compounds of the reaction, chemists determine the series of steps involved in the overall reaction. This information then can be used to develop or to improve manufacturing techniques.

 CHECK FOR UNDERSTANDING Why can radioisotopes be used to monitor what happens to the atoms in a chemical reaction?

Medical Uses of Radiotracers

Doctors use a similar process to monitor chemicals in the human body. A **radiotracer** is a radioisotope that emits nonionizing radiation and is used to signal the presence of an element or a specific substance. A patient ingests a small amount of a radioisotope, whose course through the body can be monitored by measuring its radioactive decay. One example of this use is iodine-131 tracing of thyroid problems. Iodine is used by the thyroid gland to make hormones needed by the body. When doctors suspect a thyroid problem, the patient is given a dose of the radioisotope iodine-131. By measuring the amount of the iodine that is absorbed from the bloodstream by the thyroid, they can determine whether the gland is functioning normally and then make treatment decisions.

Another medical tool that uses radiation is positron-emission transaxial tomography (PET). A radiotracer is injected into the patient's bloodstream. When the radioisotope decays, it emits a positron (identical to an electron, but carrying a positive charge) and gamma rays. An instrument detects the gamma rays and makes a map of the part of the body that is the source of the radiation. The particular isotope to be used is matched with the physiological function of the organ to be studied.

Radiation Therapy

Radioisotopes also can be used in treatment of disease. One of the effects of radiation in the body is damage to or destruction of cells. Cancer is characterized by excessive growth of abnormal cells in some parts of the body. Some cancer treatments give patients radioisotopes of elements that are likely to become concentrated in the cancer cells. Because the dosage for this application is much larger than the amount of iodine-131 used in the thyroid, the cells that concentrate the radioactive material are damaged. Although there is also some damage to healthy cells, radiation therapy is often an effective treatment for cancer.

Radiochemical Dating

Another application of radioisotopes relies on the fact that every radioactive isotope has a constant half-life, which is not affected by temperature, pressure, or concentration. As a result, by measuring the amount of radioisotope remaining in an object and comparing that amount to that of the decay products, you can determine how old the object is. The process of determining age by measuring the amount of a certain radioisotope remaining is called **radiochemical dating**.

A common procedure used to measure the age of artifacts that were once part of a living object, such as wood or bone, uses the decay of carbon-14. The radioisotope carbon-14 is produced in the upper atmosphere by the interaction of nitrogen-14 with cosmic rays. Atoms of carbon-14 then spread throughout the atmosphere and are incorporated into compounds such as carbon dioxide. Plants take in carbon-14 in carbon dioxide and use photosynthesis to build complex molecules that spread throughout their tissues and that are eaten by animals. As a result, the ratio of carbon-14 to the non-radioactive isotopes,

carbon-12 and carbon-13, in the atmosphere is also the ratio in all living organisms.

After the organism dies, however, the amount of carbon-14 decreases due to beta decay.

$$^{14}_{6}C \rightarrow ^{14}_{7}N + ^{0}_{-1}\beta$$

This nuclear reaction has a half-life of 5730 y. Because the amount of the other carbon isotopes does not change in the wood or the bone, the ratio of carbon-14 to the other isotopes steadily decreases. By measuring the ratio of radioisotope to stable isotope and comparing that to the atmospheric ratio, the age of the object can be determined. For example, if the ratio in the object is one-fourth that of the atmosphere, then two half-lives, or 11,460 y, have passed since the organism died.

Because the amount of remaining isotope gradually disappears to the point where the change is too small to measure accurately, carbon-14 is only useful for dating objects less than about 50,000 y old. A similar process with other radioisotopes having longer half-lives can be used for older objects. On a very long scale, the age of the solar system has been estimated at about 4.6 billion y using radiochemical dating of uranium-238 in rocks. The half-life of uranium-238 is about 4.5 billion y, so less than half of the original amount remains.

✓ CHECK FOR UNDERSTANDING Why does the amount of carbon-14 in an organism decrease after it dies?

Risks of Radiation

Although radiation has many useful applications in science, medicine, and industry, it also has inherent risks. Radiation that is energetic enough to ionize matter with which it collides is called **ionizing radiation**. When it collides with molecules in body tissues, ionizing radiation can fragment those molecules, disrupting the normal

Table 11.5 • Effects of Short-Term Radiation Exposure	
Dose (rem)	**Effects on Humans**
0–25	No detectable effects
25–50	Temporary decrease in white blood cell population
100–200	Nausea, substantial decrease in white blood cell population
500	50% chance of death within 30 days of exposure

Table 11.6 • Average Annual Radiation Exposure	
Source	Average Exposure (mrem/y)
Cosmic radiation	20–50
Radiation from ground	25–170
Radiation from buildings	10–160
Radiation from air	20–260
Human body (internal)	~20
Medical and dental X rays	50–75
Nuclear weapon testing	<1
Air travel	5
Total Average Exposure	100–300

operation of the cells. The effects of radiation can range from burns similar to those produced by fire, to cancer, and even death if there is sufficient exposure. Damage to reproductive tissues can cause damage that affects future generations. Because of these effects, anyone who comes in contact with radioactive materials must use protective measures to avoid damage.

Exposure to radiation is measured in a unit known as a roentgen, abbreviated as rem. Table 11.5 shows the effects of exposure to various levels of radiation. People are exposed to a certain amount of radiation from natural and human sources every day. Table 11.6 shows the average amount of exposure from a number of common sources, expressed in millirems, or mrem. By comparing the total average exposure to the table of effects, you can see that normal daily exposure to radiation carries very little risk (remember to convert mrem to rem). However, people who work with radiation sources on a daily basis, such as X-ray technicians, must leave the room or wear protective clothing to avoid too much exposure, which can add up to a dangerous dose over time.

Because of the danger to people and the long lifetime of some radioisotopes, disposal of radioactive wastes is highly regulated. Low-level wastes, such as medical radioisotopes and radioactive isotopes used to generate X rays, normally are buried in secure disposal sites to prevent contact with people. These wastes normally contain small amounts of radioisotopes and have relatively short half-lives. High-level wastes, generally from nuclear power plants or manufacturing processes that isolate or make radioisotopes, create more problems than low-level waste. These materials emit very large amounts of ionizing radiation and will remain hazardous for tens of thousands of years. Scientists and politicians are still working to find suitable disposal methods for these waste materials.

The presence and level of ionizing radiation can be measured using a Geiger counter, as illustrated in Figure 11.10. The tube of the

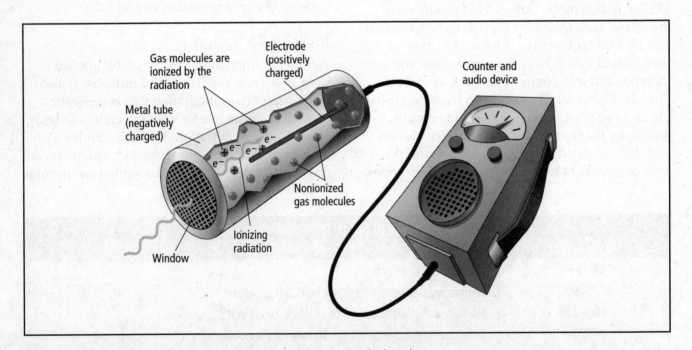

Figure 11.10 A Geiger counter detects radiation that ionizes gas inside the tube.

Geiger counter is filled with a gas, which absorbs the radiation that enters the tube and becomes ionized. Electrons that are freed from the atoms during ionization are attracted to a wire (the positively charged electrode), causing a current to flow. A current meter detects this electric current, which indicates the presence and level of radiation.

✔ CHECK FOR UNDERSTANDING Name four effects of radiation.

Quick Review

20 The radioisotope used to date archaeological specimens is
(1) carbon-12   (3) carbon-14
(2) carbon-13   (4) iodine-131

21 Uranium-238 decay can be used to date ancient rocks because it has a half-life of about
(1) 5700 y
(2) 4.5 million y
(3) 45 million y
(4) 4.5 billion y

22 Radioisotopes can be used inside the human body
(1) to reconstruct DNA molecules
(2) to absorb gamma rays
(3) as nutrients
(4) as radiotracers

23 Refer to Table 11.6. Which source may contribute the most to the total average annual radiation exposure?
(1) cosmic radiation
(2) radiation from the air
(3) radiation from the ground
(4) radiation from buildings

24 How does ionizing radiation affect the human body?

25 All of these are useful characteristics of a radiotracer for medical use, except that
(1) it has the same chemical properties as a non-radioactive isotope
(2) it emits high levels of ionizing radiation
(3) it emits nonionizing radiation
(4) it is an isotope of an element used by a specific organ

26 Radiocarbon dating is based on what nuclear reaction?
(1) $^{13}_{6}C \rightarrow {}^{13}_{7}N + {}^{0}_{-1}\beta$
(2) $^{14}_{6}C \rightarrow {}^{14}_{7}N + {}^{0}_{-1}\beta$
(3) $^{14}_{6}C \rightarrow {}^{13}_{6}C + {}^{1}_{-0}\beta$
(4) $^{14}_{6}C \rightarrow {}^{10}_{4}Be + {}^{4}_{2}He$

27 A sample of wood from an ancient building site has about one-fourth the amount of carbon-14 compared to a modern sample. About how long ago was the tree cut down?
(1) 500 y   (3) 11,500 y
(2) 5700 y   (4) 23,000 y

28 One instrument used to detect ionizing radiation is a
(1) Geiger counter
(2) PET scanner
(3) anemometer
(4) Curie

Part A

1 The spontaneous decay of an atom is called
   (1) ionization
   (2) crystallization
   (3) combustion
   (4) radioactivity

2 Artificial transmutation is brought about by using accelerated particles to bombard an atom's
   (1) nucleus
   (2) valence shells
   (3) occupied sublevels
   (4) inner principal energy levels

3 Which type of emission has the highest penetrating power?
   (1) alpha
   (2) beta
   (3) positron
   (4) gamma

4 Which product of nuclear decay has mass but no charge?
   (1) alpha particles
   (2) neutrons
   (3) gamma rays
   (4) beta positrons

5 Which type of radioactive emission has a positive charge and weak penetrating power?
   (1) alpha particle
   (2) beta particle
   (3) gamma ray
   (4) neutron

6 Which Group 16 element has only unstable isotopes?
   (1) polonuim
   (2) tellurium
   (3) selenium
   (4) sulfur

7 What is the total number of grams of a 32-gram sample of ^{32}P remaining after 71.5 days of decay? (Use the Reference Table data for half-lives.)
   (1) 1.0 g
   (2) 2.0 g
   (3) 8.0 g
   (4) 4.0 g

8 The half-life of a radioactive substance is 2.5 minutes. What fraction of the original radioactive substance remains after 10 minutes?
   (1) $\frac{1}{2}$
   (2) $\frac{1}{4}$
   (3) $\frac{1}{8}$
   (4) $\frac{1}{16}$

9 Which equation is an example of artificial transmutation?
   (1) $^{9}_{4}Be + ^{4}_{2}He \rightarrow ^{12}_{6}C + ^{1}_{0}n$
   (2) $U + 3F_2 \rightarrow UF_6$
   (3) $Mg(OH)_2 + 2HCl \rightarrow 2H_2O + MgCl_2$
   (4) $Ca + 2H_2O \rightarrow Ca(OH)_2 + H_2$

10 Which reaction represents natural nuclear decay?
   (1) $H^+ + OH^- \rightarrow H_2O$
   (2) $KClO_3 \rightarrow K^+ + ClO_3^-$
   (3) $^{235}_{92}U \rightarrow ^{4}_{2}He + ^{231}_{90}Th$
   (4) $^{14}_{7}N + ^{4}_{2}He \rightarrow ^{17}_{8}O + ^{1}_{1}H$

11 Given the reaction:
   $^{9}_{4}Be + ^{1}_{1}H \rightarrow ^{6}_{3}Li + ^{4}_{2}He$
   which type of reaction is represented?
   (1) natural transmutation
   (2) artificial transmutation
   (3) fission
   (4) fusion

12 In which reaction is mass converted to energy by the process of fission?

(1) $^{14}_{7}N + ^{1}_{0}n \rightarrow ^{14}_{6}C + ^{1}_{1}H$

(2) $^{235}_{92}U + ^{1}_{0}n \rightarrow ^{87}_{35}Br + ^{146}_{57}La + 3^{1}_{0}n$

(3) $^{226}_{88}Ra \rightarrow ^{222}_{86}Rn + ^{4}_{2}He$

(4) $^{2}_{1}H + ^{2}_{1}H \rightarrow ^{4}_{2}He$

13 Given the fusion reaction:

$^{2}_{1}H + ^{2}_{1}H \rightarrow X + energy$

which particle is represented by X?

(1) $^{1}_{1}H$ (3) $^{3}_{2}He$

(2) $^{3}_{1}H$ (4) $^{4}_{2}He$

14 Given the nuclear reaction:

$^{9}_{4}Be + X \rightarrow ^{12}_{6}C + ^{1}_{0}n$

what is the identity of particle X?

(1) alpha particle (3) proton

(2) beta particle (4) neutron

15 What mass of a 60.0-gram sample of $^{16}_{7}N$ will remain unchanged after 28.8 seconds?

(1) 3.75 g   (3) 15.0 g

(2) 7.50 g   (4) 30.0 g

16 Which substance is a gaseous radioactive waste product that is released into the atmosphere after it has decayed to a safe radiation level?

(1) radon-222

(2) radium-226

(3) cesium-137

(4) cobalt-60

17 Which radioactive isotope is used for the diagnosis of thyroid disease?

18 Which nuclide is a radioisotope used in the study of organic reaction mechanisms?

19 During a fission reaction, which type of particle is captured by a nucleus?

The diagram below represents a nuclear reaction in which a neutron bombards a heavy nucleus.

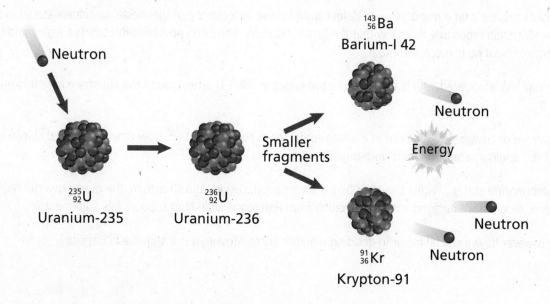

20 Which type of reaction does the diagram illustrate?

Part C

Base your answers to questions 21 through 26 on the information below.

Nuclear Waste Storage Plan for Yucca Mountain

In 1978, the United States Department of Energy began a study of Yucca Mountain, which is located 90 miles from Las Vegas, Nevada. The study was to determine if Yucca Mountain would be suitable for a long-term burial site for high-level radioactive waste. A three-dimensional (3-D) computer scale model of the site was used to simulate the Yucca Mountain area. The computer model study for Yucca Mountain included such variables as: the possibility of earthquakes, predicted water flow through the mountain, increased rainfall due to climate changes, radioactive leakage from the waste containers, and increased temperatures from the buried waste within the containers. The containers that will be used to store the radioactive waste are designed to last 10,000 years. Within the 10,000-year time period, cesium and strontium, the most powerful radioactive emitters, would have decayed. Other isotopes found in the waste would decay more slowly, but are not powerful radioactive emitters. In 1998, scientists discovered that the compressed volcanic ash making up Yucca Mountain was full of cracks. Because of the arid climate, scientists assumed that rainwater would move through the cracks at a slow rate. However, when radioactive chlorine-36 was found in rock samples at levels halfway through the mountain, it was clear that rainwater had moved quickly down through Yucca Mountain. It was only 50 years earlier when this chlorine-36 isotope had contaminated rainwater during atmospheric testing of the atom bomb. Some opponents of the Yucca Mountain plan believe that the uncertainties related to the many variables of the computer model result in limited reliability of its predictions. However, advocates of the plan believe it is safer to replace the numerous existing radioactive burial sites around the United States with the one site at Yucca Mountain. Other opponents of the plan believe that transporting the radioactive waste to Yucca Mountain from the existing 131 burial sites creates too much danger to the United States. In 2002, after years of political debate, a final legislative vote approved the development of Yucca Mountain to replace the existing 131 burial sites.

21 State one uncertainty in the computer model that limits the reliability of this computer model.

22 Scientists assume that a manufacturing defect would cause at least one of the waste containers stored in the Yucca Mountain repository to leak within the first 1000 years. State one possible effect such a leak could have on the environment near Yucca Mountain.

23 State one risk associated with leaving radioactive waste in the 131 sites around the country where it is presently stored.

24 If a sample of cesium-137 is stored in a waste container in Yucca Mountain, how much time must elapse until only $\frac{1}{32}$ of the original sample remains unchanged?

25 The information states "Within the 10,000-year time period, cesium and strontium, the most powerful radioactive emitters, would have decayed." Use information from Reference Table N to support this statement.

26 Why is water flow a crucial factor in deciding whether Yucca Mountain is a suitable burial site?

Laboratory Skills

VOCABULARY

filtration
kilogram
liter
mass
meter
safety symbol

The Regents curriculum for the *Physical Setting: Chemistry* course emphasizes that all students are expected to develop proficiency in specific process skills. These skills include the application of scientific methods, which was discussed in Section 1 of this book, and the application of laboratory techniques and procedures, which will be discussed in this section.

Safety in the Laboratory

The chemistry laboratory is a place to experiment and learn. You must assume responsibility for your own personal safety and that of people working near you. Accidents usually are caused by carelessness, but you can help prevent them by closely following instructions in this handbook, and those given to you by your teacher. **Safety symbols** shown in Figure 1 warn of dangers that may exist in a lab. Emergency information also may be listed in Material Data Safety Sheets (MDSS). Ask your instructor for their location within the laboratory.

Always be alert for dangerous situations when you are in the laboratory. The following are some safety rules to help guide you in protecting yourself and others from injury in a laboratory. Keep in mind that these rules are guidelines and you also must exercise common sense to work safely.

1 The chemistry laboratory is a place for serious work. Do not perform activities without your teacher's permission. Never work alone in the laboratory. Work only when your teacher is present.
2 Study your lab activity before you come to the lab. If you are in doubt about any procedures, ask your teacher for help.

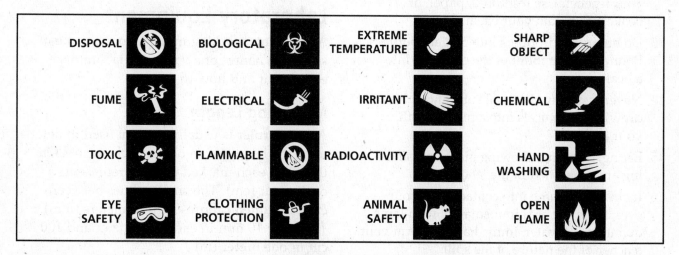

Figure 1 Safety symbols are a quick way to warn students about potential dangers in a laboratory.

3 Safety goggles and a laboratory apron must be worn whenever you work in the lab. Gloves should be worn whenever you use chemicals that cause irritations or can be absorbed through the skin.

4 Contact lenses should not be worn in the lab, even if goggles are worn. Lenses can absorb vapors and are difficult to remove in an emergency.

5 Long hair should be tied back to reduce the possibility of it catching fire.

6 Do not wear dangling jewelry or loose, draping clothing. The loose clothing may catch fire and either the clothing or the jewelry could catch on chemical apparatuses.

7 Wear shoes that cover the feet at all times. Bare feet or sandals are not permitted in the lab.

8 Know the location of the fire extinguisher, safety shower, eyewash, fire blanket, and first aid kit.

9 Know how to use the safety equipment provided for you. Immediately report any accidents, injuries, incorrect procedures, or damaged equipment to your teacher.

10 Handle chemicals carefully. Check the labels of all bottles before removing the contents. Read the labels three times: before you pick up the container, when the container is in your hand, and when you put the bottle back.

11 Do not return unused chemicals to reagent bottles.

12 Do not take reagent bottles to your work area unless specifically instructed to do so by your teacher. Use test tubes, paper, or beakers to obtain your chemicals.

13 Do not insert droppers into reagent bottles. Pour a small amount of the chemical into a beaker.

14 Never taste any chemical substances. Never draw any chemicals into a pipette with your mouth.

15 Eating, drinking, chewing gum, and smoking are prohibited in the laboratory.

16 If chemicals come into contact with your eyes, flush the area immediately with large quantities of water. Immediately inform your teacher of the nature of the spill.

17 Keep flammable materials away from open flames. (Alcohol and acetone are flammable.)

18 Handle toxic and combustible gases only under the direction of your teacher. Use the fume hood when such materials are present.

19 When heating a substance in a test tube, be careful not to point the mouth of the tube at another person or at yourself. Never look down the mouth of a test tube.

20 Use caution and the proper equipment when handling hot apparatuses or glassware. Hot glass looks the same as cool glass.

21 Dispose broken glass, unused chemicals, and products of reactions as directed by your teacher.

22 Know the correct procedure for preparing acid solutions. Always add the acid slowly to the water.

23 Keep the balance area clean. Never weigh chemicals directly on the pan of the balance.

24 Do not heat graduated cylinders, burettes, or pipettes with a laboratory burner.

25 After completing an activity, clean and put away your equipment. Clean your work area. Make sure the gas and water are turned off. Wash your hands with soap and water before you leave the lab.

✓ CHECK FOR UNDERSTANDING Which safety rules in the list should be applied at the end of an experiment?

Laboratory Equipment

All students working in the laboratory must know the names of a variety of laboratory equipment and how to use it.

Measuring Length

A metric ruler is usually the tool used to determine the length of an object in chemistry. On the ruler, each marked number represents a centimeter (cm). The smaller lines between each centimeter represent millimeters (mm). There are 10 mm in each centimeter and 100 cm in one **meter** (m).

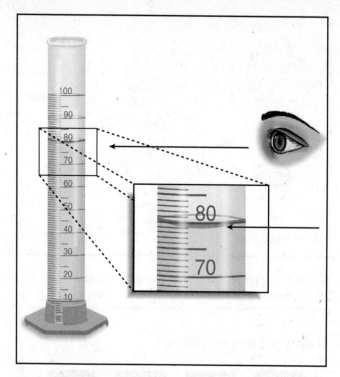

Figure 2 Liquid volume is measured at the lowest point of the meniscus. The volume of this liquid is 79 mL.

When you measure an object's length, make sure that you do not look at the ruler markings at an angle, because this will give you a reading that is too short or too long.

Measuring Volume

In the laboratory, a volume of a liquid can be measured using a graduated cylinder. The **liter** (L) is the unit used to measure volume. There are 1000 milliliters (mL).

When a liquid is poured into a graduated cylinder, the surface of the liquid curves upward at the edges of the cylinder because the molecules making up the liquid are attracted to the sides of the cylinder. This curved surface, called the meniscus, is shown in Figure 2. To make an accurate measurement with a cylinder, place the cylinder on a flat surface and, looking at it from eye level, measure the level at the lowest point of the meniscus.

Measuring Temperature

Temperatures are measured in degrees Celsius, °C, in the metric system. In this system, water freezes at 0°C, boils at 100°C, and the temperature of the human body is about 37°C. Alcohol thermometers usually are used to measure temperature, although electronic thermometers, known as

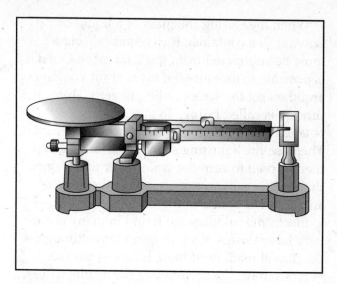

Figure 3 The centigram balance is used to measure an object's mass.

temperature probes, are used to record temperatures over time or to measure temperature with more precision.

Measuring Mass

In the chemistry laboratory, **mass**—the quantity of matter in an object—is measured with a balance. The **kilogram** (kg) is the SI unit of mass. There are 1000 grams (g) in 1 kg.

The centigram balance, shown in Figure 3, often is used to determine the mass of objects. Most centigram balances can be used to measure a mass of up to 200 g. The balance has a pan and three bars or beams that are calibrated in grams. Each beam has a moveable weight called a *rider*. The back beam is divided into 10-g units. The middle beam is divided into units of 1 g each. The front beam is divided into 0.1-g units, each of which is subdivided into 0.01-g units. Before using a centigram balance, examine it to be sure that the pan is empty, all of the riders are at zero, and the pointer at the end of the beams is aligned at zero. To mass an object, place it in the pan. Begin by moving the 10-g rider to the right, one notch at a time, until the pointer stays down, and then move the rider back one notch. Next, move the 1-g rider following the same procedure. Last, move the 0.1-g rider along its beam until the pointer at the end of the beam aligns at zero. The mass of the object is the sum of all rider positions on the three beams.

When measuring the mass of a liquid or powder in a container, the container's mass must be subtracted from the total mass. Often it is possible to measure the mass of the container and then set the scale reading to zero. This process is called taring. To tare a centigram balance, place the empty container on the pan. Then use the adjusting screw (or a tare beam if there is one) to zero the scale. After this is done, the readout will accurately reflect the mass of any material added to the container.

Electronic balances are found in many chemistry laboratories. Keep in mind that although the digital readout of these balances may seem very accurate, the accuracy of the results will depend on technique. In order to tare an electronic balance, there is usually a knob to set to "T" or "tare." Place an empty container on the pan and then push the tare button so that the scale reads zero. Then reset the scale for "measurement," and the readout will accurately reflect the mass of any material in the container.

✓ CHECK FOR UNDERSTANDING Why are there three beams on a centigram balance?

Lab Techniques

Good laboratory techniques can be developed with practice. Three important lab techniques used in the chemistry lab are filtering, using a Bunsen burner, and separating mixtures with chromatography.

Filtering

Filtration involves the use of a porous barrier to separate a solid from a liquid. Suppose you want to separate a mixture, such as sand, in water. You would place the sand and water mixture into a 250-mL beaker. Then set up a clean 250-mL beaker under a ring stand, and place a funnel into the ring so that its stem is halfway into the beaker. Using a stirring rod to prevent splashing, pour the liquid from the beaker into a second beaker through the funnel, as shown in Figure 4.

After the filter drains, you can use a water bottle to rinse the beaker and wash any remaining solid from the beaker into the filter cone. Allow the filter cone to drain, and then place it on a watch glass to record your observations.

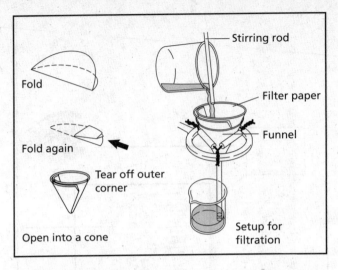

Figure 4 The proper filtration apparatus is arranged using a 250-ml beaker, a ring stand, a funnel, and a filter paper.

Using a Bunsen Burner

Always wear safety goggles and a lab apron when working with a Bunsen burner or any open flame. Assume that all glassware is hot and handle glassware with gloves. Boiling water can burn skin.

In the laboratory, you might need to use a Bunsen burner. For example, you might want to test how long it takes to boil a beaker of water. You would hold several variables constant, such

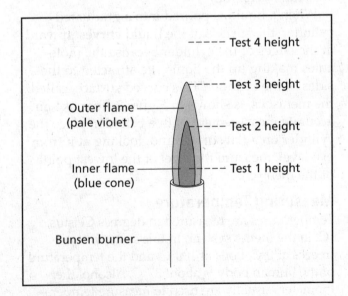

Figure 5 When using a Bunsen burner, heat substances using the blue inner flame, which is the hottest part of the flame.

Table 1 • Indicators		
Indicator	In a solution, indicates	Reaction
Litmus paper	Acid or base	Red litmus turns blue if a base; blue litmus turns red if an acid.
pH paper	pH	Color change compared to a color chart to estimate the pH
Bromthymol blue	Presence of carbon dioxide	Turns yellow if carbon dioxide is present; changes back to blue from yellow when carbon dioxide is removed
Phenolphthalein solution	Presence of carbon dioxide or a basic solution	Turns from clear to a pink in the presence of either substance
Benedict's solution	Presence of simple sugars when heated	High sugar concentration, changes from blue to red; low sugar concentration, changes from blue to yellow
Biuret solution	Presence of protein	Turns from light blue to purple
Lugol's solution	Presence of starch	Turns from deep brown to blue-black

as the height of the platform holding the beaker, the volume of H_2O, and the intensity of the flame. With careful experimentation, you could discover that the same quantity of room-temperature water will always require the same amount of energy to boil.

To heat water in a beaker, place wire gauze on a ring stand to serve as a platform for the beaker. To light a Bunsen burner safely, you will use a striker to make a spark. Test the striker beforehand to make sure that it is working. Then connect the Bunsen burner to the gas inlet. Light the burner by turning on the gas flow first, then use the striker to make a spark at the bottom side of the burner nozzle. When the flame is lit, adjust the gas flow and the oxygen so that you see a blue flame with an inner light-blue cone. Move the burner to the ring stand, making sure the wire gauze is about halfway up the inner light-blue cone. Figure 5 shows the flame of a Bunsen burner.

✓ CHECK FOR UNDERSTANDING What part of a Bunsen burner flame is used to heat substances?

Using Indicators

Indicators are used to test for the presence of specific substances or chemicals. An indicator will change color when it contacts or reacts with a specific type of substance. Table 1 lists commonly used indicators, what they test for, and how they react.

REGENTS EXAM
Strategies for Success

STEP 1 READ the Regents Question . . .
If the pH of a solution is 9, the solution is
(1) acidic, which turns phenolphthalein pink
(2) acidic, which turns phenolphthalein colorless
(3) basic, which turns phenolphthalein pink
(4) basic, which turns phenolphthalein colorless

STEP 2 ANALYZE each choice . . .
(1) Phenolphthalein turns pink in the presence of a basic solution. Since acids have a pH of less than 7, this solution is not acidic.
(2) This solution would turn phenolphthalein pink because it has a pH of greater than 7.
(3) Since phenolphthalein turns pink in the presence of a basic solution, this solution would turn phenolphthalein pink because it has a pH of greater than 7.
(4) The pH of the solution indicates that the solution is basic, but the phenolphthalein would not be colorless in a basic solution.

STEP 3 CHOOSE the best answer . . .
After considering all of the choices, number 3 is the correct choice. A solution with a pH of 9 indicates that the solution is basic and phenolphthalein would turn pink.

Chromatography

A commonly used technique in the chemistry laboratory for separating mixtures of molecules is chromatography. Dyes in inks, for example, can be separated by chromatography. In chromatography, the substance to be separated is placed on filter paper or special chromatography paper. A dot of the ink is placed near one end of the strip of paper. The end of the paper nearest the dot is placed in a solvent, such as alcohol. The solvent should not touch the sample to be separated, but should be just below it. The solvent then moves up the paper and picks up substances in the dot. Substances in the sample that have a strong attraction to the paper will move slowly up the paper, while substances that are not as tightly held move quickly up the paper. This results in bands of different substances on the chromatography paper.

✓ CHECK FOR UNDERSTANDING How is chromatography used to separate a mixture?

Quick Review

1 What is the purpose of performing chromatography?

2 If you were performing an experiment which involved measuring the time it takes to boil water, which factor(s) would you keep constant from trial to trial?

   (1) air pressure
   (2) temperature of flame
   (3) the container holding the water
   (4) all of the above

3 Why is a stirring rod helpful when pouring a liquid?

4 What is the purpose of filtration?

5 The SI unit of mass is the

   (1) gram   (2) kilogram
   (3) pound   (4) metric ton

6 What is the name for a movable weight used on a triple-beam balance?

7 The meniscus of a liquid in a graduated cylinder is used to

   (1) precisely measure the height of the liquid
   (2) directly measure the volume of liquid
   (3) estimate the density of the liquid
   (4) reduce evaporation of the liquid

Part A

1 You are working with a small lab group when someone spills an unknown chemical on the lab table. What is your first action?

(1) Wipe up the spill with a paper towel

(2) Continue working as if nothing has happened

(3) Notify your teacher

(4) Move to another lab station

2 In the metric system, temperature is measured in degrees

(1) Celsius

(2) centigrade

(3) centimeter

(4) celtic

3 Safety goggles should be worn in the lab

(1) only when working with liquid solutions

(2) only when a chemical reaction is expected

(3) only when your teacher tells you to

(4) at all times

4 A laboratory procedure calls for heating 10 milliliters of a saltwater solution to 37° Celsius. Which piece of laboratory equipment will not be needed?

(1) protective eyewear

(2) metric ruler

(3) bulb thermometer

(4) graduated cylinder

5 Which of the following solutions would you use to test for the presence of simple sugars in a substance?

(1) phenolphthalein solution

(2) Benedict's solution

(3) Biuret solution

(4) Lugol's solution

6 The picture shows a student reading a graduated cylinder. Which change would help ensure that a more accurate measurement is made?

(1) The student should be seated.

(2) The cylinder should be held with two hands.

(3) The student should be wearing insulated gloves.

(4) The cylinder should be on a flat surface.

7 A scientist is testing milk for the presence of bacteria. Exactly 25 milliliters of a test solution must be added to each milk sample. Which of these instruments would most accurately measure the volume of the test solution?

(1) a beaker

(2) a test tube

(3) a measuring cup

(4) a graduated cylinder

Part B–1

8 The diagram below represents the measurements of two leaves. The difference in length between leaves A and B is closest to

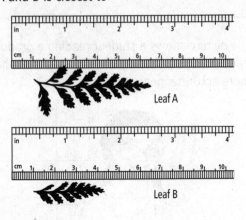

Leaf A

Leaf B

(1) 20. mm   (2) 20. cm

(3) 0.65 m   (4) 1.6 μm

9 The diagram below represents a section of a buret containing acid used in an acid-base titration. What is the total volume of acid that was used?

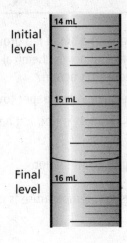

Initial level

14 mL

15 mL

Final level

16 mL

(1) 1.10 mL   (2) 1.30 mL

(3) 1.40 mL   (4) 1.45 mL

Part B–2

10 Which piece of glassware is used for measuring volumes of an acid or a base with the greatest precision and accuracy?

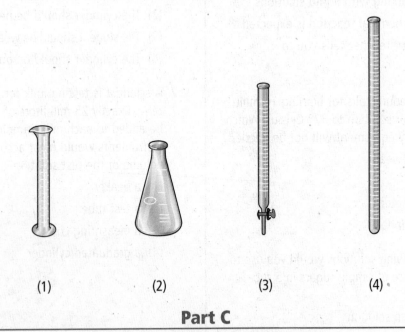

(1)   (2)   (3)   (4)

Part C

11 You are testing a hypothesis regarding how you think temperature will affect the rate at which the enzyme peroxidase breaks down hydrogen peroxide. Consider what materials you will need. Use the following safety symbols to help determine the safety precautions you should take during your experiment. List those precautions.

Part A

Answer all questions in this part.

Directions (1–33): For *each* statement or question, write on the separate answer sheet the *number* of the word or expression that, of those given, best completes the statement or answers the question. Some questions may require the use of the *Reference Tables for Physical Setting/Chemistry*.

1 Which of these phrases best describes an atom?

  (1) a positive nucleus surrounded by a hard negative shell

  (2) a positive nucleus surrounded by a cloud of negative charges

  (3) a hard sphere with positive particles uniformly embedded

  (4) a hard sphere with negative particles uniformly embedded

2 Which statement is true about a proton and an electron?

  (1) They have the same masses and the same charges.

  (2) They have the same masses and different charges.

  (3) They have different masses and the same charges.

  (4) They have different masses and different charges.

3 The atomic mass of an element is the weighted average of the masses of

  (1) its two most abundant isotopes

  (2) its two least abundant isotopes

  (3) all of its naturally occurring isotopes

  (4) all of its radioactive isotopes

4 What determines the order of placement of the elements on the modern Periodic Table?

  (1) atomic number

  (2) atomic mass

  (3) the number of neutrons, only

  (4) the number of neutrons and protons

5 Which compound contains only covalent bonds?

  (1) $NaOH$ (3) $Ca(OH)_2$

  (2) $Ba(OH)_2$ (4) CH_3OH

6 At 298 K, oxygen (O_2) and ozone (O_3) have different properties because their

  (1) atoms have different atomic numbers

  (2) atoms have different atomic masses

  (3) molecules have different molecular structures

  (4) molecules have different average kinetic energies

7 Which substance represents a compound?

  (1) $C(s)$ (3) $CO(g)$

  (2) $Co(s)$ (4) $O_2(g)$

8 All chemical reactions have a conservation of

  (1) mass, only

  (2) mass and charge, only

  (3) charge and energy, only

  (4) mass, charge, and energy

9 Which characteristic is a property of molecular substances?

  (1) good heat conductivity

  (2) good electrical conductivity

  (3) low melting point

  (4) high melting point

10 Given the Lewis electron-dot diagram:

$$\begin{array}{c} H \\ \cdot\cdot \\ H : C : H \\ \cdot\cdot \\ H \end{array}$$

Which electrons are represented by all of the dots?

  (1) the carbon valence electrons, only

  (2) the hydrogen valence electrons, only

  (3) the carbon and hydrogen valence electrons

  (4) all of the carbon and hydrogen electrons

11 Which grouping of the three phases of bromine is listed in order from left to right for increasing distance between bromine molecules?

(1) gas, liquid, solid
(2) liquid, solid, gas
(3) solid, gas, liquid
(4) solid, liquid, gas

12 Which statement concerning elements is true?

(1) Different elements must have different numbers of isotopes.
(2) Different elements must have different numbers of neutrons.
(3) All atoms of a given element must have the same mass number.
(4) All atoms of a given element must have the same atomic number.

13 At room temperature, the solubility of which solute in water would be most affected by a change in pressure?

(1) methanol
(2) sugar
(3) carbon dioxide
(4) sodium nitrate

14 Based on Reference Table I, which change occurs when pellets of solid NaOH are added to water and stirred?

(1) The water temperature increases as chemical energy is converted to heat energy.
(2) The water temperature increases as heat energy is stored as chemical energy.
(3) The water temperature decreases as chemical energy is converted to heat energy.
(4) The water temperature decreases as heat energy is stored as chemical energy.

15 The concept of an ideal gas is used to explain

(1) the mass of a gas sample
(2) the behavior of a gas sample
(3) why some gases are monatomic
(4) why some gases are diatomic

16 Molecules in a sample of $NH_3(\ell)$ are held closely together by intermolecular forces

(1) existing between ions
(2) existing between electrons
(3) caused by different numbers of neutrons
(4) caused by unequal charge distribution

17 Which process represents a chemical change?

(1) melting of ice
(2) corrosion of copper
(3) evaporation of water
(4) crystallization of sugar

18 At STP, which 4.0-gram zinc sample will react fastest with dilute hydrochloric acid?

(1) lump
(2) bar
(3) powdered
(4) sheet metal

19 Which information about a chemical reaction is provided by a potential energy diagram?

(1) the oxidation states of the reactants and products
(2) the average kinetic energy of the reactants and products
(3) the change in solubility of the reacting substances
(4) the energy released or absorbed during the reaction

20 A catalyst works by

(1) increasing the potential energy of the reactants
(2) increasing the energy released during a reaction
(3) decreasing the potential energy of the products
(4) decreasing the activation energy required for a reaction

21 Even though the process is endothermic, snow can sublime. Which tendency in nature accounts for this phase change?

(1) a tendency toward greater entropy
(2) a tendency toward greater energy
(3) a tendency toward less entropy
(4) a tendency toward less energy

22 What is the IUPAC name of the compound with the structural formula shown below?

(1) 2-pentene
(2) 3-pentene
(3) 2-pentyne
(4) 3-pentyne

23 Molecules of 1-bromopropane and 2-bromo-propane differ in

(1) molecular formula
(2) structural formula
(3) number of carbon atoms per molecule
(4) number of bromine atoms per molecule

24 Which half-reaction correctly represents reduction?

(1) $Ag \rightarrow Ag^+ + e^-$
(2) $F_2 \rightarrow 2\ F^- + 2e^-$
(3) $Au^{3+} + 3e^- \rightarrow Au$
(4) $Fe^{2+} + e^- \rightarrow Fe^{3+}$

25 In a redox reaction, how does the total number of electrons lost by the oxidized substance compare to the total number of electrons gained by the reduced substance?

(1) The number lost is always greater than the number gained.
(2) The number lost is always equal to the number gained.
(3) The number lost is sometimes equal to the number gained.
(4) The number lost is sometimes less than the number gained.

26 Which reaction is an example of an oxidation-reduction reaction?

(1) $AgNO_3 + KI \rightarrow AgI + KNO_3$
(2) $Cu + 2\ AgNO_3 \rightarrow Cu(NO_3)_2 + 2\ Ag$
(3) $2\ KOH + H_2SO_4 \rightarrow K_2SO_4 + 2\ H_2O$
(4) $Ba(OH)_2 + 2\ HCl \rightarrow BaCl_2 + 2\ H_2O$

27 Which compound is an Arrhenius base?

(1) CH_3OH
(2) CO_2
(3) $LiOH$
(4) NO_2

28 The only positive ion found in an aqueous solution of sulfuric acid is the

(1) hydroxide ion
(2) hydronium ion
(3) sulfite ion
(4) sulfate ion

29 Which process uses a volume of solution of known concentration to determine the concentration of another solution?

(1) distillation
(2) substitution
(3) transmutation
(4) titration

30 Which pH change represents a hundredfold increase in the concentration of H_3O^+?

(1) pH 5 to pH 7
(2) pH 13 to pH 14
(3) pH 3 to pH 1
(4) pH 4 to pH 3

31 Which radioisotope undergoes beta decay and has a half-life of less than 1 minute?

(1) Fr-220
(2) K-42
(3) N-16
(4) P-32

32 Which set of symbols represents atoms with valence electrons in the same electron shell?

(1) Ba, Br, Bi
(2) Sr, Sn, I
(3) O, S, Te
(4) Mn, Hg, Cu

Note that question 33 has only three choices.

33 When compared with the energy of an electron in the first shell of a carbon atom, the energy of an electron in the second shell of a carbon atom is

(1) less
(2) greater
(3) the same

Part B–1

Answer all questions in this part.

Directions (34–50): For *each* statement or question, write on the separate answer sheet the *number* of the word or expression that, of those given, best completes the statement or answers the question. Some questions may require the use of the *Reference Tables for Physical Setting/Chemistry*.

34 What is the total number of electrons found in an atom of sulfur?

(1) 6   (3) 16
(2) 8   (4) 32

35 Which electron configuration represents the electrons of an atom in an excited state?

(1) 2–8–1   (3) 2–8–17–6
(2) 2–8–6   (4) 2–8–18–5

36 The nucleus of an atom of cobalt-58 contains

(1) 27 protons and 31 neutrons
(2) 27 protons and 32 neutrons
(3) 59 protons and 60 neutrons
(4) 60 protons and 60 neutrons

37 Which pair of formulas correctly represents a molecular formula and its corresponding empirical formula?

(1) C_2H_2 and CH (3) C_4H_6 and CH
(2) C_3H_4 and CH_2 (4) C_5H_8 and C_2H_2

38 Which substance is correctly paired with its type of bonding?

(1) NaBr—nonpolar covalent
(2) HCl—nonpolar covalent
(3) NH_3—polar covalent
(4) Br_2—polar covalent

39 A gas occupies a volume of 444 mL at 273 K and 79.0 kPa. What is the final kelvin temperature when the volume of the gas is changed to 1880 mL and the pressure is changed to 38.7 kPa?

(1) 31.5 K   (3) 566 K
(2) 292 K   (4) 2360 K

40 At STP, which of these substances is most soluble in H_2O?

(1) CCl_4 (3) HCl
(2) CO_2 (4) N_2

41 Based on intermolecular forces, which of these substances would have the highest boiling point?

(1) He   (3) CH_4
(2) O_2 (4) NH_3

42 How much heat energy must be absorbed to completely melt 35.0 grams of $H_2O(s)$ at 0°C?

(1) 9.54 J   (3) 11 700 J
(2) 146 J   (4) 79 100 J

43 The graph below represents the uniform heating of a substance, starting below its melting point, when the substance is solid.

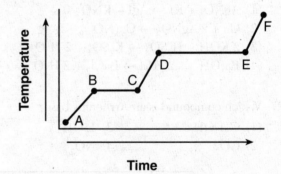

Which line segments represent an increase in average kinetic energy?

(1) $\overline{AB}$ and $\overline{BC}$ (3) $\overline{BC}$ and $\overline{DE}$
(2) $\overline{AB}$ and $\overline{CD}$ (4) $\overline{DE}$ and $\overline{EF}$

44 Given the three organic structural formulas shown below:

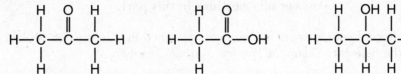

Which organic-compound classes are represented by these structural formulas, as shown from left to right?

(1) ester, organic acid, ketone
(2) ester, aldehyde, organic acid
(3) ketone, aldehyde, alcohol
(4) ketone, organic acid, alcohol

45 Given the reaction at equilibrium:

$$N_2(g) + O_2(g) + energy \rightleftharpoons 2\ NO(g)$$

Which change will result in a *decrease* in the amount of NO(g) formed?

(1) decreasing the pressure
(2) decreasing the concentration of $N_2(g)$
(3) increasing the concentration of $O_2(g)$
(4) increasing the temperature

46 Given the equation:

$$X + Cl_2 \rightarrow C_2H_5Cl + HCl$$

Which molecule is represented by X?

(1) C_2H_4 (3) C_3H_6
(2) C_2H_6 (4) C_3H_8

47 Which metal reacts spontaneously with a solution containing zinc ions?

(1) magnesium   (3) copper
(2) nickel   (4) silver

48 Which statement correctly describes a solution with a pH of 9?

(1) It has a higher concentration of H_3O^+ than OH^- and causes litmus to turn blue.
(2) It has a higher concentration of OH^- than H_3O^+ and causes litmus to turn blue.
(3) It has a higher concentration of H_3O^+ than OH^- and causes methyl orange to turn yellow.
(4) It has a higher concentration of OH^- than H_3O^+ and causes methyl orange to turn red.

49 How many days are required for 200. grams of radon-222 to decay to 50.0 grams?

(1) 1.91 days   (3) 7.64 days
(2) 3.82 days   (4) 11.5 days

50 A student calculates the density of an unknown solid. The mass is 10.04 grams, and the volume is 8.21 cubic centimeters. How many significant figures should appear in the final answer?

(1) 1   (3) 3
(2) 2   (4) 4

Part B–2

Answer all questions in this part.

Directions (51–65): Record your answers in the spaces provided in your answer booklet. Some questions may require the use of the *Reference Tables for Physical Setting/Chemistry.*

51 In the 19th century, Dmitri Mendeleev predicted the existence of a then unknown element X with a mass of 68. He also predicted that an oxide of X would have the formula X_2O_3. On the modern Periodic Table, what is the group number and period number of element X? [1]

52 Given the equation: $2 H_2(g) + O_2(g) \rightarrow 2 H_2O(g)$

If 8.0 moles of O_2 are completely consumed, what is the total number of moles of H_2O produced? [1]

53 In the space provided *in your answer booklet,* show a correct numerical setup for determining how many liters of a 1.2 M solution can be prepared with 0.50 mole of $C_6H_{12}O_6$. [1]

Base your answers to questions 54 through 57 on the particle diagrams below. Samples *A*, *B*, and *C* contain molecules at STP.

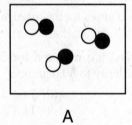
A

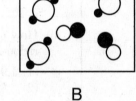
B

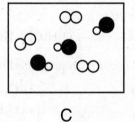
C

54 Explain why the average kinetic energy of sample *B* is equal to the average kinetic energy of sample *C*. [1]

55 Explain, in terms of the *composition*, why sample *A* represents a pure substance. [1]

56 Explain why sample *C* could represent a mixture of fluorine and hydrogen chloride. [1]

57 Contrast sample *A* and sample *B*, in terms of *compounds and mixtures*. Include both sample *A* and sample *B* in your answer. [1]

Base your answers to questions 58 through 60 on the electronegativity values and atomic numbers of fluorine, chlorine, bromine, and iodine that are listed on Reference Table S.

58 On the grid provided *in your answer booklet*, mark an appropriate scale on the axis labeled "Electronegativity." An appropriate scale is one that allows a trend to be seen.   [1]

59 On the same grid, plot the electronegativity and atomic number data from Reference Table S. Circle and connect the points.   [1]

Example: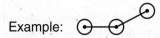

60 Explain, in terms of *electronegativity*, why the H–F bond is expected to be more polar than the H–I bond.   [1]

_____

61 What is the gram-formula mass of $(NH_4)_2CO_3$? Use atomic masses rounded to the *nearest whole number*.   [1]

62 In the space provided *in your answer booklet*, show a correct numerical setup for calculating the number of moles of CO_2 (gram-formula mass = 44 g/mol) present in 11 grams of CO_2.   [1]

Base your answers to questions 63 and 64 on the information below.

Given the equilibrium equation at 298 K:

$$KNO_3(s) + 34.89 \text{ kJ} \overset{H_2O}{\rightleftharpoons} K^+(aq) + NO_3^-(aq)$$

63 Describe, in terms of *LeChatelier's principle*, why an increase in temperature increases the solubility of KNO_3.   [1]

64 The equation indicates that KNO_3 has formed a saturated solution. Explain, in terms of *equilibrium*, why the solution is saturated.   [1]

_____

65 In the space provided *in your answer booklet*, draw the structural formula for butanoic acid.   [1]

_____

Part C

Answer all questions in this part.

Directions (66–85): Record your answers in the spaces provided in your answer booklet. Some questions may require the use of the *Reference Tables for Physical Setting/Chemistry*.

Base your answers to questions 66 through 69 on the information below, which describes the smelting of iron ore, and on your knowledge of chemistry.

In the smelting of iron ore, Fe_2O_3 is reduced in a blast furnace at high temperature by a reaction with carbon monoxide. Crushed limestone, $CaCO_3$, is also added to the mixture to remove impurities in the ore. The carbon monoxide is formed by the oxidation of carbon (coke), as shown in the reaction below:

$$2 C + O_2 \rightarrow 2 CO + energy$$

Liquid iron flows from the bottom of the blast furnace and is processed into different alloys of iron.

66 Balance the equation for the reaction of Fe_2O_3 and CO *in your answer booklet*, using the smallest whole-number coefficients. [1]

67 Using the set of axes provided *in your answer booklet*, sketch a potential energy diagram for the reaction of carbon and oxygen that produces carbon monoxide. [1]

68 What is the oxidation number of carbon in $CaCO_3$? [1]

69 Convert the melting point of iron metal to degrees Celsius. [1]

Base your answers to questions 70 through 72 on the information below.

Potassium ions are essential to human health. The movement of dissolved potassium ions, $K^+(aq)$, in and out of a nerve cell allows that cell to transmit an electrical impulse.

70 What is the total number of electrons in a potassium ion? [1]

71 Explain, in terms of *atomic structure*, why a potassium ion is smaller than a potassium atom. [1]

72 What property of potassium ions allows them to transmit an electrical impulse? [1]

Base your answers to questions 73 through 75 on the information below.

Ethene (common name ethylene) is a commercially important organic compound. Millions of tons of ethene are produced by the chemical industry each year. Ethene is used in the manufacture of synthetic fibers for carpeting and clothing, and it is widely used in making polyethylene. Low-density polyethylene can be stretched into a clear, thin film that is used for wrapping food products and consumer goods. High-density polyethylene is molded into bottles for milk and other liquids.

Ethene can also be oxidized to produce ethylene glycol, which is used in antifreeze for automobiles. The structural formula for ethylene glycol is:

$$
\begin{array}{ccc}
& H & H \\
& | & | \\
H - & C - & C - H \\
& | & | \\
& OH & OH
\end{array}
$$

At standard atmospheric pressure, the boiling point of ethylene glycol is 198°C, compared to ethene that boils at –104°C.

73 Identify the type of organic reaction by which ethene (ethylene) is made into polyethylene. [1]

74 According to the information in the reading passage, state *two* consumer products manufactured from ethene. [1]

75 Explain, in terms of *bonding*, why ethene is an unsaturated hydrocarbon. [1]

Base your answers to questions 76 through 78 on the diagram below, which represents a voltaic cell at 298 K and 1 atm.

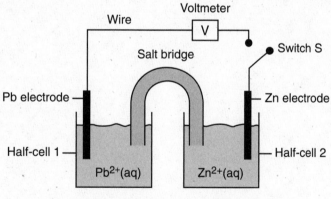

$$Pb^{2+}(aq) + Zn \rightarrow Pb + Zn^{2+}(aq)$$

76 In which half-cell will oxidation occur when switch S is closed? [1]

77 Write the balanced half-reaction equation that will occur in half-cell 1 when switch S is closed. [1]

78 Describe the direction of electron flow between the electrodes when switch S is closed. [1]

Base your answers to questions 79 through 81 on the information and data table below.

Indigestion may be caused by excess stomach acid (hydrochloric acid). Some products used to treat indigestion contain magnesium hydroxide. The magnesium hydroxide neutralizes some of the stomach acid.

The amount of acid that can be neutralized by three different brands of antacids is shown in the data table below.

Antacid Brand	Mass of Antacid Tablet (g)	Volume of HCl(aq) Neutralized (mL)
X	2.00	25.20
Y	1.20	18.65
Z	1.75	22.50

79 Based on Reference Table F, describe the solubility of magnesium hydroxide in water.   [1]

80 In the space provided *in your answer booklet*, show a correct numerical setup for calculating the milliliters of HCl(aq) neutralized per gram of antacid tablet for *each* brand of antacid.   [1]

81 Which antacid brand neutralizes the most acid per gram of antacid tablet?   [1]

Base your answers to questions 82 through 85 on the reading passage below and on your knowledge of chemistry.

A Glow in the Dark, and Scientific Peril

The [Marie and Pierre] Curies set out to study radioactivity in 1898. Their first accomplishment was to show that radioactivity was a property of atoms themselves. Scientifically, that was the most important of their findings, because it helped other researchers refine their understanding of atomic structure.

More famous was their discovery of polonium and radium. Radium was the most radioactive substance the Curies had encountered. Its radioactivity is due to the large size of the atom, which makes the nucleus unstable and prone to decay, usually to radon and then lead, by emitting particles and energy as it seeks a more stable configuration.

Marie Curie struggled to purify radium for medical uses, including early radiation treatment for tumors. But radium's bluish glow caught people's fancy, and companies in the United States began mining it and selling it as a novelty: for glow-in-the-dark light pulls, for instance, and bogus cure-all patent medicines that actually killed people.

What makes radium so dangerous is that it forms chemical bonds in the same way as calcium, and the body can mistake it for calcium and absorb it into the bones. Then, it can bombard cells with radiation at close range, which may cause bone tumors or bone-marrow damage that can give rise to anemia or leukemia.

— Denise Grady, *The New York Times*, October 6, 1998

82 State one risk associated with the use of radium. [1]

83 Using Reference Table *N*, complete the equation provided *in your answer booklet* for the nuclear decay of $^{226}_{88}Ra$. Include *both* atomic number and mass number for *each* particle. [1]

84 Using information from the Periodic Table, explain why radium forms chemical bonds in the same way as calcium does. [1]

85 If a scientist purifies 1.0 gram of radium-226, how many years must pass before only 0.50 gram of the original radium-226 sample remains unchanged? [1]

Part A

Answer all questions in this part.

Directions (1–30): For *each* statement or question, write on the separate answer sheet the *number* of the word or expression that, of those given, best completes the statement or answers the question. Some questions may require the use of the *Reference Tables for Physical Setting/Chemistry*.

1 As an electron in an atom moves from the ground state to the excited state, the electron

(1) gains energy as it moves to a higher energy level
(2) gains energy as it moves to a lower energy level
(3) loses energy as it moves to a higher energy level
(4) loses energy as it moves to a lower energy level

2 Which subatomic particle will be attracted by a positively charged object?

(1) proton   (3) electron
(2) neutron   (4) positron

3 Which conclusion is based on the "gold foil experiment" and the resulting model of the atom?

(1) An atom is mainly empty space, and the nucleus has a positive charge.
(2) An atom is mainly empty space, and the nucleus has a negative charge.
(3) An atom has hardly any empty space, and the nucleus has a positive charge.
(4) An atom has hardly any empty space, and the nucleus has a negative charge.

4 Which two particles have approximately the same mass?

(1) proton and neutron
(2) proton and electron
(3) neutron and electron
(4) neutron and positron

5 Which element has chemical properties that are most similar to the chemical properties of sodium?

(1) Mg   (3) Se
(2) K   (4) Cl

6 Germanium is classified as a

(1) metal   (3) nonmetal
(2) metalloid   (4) noble gas

7 Which statement correctly describes diamond and graphite, which are different forms of solid carbon?

(1) They differ in their molecular structure, only.
(2) They differ in their properties, only.
(3) They differ in their molecular structure and properties.
(4) They do not differ in their molecular structure or properties.

8 What is the chemical formula for copper(II) hydroxide?

(1) $CuOH$ (3) $Cu_2(OH)$
(2) $CuOH_2$ (4) $Cu(OH)_2$

9 What is the percent composition by mass of aluminum in $Al_2(SO_4)_3$ (gram-formula mass = 342 grams/mole)?

(1) 7.89%   (3) 20.8%
(2) 15.8%   (4) 36.0%

10 Which statement describes a chemical property that can be used to distinguish between compound *A* and compound *B*?

(1) *A* is a blue solid, and *B* is a white solid.
(2) *A* has a high melting point, and *B* has a low melting point.
(3) *A* dissolves in water, and *B* does not dissolve in water.
(4) *A* does not burn in air, and *B* does burn in air.

11 Which compound contains both ionic and covalent bonds?

(1) $CaCO_3$

(3) MgF_2

(2) PCl_3

(4) CH_2O

12 Which formula represents a nonpolar molecule?

(1) HCl

(3) NH_3

(2) H_2O

(4) CF_4

13 When a lithium atom forms an Li^+ ion, the lithium atom

(1) gains a proton
(2) gains an electron
(3) loses a proton
(4) loses an electron

14 Which Lewis electron-dot diagram represents a boron atom in the ground state?

(1) $\cdot$B

(3) $:$B$\cdot$

(2) $:$B

(4) $:$B$\cdot$

15 A sample is prepared by completely dissolving 10.0 grams of NaCl in 1.0 liter of H_2O. Which classification best describes this sample?

(1) homogeneous compound
(2) homogeneous mixture
(3) heterogeneous compound
(4) heterogeneous mixture

16 Which form of energy is converted to thermal energy when propane burns in air?

(1) electromagnetic
(3) electrical
(2) nuclear
(4) chemical

17 Which physical changes are endothermic?

(1) melting and freezing
(2) melting and evaporating
(3) condensation and sublimation
(4) condensation and deposition

18 Which transfer of energy occurs when ice cubes are placed in water that has a temperature of 45°C?

(1) Chemical energy is transferred from the ice to the water.
(2) Chemical energy is transferred from the water to the ice.
(3) Thermal energy is transferred from the ice to the water.
(4) Thermal energy is transferred from the water to the ice.

19 At STP, 4 liters of O_2 contains the same total number of molecules as

(1) 1 L of NH_3

(3) 8 L of He

(2) 2 L of Cl_2

(4) 4 L of CO_2

20 What is the total number of electron pairs that are shared between the two carbon atoms in a molecule of ethyne?

(1) 1

(3) 3

(2) 2

(4) 4

21 Which pair of compounds are isomers?

(1) NO_2 and N_2O_4
(2) P_2O_5 and P_4O_{10}
(3) HCOOH and CH_3COOH
(4) CH_3OCH_3 and C_2H_5OH

22 Which organic compound is unsaturated?

(1) 2-methylbutane
(3) 2-hexanol
(2) 2-chloropropane
(4) 2-pentene

23 Which change in oxidation number indicates oxidation?

(1) –1 to +2
(3) +2 to –3
(2) –1 to –2
(4) +3 to +2

24 Given the redox reaction:

$$Cr^{3+} + Al \rightarrow Cr + Al^{3+}$$

As the reaction takes place, there is a transfer of

(1) electrons from Al to Cr^{3+}
(2) electrons from Cr^{3+} to Al
(3) protons from Al to Cr^{3+}
(4) protons from Cr^{3+} to Al

25 The compound HNO_3 can be described as an

(1) Arrhenius acid and an electrolyte
(2) Arrhenius acid and a nonelectrolyte
(3) Arrhenius base and an electrolyte
(4) Arrhenius base and a nonelectrolyte

26 According to Reference Table M, what is the color of the indicator methyl orange in a solution that has a pH of 2?

(1) blue   (3) orange
(2) yellow   (4) red

27 Given the reaction:

$$NH_3 + HCl \rightarrow NH_4Cl$$

In this reaction, ammonia molecules (NH_3) act as a base because they

(1) accept hydrogen ions (H^+)
(2) accept hydroxide ions (OH^-)
(3) donate hydrogen ions (H^+)
(4) donate hydroxide ions (OH^-)

28 Which reaction is an example of natural transmutation?

(1) $^{239}_{94}Pu \rightarrow ^{235}_{92}U + ^{4}_{2}He$
(2) $^{27}_{13}Al + ^{4}_{2}He \rightarrow ^{30}_{15}P + ^{1}_{0}n$
(3) $^{238}_{92}U + ^{1}_{0}n \rightarrow ^{239}_{94}Pu + 2^{0}_{-1}e$
(4) $^{239}_{94}Pu + ^{1}_{0}n \rightarrow ^{147}_{56}Ba + ^{90}_{38}Sr + 3^{1}_{0}n$

29 Which statement best describes gamma radiation?

(1) It has a mass of 1 and a charge of 1.
(2) It has a mass of 0 and a charge of –1.
(3) It has a mass of 0 and a charge of 0.
(4) It has a mass of 4 and a charge of +2.

30 Which change takes place in a nuclear fusion reaction?

(1) Matter is converted to energy.
(2) Energy is converted to matter.
(3) Ionic bonds are converted to covalent bonds.
(4) Covalent bonds are converted to ionic bonds.

Part B-1

Answer all questions in this part.

Directions (31–50): For *each* statement or question, write on the separate answer sheet the *number* of the word or expression that, of those given, best completes the statement or answers the question. Some questions may require the use of the *Reference Tables for Physical Setting/Chemistry*.

31 What is the total number of neutrons in the nucleus of a neutral atom that has 19 electrons and a mass number of 39?

(1) 19   (3) 39
(2) 20   (4) 58

32 An unknown element X can form a compound with the formula XBr_3. In which group on the Periodic Table would element X be found?

(1) 1   (3) 13
(2) 2   (4) 14

33 As the elements in Group 17 on the Periodic Table are considered from top to bottom, what happens to the atomic radius and the metallic character of each successive element?

(1) The atomic radius and the metallic character both increase.
(2) The atomic radius increases and the metallic character decreases.
(3) The atomic radius decreases and the metallic character increases.
(4) The atomic radius and the metallic character both decrease.

34 Which pair of compounds has the same empirical formula?

(1) C_2H_2 and C_6H_6
(2) C_2H_6 and C_3H_8
(3) CH_3OH and C_2H_5OH
(4) CH_3CHO and CH_3COOH

35 Which equation shows a conservation of mass?

(1) $Na + Cl_2 \rightarrow NaCl$
(2) $Al + Br_2 \rightarrow AlBr_3$
(3) $H_2O \rightarrow H_2 + O_2$
(4) $PCl_5 \rightarrow PCl_3 + Cl_2$

36 How many electrons are in an Fe^{2+} ion?

(1) 24   (3) 28
(2) 26   (4) 56

37 A substance that does not conduct electricity as a solid but does conduct electricity when melted is most likely classified as

(1) an ionic compound
(2) a molecular compound
(3) a metal
(4) a nonmetal

38 According to Reference Table H, what is the boiling point of ethanoic acid at 80 kPa?

(1) 28°C   (3) 111°C
(2) 100°C   (4) 125°C

39 Which particle diagram represents one pure substance, only?

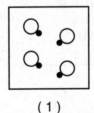

(1)   (3)

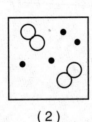

(2)   (4)

40 A sample of helium gas has a volume of 900. milliliters and a pressure of 2.50 atm at 298 K. What is the new pressure when the temperature is changed to 336 K and the volume is decreased to 450. milliliters?

(1) 0.177 atm   (3) 5.64 atm
(2) 4.43 atm   (4) 14.1 atm

41 Given the particle diagram:

At 101.3 kPa and 298 K, which element could this diagram represent?

(1) Rn   (3) Ag
(2) Xe   (4) Kr

42 For most atoms with an atomic number less than 20, nuclear stability occurs when the ratio of neutrons to protons is 1:1. Which of the following atoms would be most likely to have an unstable nucleus?

(1) $^{4}_{2}$He   (3) $^{16}_{7}$N
(2) $^{12}_{6}$C   (4) $^{24}_{12}$Mg

43 Which of these changes produces the greatest increase in entropy?

(1) $CaCO_3(s) \rightarrow CaO(s) + CO_2(g)$
(2) $2\ Mg(s) + O_2(g) \rightarrow 2\ MgO(s)$
(3) $H_2O(g) \rightarrow H_2O(\ell)$
(4) $CO_2(g) \rightarrow CO_2(s)$

44 Given the structural formula:

$$H-\overset{\overset{\displaystyle H}{|}}{\underset{\underset{\displaystyle H}{|}}{C}}-\overset{\overset{\displaystyle H}{|}}{\underset{\underset{\displaystyle N}{|}}{C}}-\overset{\displaystyle O}{C}-OH$$

This structural formula represents a molecule of

(1) an aldehyde   (3) a ketone
(2) an ester   (4) an amino acid

45 Which half-reaction can occur at the anode in a voltaic cell?

(1) $Ni^{2+} + 2e^- \rightarrow Ni$ (3) $Zn \rightarrow Zn^{2+} + 2e^-$
(2) $Sn + 2e^- \rightarrow Sn^{2+}$ (4) $Fe^{3+} \rightarrow Fe^{2+} + e^-$

46 Given the reaction:

$$Ba(OH)_2(aq) + H_2SO_4(aq) \rightarrow$$
$$BaSO_4(s) + 2\ H_2O(\ell) + energy$$

As the barium hydroxide solution is added to the solution of sulfuric acid, the electrical conductivity of the acid solution decreases because the

(1) volume of the reaction mixture increases
(2) temperature of the reaction mixture decreases
(3) concentration of ions increases
(4) concentration of ions decreases

47 Which chemical equation represents the reaction of an Arrhenius acid and an Arrhenius base?

(1) $HC_2H_3O_2(aq) + NaOH(aq) \rightarrow$
$NaC_2H_3O_2(aq) + H_2O(\ell)$
(2) $C_3H_8(g) + 5\ O_2(g) \rightarrow 3\ CO_2(g) + 4\ H_2O(\ell)$
(3) $Zn(s) + 2\ HCl(aq) \rightarrow ZnCl_2(aq) + H_2(g)$
(4) $BaCl_2(aq) + Na_2SO_4(aq) \rightarrow$
$BaSO_4(s) + 2\ NaCl(aq)$

48 Based on Reference Table F, which of these saturated solutions has the *lowest* concentration of dissolved ions?

(1) NaCl(aq)   (3) $NiCl_2$(aq)
(2) $MgCl_2$(aq)   (4) AgCl(aq)

49 Based on Reference Table N, what fraction of a radioactive ^{90}Sr sample would remain unchanged after 56.2 years?

(1) $\frac{1}{2}$ (3) $\frac{1}{8}$
(2) $\frac{1}{4}$ (4) $\frac{1}{16}$

50 Given the nuclear equation:

$$^{19}_{10}Ne \rightarrow X + ^{19}_{9}F$$

Which particle is represented by X?

(1) alpha   (3) neutron
(2) beta   (4) positron

Part B–2

Answer all questions in this part.

Directions (51–65): Record your answers in the spaces provided in your answer booklet. Some questions may require the use of the *Reference Tables for Physical Setting/Chemistry*.

Base your answers to questions 51 through 53 on your knowledge of chemical bonding and on the Lewis electron-dot diagrams of H_2S, CO_2, and F_2 below.

$$H : \overset{\displaystyle ..}{\underset{\displaystyle H}{\overset{\displaystyle ..}{S}}} : \qquad : \overset{..}{O} :: C :: \overset{..}{O} : \qquad : \overset{..}{\underset{..}{F}} : \overset{..}{\underset{..}{F}} :$$

51 Which atom, when bonded as shown, has the same electron configuration as an atom of argon? [1]

52 Explain, in terms of *structure* and/or *distribution of charge*, why CO_2 is a nonpolar molecule. [1]

53 Explain, in terms of *electronegativity*, why a C=O bond in CO_2 is more polar than the F–F bond in F_2. [1]

Base your answers to questions 54 and 55 on the heating curve below, which represents a substance starting as a solid below its melting point and being heated at a constant rate over a period of time.

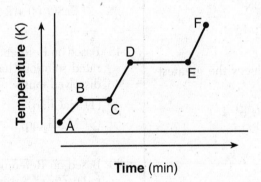

Time (min)

54 What is happening to the average kinetic energy of the particles during segment $\overline{BC}$? [1]

55 How does this heating curve illustrate that the heat of vaporization is greater than the heat of fusion? [1]

Base your answers to questions 56 through 58 on the potential energy diagram and the equation below.

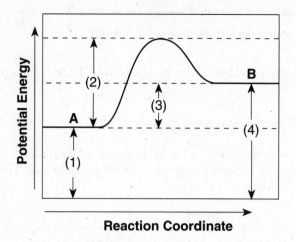

$$2\ C(s) + H_2(g) + 227.4\ kJ \rightarrow C_2H_2(g)$$

56 The letter *B* represents which chemical formula or formulas in the equation?   [1]

57 If 682.2 kilojoules are absorbed, how many moles of $C_2H_2(g)$ are produced?   [1]

58 Describe how the potential energy diagram will change if a catalyst is added.   [1]

___

Base your answers to questions 59 and 60 on the condensed structural formula below.

$$CH_3CH_2CHCH_2$$

59 In the space provided *in your answer booklet*, draw the structural formula for this compound.   [1]

60 The formula below represents a product formed when HCl reacts with $CH_3CH_2CHCH_2$.

```
      H   H   H   H
      |   |   |   |
  H — C — C — C — C — H
      |   |   |   |
      H   Cl  H   H
```

What is an IUPAC name for this product?   [1]

___

61 Given the equation:

butanoic acid + 1-pentanol $\xrightarrow{\text{catalyst}}$ water + X

To which class of organic compounds does product X belong?   [1]

62 Identify the homologous series of hydrocarbons to which CH_3CHCH_2 belongs.   [1]

Base your answers to questions 63 through 65 on the information below.

In a titration experiment, a student uses a 1.4 M HBr(aq) solution and the indicator phenolphthalein to determine the concentration of a KOH(aq) solution. The data for trial 1 is recorded in the table below.

Trial 1

Buret Readings	HBr(aq)	KOH(aq)
Initial volume (mL)	7.50	11.00
Final volume (mL)	22.90	33.10
Volume used (mL)	15.40	22.10

63 In the space provided *in your answer booklet*, show a correct numerical setup for calculating the molarity of the KOH(aq) solution for trial 1.   [1]

64 Why is it better to use several trials of a titration rather than one trial to determine the molarity of a solution of an unknown concentration?   [1]

65 In a second trial of this experiment, the molarity of KOH(aq) was determined to be 0.95 M. The actual molarity was 0.83 M. What is the percent error in the second trial?   [1]

Part C

Answer all questions in this part.

Directions (66–84): Record your answers in the spaces provided in your answer booklet. Some questions may require the use of the *Reference Tables for Physical Setting/Chemistry*.

Base your answers to questions 66 and 67 on the information below.

Naturally occurring elemental carbon is a mixture of isotopes. The percent composition of the two most abundant isotopes is listed below.

- 98.93% of the carbon atoms have a mass of 12.00 atomic mass units.
- 1.07% of the carbon atoms have a mass of 13.00 atomic mass units.

66 In the space provided *in your answer booklet*, show a correct numerical setup for calculating the average atomic mass of carbon. [1]

67 Describe, in terms of *subatomic particles found in the nucleus*, one difference between the nuclei of carbon-12 atoms and the nuclei of carbon-13 atoms. The response must include both isotopes. [1]

Base your answers to questions 68 and 69 on the information below.

A scientist in a chemistry laboratory determined the molecular formulas for two compounds containing nitrogen and oxygen to be NO_2 and N_2O_5.

68 Write an IUPAC name for the compound N_2O_5. [1]

69 In the space provided *in your answer booklet*, show a correct numerical setup for calculating the percent composition by mass of oxygen in NO_2. [1]

Base your answers to questions 70 through 72 on the information below.

In a laboratory experiment, 10.00 grams of an unknown solid is added to 100.0 milliliters of water and the temperature of the resulting solution is measured over several minutes, as recorded in the table below.

Data Table

Time (minutes)	Temperature (°C)
0	24.0
0.5	28.5
1.0	31.0
1.5	34.5
2.0	41.0
2.5	45.5
3.0	46.5

70 On the grid provided *in your answer booklet*, mark an appropriate scale on the axis labeled "Temperature (°C)." An appropriate scale is one that allows a trend to be seen. [1]

71 Plot the data from the data table. Circle and connect the points. [1]

Example:

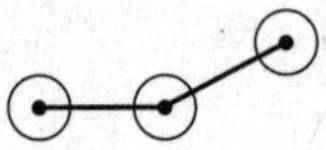

72 Given the statement:

The unknown solid is either sodium hydroxide or lithium bromide, and both of these compounds dissolve in water exothermically.

a Explain how the experimental data support the statement. [1]

b State specific information from Reference Table *I* to support the statement. [1]

Base your answers to questions 73 through 76 on the information below.

Figure 1

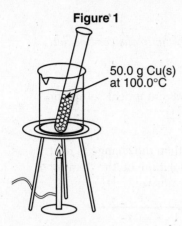

50.0 g Cu(s)
at 100.0°C

In a laboratory investigation, a 50.0-gram sample of copper is at 100.0°C in a boiling water bath.

Figure 2

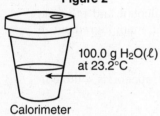

100.0 g H₂O(ℓ)
at 23.2°C

Calorimeter

A Styrofoam cup with a lid is used as a calorimeter. The cup contains 100.0 grams of distilled water at 23.2°C.

Figure 3

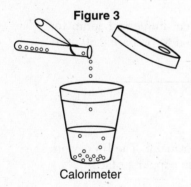

Calorimeter

The hot copper is poured into the cup of water, and the cup is quickly covered with the lid.

Figure 4

Calorimeter

A thermometer is inserted through the lid. The copper and water are gently stirred in the cup. The temperature is checked periodically. The highest temperature noted is 26.3°C.

73 In terms of *energy flow,* explain why the temperature of the water in the calorimeter increases. [1]

74 Using the information given, complete the data table provided *in your answer booklet.* [1]

75 In the space provided *in your answer booklet,* show a correct numerical setup for calculating the number of joules of heat gained by the water. [1]

76 In this investigation, the change in heat of the copper is greater than the change in heat of the water. What error could account for this apparent violation of the Law of Conservation of Energy? Do *not* use human error as part of the answer. [1]

Base your answers to questions 77 through 79 on the information below.

Two alcohols that are used in our everyday lives are rubbing alcohol and ethylene glycol. Rubbing alcohol is used as an antiseptic. Ethylene glycol is the main ingredient in antifreeze, which is used in automobile cooling systems.

77 Explain, in terms of *molecular polarity,* why rubbing alcohol, 2-propanol, is soluble in water. [1]

78 What is the gram-formula mass of ethylene glycol, $C_2H_4(OH)_2$? [1]

79 In the space provided *in your answer booklet,* show a correct numerical setup for calculating the total number of moles of ethylene glycol needed to prepare 2.50 liters of a 10.0 M solution. [1]

Base your answers to questions 80 and 81 on the information below.

The outer structure of the Statue of Liberty is made of copper metal. The framework is made of iron. Over time, a thin green layer (patina) forms on the copper surface.

80 When copper oxidized to form this patina layer, the copper atoms became copper(II) ions (Cu^{2+}). Write a balanced half-reaction for this oxidation of copper. [1]

81 Where the iron framework came in contact with the copper surface, a reaction occurred in which iron was oxidized. Using information from Reference Table *J,* explain why the iron was oxidized. [1]

Base your answers to questions 82 through 84 on the information below, the *Reference Tables for Physical Setting/Chemistry*, and your knowledge of chemistry.

Radioactivity and radioactive isotopes have the potential for both benefiting and harming living organisms. One use of radioactive isotopes is in radiation therapy as a treatment for cancer. Cesium-137 is sometimes used in radiation therapy.

A sample of cesium-137 was left in an abandoned clinic in Brazil in 1987. Cesium-137 gives off a blue glow because of its radioactivity. The people who discovered the sample were attracted by the blue glow and had no idea of any danger. Hundreds of people were treated for overexposure to radiation, and four people died.

82 Using Reference Table *N*, complete the equation provided *in your answer booklet* for the radioactive decay of $^{137}_{55}$Cs. Include *both* atomic number and mass number for *each* particle. [1]

83 If 12.5 grams of the original sample of cesium-137 remained after 90.69 years, what was the mass of the original sample? [1]

84 Suppose a 40-gram sample of iodine-131 and a 40-gram sample of cesium-137 were both abandoned in the clinic in 1987. Explain why the sample of iodine-131 would *not* pose as great a radiation risk to people today as the sample of cesium-137 would. [1]

Part A

Answer all questions in this part.

Directions (1–33): For *each* statement or question, write on the separate answer sheet the *number* of the word or expression that, of those given, best completes the statement or answers the question. Some questions may require the use of the *Reference Tables for Physical Setting/Chemistry*.

1 In the modern wave-mechanical model of the atom, the orbitals are regions of the most probable location of

(1) protons   (3) electrons
(2) neutrons   (4) positrons

2 Compared to a proton, an electron has

(1) a greater quantity of charge and the same sign
(2) a greater quantity of charge and the opposite sign
(3) the same quantity of charge and the same sign
(4) the same quantity of charge and the opposite sign

3 Which two notations represent atoms that are isotopes of the same element?

(1) $^{121}_{50}Sn$ and $^{119}_{50}Sn$ (3) $^{19}_{8}O$ and $^{19}_{9}F$
(2) $^{121}_{50}Sn$ and $^{121}_{50}Sn$ (4) $^{39}_{17}Cl$ and $^{39}_{19}K$

4 The elements in Period 5 on the Periodic Table are arranged from left to right in order of

(1) decreasing atomic mass
(2) decreasing atomic number
(3) increasing atomic mass
(4) increasing atomic number

5 Which list of elements contains a metal, a metalloid, and a nonmetal?

(1) Zn, Ga, Ge   (3) Cd, Sb, I
(2) Si, Ge, Sn   (4) F, Cl, Br

6 An example of a physical property of an element is the element's ability to

(1) react with an acid
(2) react with oxygen
(3) form a compound with chlorine
(4) form an aqueous solution

7 Which element is malleable and conducts electricity?

(1) iron   (3) sulfur
(2) iodine   (4) phosphorus

8 At STP, solid carbon can exist as graphite or as diamond. These two forms of carbon have

(1) the same properties and the same crystal structures
(2) the same properties and different crystal structures
(3) different properties and the same crystal structures
(4) different properties and different crystal structures

9 What is the formula of titanium(II) oxide?

(1) TiO   (3) Ti_2O
(2) TiO_2 (4) Ti_2O_3

10 Which substance can be decomposed by a chemical change?

(1) calcium   (3) copper
(2) potassium   (4) ammonia

11 As a chlorine atom becomes a negative ion, the atom

(1) gains an electron and its radius increases
(2) gains an electron and its radius decreases
(3) loses an electron and its radius increases
(4) loses an electron and its radius decreases

12 Based on Reference Table S, the atoms of which of these elements have the strongest attraction for electrons in a chemical bond?

(1) N   (3) P
(2) Na   (4) Pt

13 Which terms are used to identify pure substances?

(1) an element and a mixture
(2) an element and a compound
(3) a solution and a mixture
(4) a solution and a compound

14 The solubility of $KClO_3(s)$ in water increases as the

(1) temperature of the solution increases
(2) temperature of the solution decreases
(3) pressure on the solution increases
(4) pressure on the solution decreases

15 Compared to a 0.1 M aqueous solution of NaCl, a 0.8 M aqueous solution of NaCl has a

(1) higher boiling point and a higher freezing point
(2) higher boiling point and a lower freezing point
(3) lower boiling point and a higher freezing point
(4) lower boiling point and a lower freezing point

16 The kinetic molecular theory assumes that the particles of an ideal gas

(1) are in random, constant, straight-line motion
(2) are arranged in a regular geometric pattern
(3) have strong attractive forces between them
(4) have collisions that result in the system losing energy

17 In which process does a solid change directly into a vapor?

(1) condensation   (3) deposition
(2) sublimation   (4) solidification

18 Which statement must be true about a chemical system at equilibrium?

(1) The forward and reverse reactions stop.
(2) The concentration of reactants and products are equal.
(3) The rate of the forward reaction is equal to the rate of the reverse reaction.
(4) The number of moles of reactants is equal to the number of moles of product.

19 Adding a catalyst to a chemical reaction results in

(1) a decrease in activation energy and a decrease in the reaction rate
(2) a decrease in activation energy and an increase in the reaction rate
(3) an increase in activation energy and a decrease in the reaction rate
(4) an increase in activation energy and an increase in the reaction rate

20 Systems in nature tend to undergo changes toward

(1) lower energy and lower entropy
(2) lower energy and higher entropy
(3) higher energy and lower entropy
(4) higher energy and higher entropy

21 Which element has atoms that can bond with each other to form long chains or rings?

(1) carbon   (3) oxygen
(2) nitrogen   (4) fluorine

22 Which formula represents an unsaturated hydrocarbon?

(1) C_2H_6 (3) C_5H_8
(2) C_3H_8 (4) C_6H_{14}

23 Given the structural formula:

What is the IUPAC name of this compound?

(1) propane   (3) propanone
(2) propene   (4) propanal

24 What is the oxidation state of nitrogen in $NaNO_2$?

(1) +1   (3) +3
(2) +2   (4) +4

25 The three isomers of pentane have different

(1) formula masses
(2) molecular formulas
(3) empirical formulas
(4) structural formulas

26 Where does oxidation occur in an electro-chemical cell?

(1) at the cathode in both an electrolytic cell and a voltaic cell
(2) at the cathode in an electrolytic cell and at the anode in a voltaic cell
(3) at the anode in both an electrolytic cell and a voltaic cell
(4) at the anode in an electrolytic cell and at the cathode in a voltaic cell

27 Which formula represents an electrolyte?

(1) CH_3OCH_3 (3) CH_3COOH
(2) CH_3OH (4) C_2H_5CHO

28 When an Arrhenius acid dissolves in water, the only positive ion in the solution is

(1) H^+ (3) Na^+
(2) Li^+ (4) K^+

29 What is the half-life and decay mode of Rn-222?

(1) 1.91 days and alpha decay
(2) 1.91 days and beta decay
(3) 3.82 days and alpha decay
(4) 3.82 days and beta decay

30 Which equation represents a transmutation reaction?

(1) $^{239}_{92}U \rightarrow ^{239}_{92}U + ^{0}_{0}\gamma$

(2) $^{14}_{6}C \rightarrow ^{14}_{7}N + ^{0}_{-1}e$

(3) $C_3H_8 + 5O_2 \rightarrow 3CO_2 + 4H_2O$

(4) $nC_2H_4 \xrightarrow{\text{catalyst}} (-C_2H_4-)_n$

31 Which equation represents positron decay?

(1) $^{87}_{37}Rb \rightarrow ^{0}_{-1}e + ^{87}_{38}Sr$

(2) $^{227}_{92}U \rightarrow ^{223}_{90}Th + ^{4}_{2}He$

(3) $^{27}_{13}Al + ^{4}_{2}He \rightarrow ^{30}_{15}P + ^{1}_{0}n$

(4) $^{11}_{6}C \rightarrow ^{0}_{+1}e + ^{11}_{5}B$

32 Which equation represents a fusion reaction?

(1) $H_2O(g) \rightarrow H_2O(\ell)$

(2) $C(s) + O_2(g) \rightarrow CO_2(g)$

(3) $^{2}_{1}H + ^{3}_{1}H \rightarrow ^{4}_{2}He + ^{1}_{0}n$

(4) $^{235}_{92}U + ^{1}_{0}n \rightarrow ^{142}_{56}Ba + ^{91}_{36}Kr + 3^{1}_{0}n$

Note that question 33 has only three choices.

33 An electron in an atom moves from the ground state to an excited state when the energy of the electron

(1) decreases
(2) increases
(3) remains the same

Part B–1

Answer all questions in this part.

Directions (34–50): For *each* statement or question, write on the separate answer sheet the *number* of the word or expression that, of those given, best completes the statement or answers the question. Some questions may require the use of the *Reference Tables for Physical Setting/Chemistry*.

34 Which symbol represents a particle that has the same total number of electrons as S^{2-}?

(1) O^{2-}
(2) Si
(3) Se^{2-}
(4) Ar

35 The data table below shows elements Xx, Yy, and Zz from the same group on the Periodic Table.

Element	Atomic Mass (atomic mass unit)	Atomic Radius (pm)
Xx	69.7	141
Yy	114.8	?
Zz	204.4	171

What is the most likely atomic radius of element Yy?

(1) 103 pm
(2) 127 pm
(3) 166 pm
(4) 185 pm

36 Which substance has a chemical formula with the same ratio of metal ions to nonmetal ions as in potassium sulfide?

(1) sodium oxide
(2) sodium chloride
(3) magnesium oxide
(4) magnesium chloride

37 The molecular formula of glucose is $C_6H_{12}O_6$. What is the empirical formula of glucose?

(1) CHO
(2) CH_2O
(3) $C_6H_{12}O_6$
(4) $C_{12}H_{24}O_{12}$

38 According to Reference Table F, which of these compounds is the *least* soluble in water?

(1) K_2CO_3
(2) $KC_2H_3O_2$
(3) $Ca_3(PO_4)_2$
(4) $Ca(NO_3)_2$

39 A sample of a substance containing only magnesium and chlorine was tested in the laboratory and was found to be composed of 74.5% chlorine by mass. If the total mass of the sample was 190.2 grams, what was the mass of the magnesium?

(1) 24.3 g
(2) 48.5 g
(3) 70.9 g
(4) 142 g

40 Which molecule contains a nonpolar covalent bond?

$$O=C=O$$
(1)

$$C\equiv O$$
(2)

$$Br-Br$$
(3)

$$\begin{array}{c} Cl \\ | \\ Cl-C-Cl \\ | \\ Cl \end{array}$$
(4)

41 According to Reference Table G, which substance forms an unsaturated solution when 80 grams of the substance is dissolved in 100 grams of H_2O at 10°C?

(1) KI
(2) KNO_3
(3) $NaNO_3$
(4) NaCl

42 What is the concentration of a solution, in parts per million, if 0.02 gram of Na_3PO_4 is dissolved in 1000 grams of water?

(1) 20 ppm
(2) 2 ppm
(3) 0.2 ppm
(4) 0.02 ppm

43 Given the simple representations for atoms of two elements:

○ = an atom of an element
● = an atom of a different element

Which particle diagram represents molecules of only one compound in the gaseous phase?

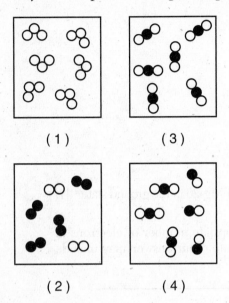

(1)   (3)

(2)   (4)

44 Given the balanced equation:

$$KNO_3(s) + 34.89 \text{ kJ} \xrightarrow{H_2O} K^+(aq) + NO_3^-(aq)$$

Which statement best describes this process?

(1) It is endothermic and entropy increases.
(2) It is endothermic and entropy decreases.
(3) It is exothermic and entropy increases.
(4) It is exothermic and entropy decreases.

45 A 1.0-gram piece of zinc reacts with 5 milliliters of HCl(aq). Which of these conditions of concentration and temperature would produce the greatest rate of reaction?

(1) 1.0 M HCl(aq) at 20.°C
(2) 1.0 M HCl(aq) at 40.°C
(3) 2.0 M HCl(aq) at 20.°C
(4) 2.0 M HCl(aq) at 40.°C

46 At STP, fluorine is a gas and iodine is a solid. This observation can be explained by the fact that fluorine has

(1) weaker intermolecular forces of attraction than iodine
(2) stronger intermolecular forces of attraction than iodine
(3) lower average kinetic energy than iodine
(4) higher average kinetic energy than iodine

47 Given the structural formula:

$$\begin{array}{ccccc} & H & H & & H & H \\ & | & | & & | & | \\ H- & C- & C- & O- & C- & C-H \\ & | & | & & | & | \\ & H & H & & H & H \end{array}$$

The compound represented by this formula can be classified as an

(1) organic acid   (3) ester
(2) ether   (4) aldehyde

48 Sulfuric acid, $H_2SO_4(aq)$, can be used to neutralize barium hydroxide, $Ba(OH)_2(aq)$. What is the formula for the salt produced by this neutralization?

(1) BaS   (3) $BaSO_3$
(2) $BaSO_2$ (4) $BaSO_4$

49 Given the balanced ionic equation:

$$Zn(s) + Cu^{2+}(aq) \rightarrow Zn^{2+}(aq) + Cu(s)$$

Which equation represents the oxidation half-reaction?

(1) $Zn(s) + 2e^- \rightarrow Zn^{2+}(aq)$
(2) $Zn(s) \rightarrow Zn^{2+}(aq) + 2e^-$
(3) $Cu^{2+}(aq) \rightarrow Cu(s) + 2e^-$
(4) $Cu^{2+}(aq) + 2e^- \rightarrow Cu(s)$

50 In which solution will thymol blue indicator appear blue?

(1) 0.1 M CH_3COOH (3) 0.1 M HCl
(2) 0.1 M KOH   (4) 0.1 M H_2SO_4

Part B–2

Answer all questions in this part.

Directions (51–64): Record your answers in the spaces provided in your answer booklet. Some questions may require the use of the *Reference Tables for Physical Setting/Chemistry*.

Base your answers to questions 51 and 52 on the diagram below, which represents an atom of magnesium-26 in the ground state.

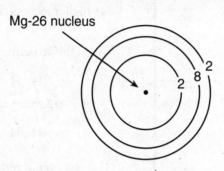

Mg-26 nucleus

51 What is the total number of valence electrons in an atom of Mg-26 in the ground state? [1]

52 On the diagram *in your answer booklet*, write an appropriate number of electrons in *each* shell to represent a Mg-26 atom in an excited state. Your answer may include additional shells. [1]

_____

53 Explain, in terms of atomic structure, why germanium is chemically similar to silicon. [1]

54 Given the balanced equation:

$$4Al(s) + 3O_2(g) \rightarrow 2Al_2O_3(s)$$

What is the total number of moles of $O_2(g)$ that must react completely with 8.0 moles of Al(s) in order to form $Al_2O_3(s)$? [1]

Base your answers to questions 55 and 56 on the balanced equation below.

$$2Na(s) + Cl_2(g) \rightarrow 2NaCl(s)$$

55 In the box *in your answer booklet,* draw a Lewis electron-dot diagram for a molecule of chlorine, Cl_2. [1]

56 Explain, in terms of electrons, why the bonding in NaCl is ionic. [1]

_____

Base your answers to questions 57 and 58 on the information below.

Given the reaction at equilibrium:

$$2NO_2(g) + 7H_2(g) \rightleftharpoons 2NH_3(g) + 4H_2O(g) + 1127 \text{ kJ}$$

57 On the diagram *in your answer booklet*, complete the potential energy diagram for the forward reaction. Be sure your drawing shows the activation energy and the potential energy of the products. [2]

58 Explain, in terms of Le Chatelier's principle, why the concentration of $NH_3(g)$ *decreases* when the temperature of the equilibrium system increases. [1]

Base your answers to questions 59 and 60 on the information below.

Given the reaction between 1-butene and chlorine gas:

$$C_4H_8 + Cl_2 \rightarrow C_4H_8Cl_2$$

59 Which type of chemical reaction is represented by this equation? [1]

60 In the space *in your answer booklet*, draw the structural formula of the product 1,2-dichlorobutane. [1]

Base your answers to questions 61 through 64 on the information below, which relates the numbers of neutrons and protons for specific nuclides of C, N, Ne, and S.

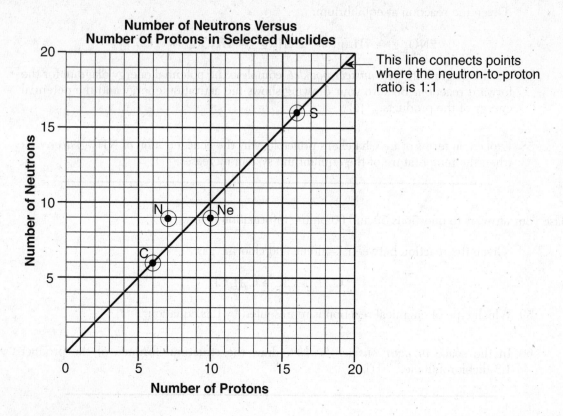

Number of Neutrons Versus Number of Protons in Selected Nuclides

This line connects points where the neutron-to-proton ratio is 1:1

61 Using the point plotted on the graph for neon, complete the table *in your answer booklet*. [1]

62 Explain, in terms of atomic particles, why S-32 is a stable nuclide. [1]

63 Using the point plotted on the graph for nitrogen, what is the neutron-to-proton ratio of this nuclide? [1]

64 Based on Reference Table *N*, complete the decay equation for N-16 *in your answer booklet*. [1]

Part C

Answer all questions in this part.

Directions (65–83): Record your answers in the spaces provided in your answer booklet. Some questions may require the use of the *Reference Tables for Physical Setting/Chemistry.*

65 In the early 1900s, experiments were conducted to determine the structure of the atom. One of these experiments involved bombarding gold foil with alpha particles. Most alpha particles passed directly through the foil. Some, however, were deflected at various angles. Based on this alpha particle experiment, state *two* conclusions that were made concerning the structure of an atom.   [2]

Base your answers to questions 66 through 70 on the information below.

A substance is a solid at 15°C. A student heated a sample of the solid substance and recorded the temperature at one-minute intervals in the data table below.

Time (min)	0	1	2	3	4	5	6	7	8	9	10	11	12
Temperature (°C)	15	32	46	53	53	53	53	53	53	53	53	60	65

66 On the grid *in your answer booklet,* mark an appropriate scale on the axis labeled "Temperature (°C)." An appropriate scale is one that allows a trend to be seen.   [1]

67 Plot the data from the data table. Circle and connect the points.   [1]

Example:

68 Based on the data table, what is the melting point of this substance?   [1]

69 What is the evidence that the average kinetic energy of the particles of this substance is increasing during the first three minutes?   [1]

70 The heat of fusion for this substance is 122 joules per gram. How many joules of heat are needed to melt 7.50 grams of this substance at its melting point?   [1]

Base your answers to questions 71 through 73 on the diagram of a voltaic cell and the balanced ionic equation below.

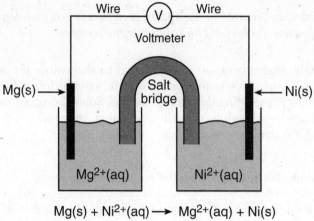

$$Mg(s) + Ni^{2+}(aq) \longrightarrow Mg^{2+}(aq) + Ni(s)$$

71 What is the total number of moles of electrons needed to completely reduce 6.0 moles of $Ni^{2+}(aq)$ ions?   [1]

72 Identify *one* metal from Reference Table *J* that is more easily oxidized than Mg(s).   [1]

73 Explain the function of the salt bridge in the voltaic cell.   [1]

___

Base your answers to questions 74 through 76 on the passage below.

Acid rain is a problem in industrialized countries around the world. Oxides of sulfur and nitrogen are formed when various fuels are burned. These oxides dissolve in atmospheric water droplets that fall to earth as acid rain or acid snow.

While normal rain has a pH between 5.0 and 6.0 due to the presence of dissolved carbon dioxide, acid rain often has a pH of 4.0 or lower. This level of acidity can damage trees and plants, leach minerals from the soil, and cause the death of aquatic animals and plants.

If the pH of the soil is too low, then quicklime, CaO, can be added to the soil to increase the pH. Quicklime produces calcium hydroxide when it dissolves in water.

74 Balance the neutralization equation *in your answer booklet,* using the smallest whole-number coefficients.   [1]

75 A sample of wet soil has a pH of 4.0. After the addition of quicklime, the H^+ ion concentration of the soil is $\frac{1}{100}$ of the original H^+ ion concentration of the soil. What is the new pH of the soil sample?   [1]

76 Samples of acid rain are brought to a laboratory for analysis. Several titrations are performed and it is determined that a 20.0-milliliter sample of acid rain is neutralized with 6.50 milliliters of 0.010 M NaOH. What is the molarity of the H^+ ions in the acid rain?   [1]

___

Base your answers to questions 77 through 79 on the information and diagrams below.

Cylinder A contains 22.0 grams of $CO_2(g)$ and cylinder B contains $N_2(g)$. The volumes, pressures, and temperatures of the two gases are indicated under each cylinder.

Cylinder A   **Cylinder B**

$CO_2(g)$ $N_2(g)$

V = 12.3 L   V = 12.3 L
P = 1.0 atm   P = 1.0 atm
T = 300. K   T = 300. K

77 What is the total number of moles of $CO_2(g)$ in cylinder A? [1]

78 Explain why the number of molecules of $N_2(g)$ in cylinder B is the same as the number of molecules of $CO_2(g)$ in cylinder A. [1]

79 The temperature of the $CO_2(g)$ is increased to 450. K and the volume of cylinder A remains constant. In the space *in your answer booklet*, show a correct numerical setup for calculating the new pressure of the $CO_2(g)$ in cylinder A. [1]

_____

Base your answers to questions 80 through 83 on the information and diagram below and on your knowledge of chemistry.

Crude oil is a mixture of many hydrocarbons that have different numbers of carbon atoms. The use of a fractionating tower allows the separation of this mixture based on the boiling points of the hydrocarbons.

To begin the separation process, the crude oil is heated to about 400°C in a furnace, causing many of the hydrocarbons of the crude oil to vaporize. The vaporized mixture is pumped into a fractionating tower that is usually more than 30 meters tall. The temperature of the tower is highest at the bottom. As vaporized samples of hydrocarbons travel up the tower, they cool and condense. The liquid hydrocarbons are collected on trays and removed from the tower. The diagram below illustrates the fractional distillation of the crude oil and the temperature ranges in which the different hydrocarbons condense.

Distillation of Crude Oil

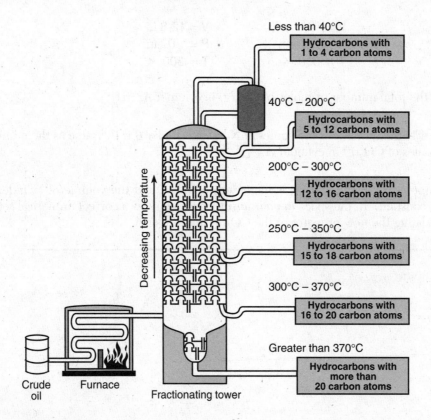

80 State the trend between the boiling point of the hydrocarbons contained in the crude oil and the number of carbon atoms in these molecules. [1]

81 Describe the relationship between the strength of the intermolecular forces and the number of carbon atoms in the different hydrocarbon molecules. [1]

82 Write an IUPAC name of *one* saturated hydrocarbon that leaves the fractionating tower at *less than* 40°C. [1]

83 How many hydrogen atoms are present in one molecule of octane? [1]

Part A

Answer all questions in this part.

Directions (1–30): For *each* statement or question, write on the separate answer sheet the *number* of the word or expression that, of those given, best completes the statement or answers the question. Some questions may require the use of the *Reference Tables for Physical Setting/Chemistry*.

1 Which subatomic particle has a negative charge?
  (1) proton   (3) neutron
  (2) electron   (4) positron

2 Which statement best describes the nucleus of an aluminum atom?
  (1) It has a charge of +13 and is surrounded by a total of 10 electrons.
  (2) It has a charge of +13 and is surrounded by a total of 13 electrons.
  (3) It has a charge of –13 and is surrounded by a total of 10 electrons.
  (4) It has a charge of –13 and is surrounded by a total of 13 electrons.

3 The atomic mass of an element is the weighted average of the
  (1) number of protons in the isotopes of that element
  (2) number of neutrons in the isotopes of that element
  (3) atomic numbers of the naturally occurring isotopes of that element
  (4) atomic masses of the naturally occurring isotopes of that element

4 In which pair do the particles have approximately the same mass?
  (1) proton and electron
  (2) proton and neutron
  (3) neutron and electron
  (4) neutron and beta particle

5 Two different samples decompose when heated. Only one of the samples is soluble in water. Based on this information, these two samples are
  (1) both the same element
  (2) two different elements
  (3) both the same compound
  (4) two different compounds

6 The elements located in the lower left corner of the Periodic Table are classified as
  (1) metals   (3) metalloids
  (2) nonmetals   (4) noble gases

7 Which of these elements has the *lowest* melting point?
  (1) Li   (3) K
  (2) Na   (4) Rb

8 Which list consists of elements that have the most similar chemical properties?
  (1) Mg, Al, and Si   (3) K, Al, and Ni
  (2) Mg, Ca, and Ba   (4) K, Ca, and Ga

9 The correct chemical formula for iron(II) sulfide is
  (1) FeS (3) $FeSO_4$
  (2) Fe_2S_3 (4) $Fe_2(SO_4)_3$

10 Which list consists of types of chemical formulas?
  (1) atoms, ions, molecules
  (2) metals, nonmetals, metalloids
  (3) empirical, molecular, structural
  (4) synthesis, decomposition, neutralization

11 Which type of bonding is found in all molecular substances?
  (1) covalent bonding   (3) ionic bonding
  (2) hydrogen bonding   (4) metallic bonding

12 An aqueous solution of sodium chloride is best classified as a
  (1) homogeneous compound
  (2) homogeneous mixture
  (3) heterogeneous compound
  (4) heterogeneous mixture

13 What is the total number of electrons shared in a double covalent bond between two atoms?

(1) 1   (3) 8
(2) 2   (4) 4

14 Which formula represents a nonpolar molecule?

(1) H_2S (3) CH_4
(2) HCl   (4) NH_3

15 What occurs when an atom loses an electron?

(1) The atom's radius decreases and the atom becomes a negative ion.
(2) The atom's radius decreases and the atom becomes a positive ion.
(3) The atom's radius increases and the atom becomes a negative ion.
(4) The atom's radius increases and the atom becomes a positive ion.

16 Two samples of gold that have different temperatures are placed in contact with one another. Heat will flow spontaneously from a sample of gold at 60°C to a sample of gold that has a temperature of

(1) 50°C   (3) 70°C
(2) 60°C   (4) 80°C

17 Under which conditions of temperature and pressure would helium behave most like an ideal gas?

(1) 50 K and 20 kPa   (3) 750 K and 20 kPa
(2) 50 K and 600 kPa   (4) 750 K and 600 kPa

18 A sample of oxygen gas is sealed in container X. A sample of hydrogen gas is sealed in container Z. Both samples have the same volume, temperature, and pressure. Which statement is true?

(1) Container X contains more gas molecules than container Z.
(2) Container X contains fewer gas molecules than container Z.
(3) Containers X and Z both contain the same number of gas molecules.
(4) Containers X and Z both contain the same mass of gas.

19 Which formula represents an unsaturated hydrocarbon?

(1)   (3)

(2)   (4)

20 Given the formula:

What is the IUPAC name of this compound?

(1) 2-pentene   (3) 2-butene
(2) 2-pentyne   (4) 2-butyne

21 Given the reaction system in a closed container at equilibrium and at a temperature of 298 K:

$$N_2O_4(g) \rightleftharpoons 2NO_2(g)$$

The measurable quantities of the gases at equilibrium must be

(1) decreasing   (3) equal
(2) increasing   (4) constant

22 Atoms of which element can bond with each other to form ring and chain structures in compounds?

(1) C   (3) H
(2) Ca   (4) Na

23 In a voltaic cell, chemical energy is converted to

(1) electrical energy, spontaneously
(2) electrical energy, nonspontaneously
(3) nuclear energy, spontaneously
(4) nuclear energy, nonspontaneously

24 In each of the four beakers shown below, a 2.0-centimeter strip of magnesium ribbon reacts with 100 milliliters of HCl(aq) under the conditions shown.

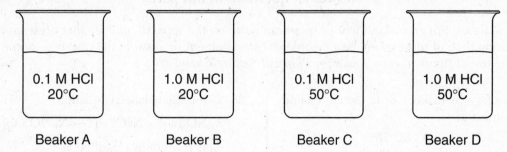

0.1 M HCl 20°C	1.0 M HCl 20°C	0.1 M HCl 50°C	1.0 M HCl 50°C
Beaker A	Beaker B	Beaker C	Beaker D

In which beaker will the reaction occur at the fastest rate?

(1) A

(2) B

(3) C

(4) D

25 Which aqueous solution is the best conductor of an electrical current?

(1) 0.01 M CH$_3$OH

(2) 0.01 M KOH

(3) 0.1 M CH$_3$OH

(4) 0.1 M KOH

26 A hydrogen ion, H$^+$, in aqueous solution may also be written as

(1) H$_2$O

(2) H$_2$O$_2$

(3) H$_3$O$^+$

(4) OH$^-$

27 One acid-base theory states that an acid is

(1) an electron donor

(2) a neutron donor

(3) an H$^+$ donor

(4) an OH$^-$ donor

28 Which isotope will spontaneously decay and emit particles with a charge of +2?

(1) ^{53}Fe

(2) ^{137}Cs

(3) ^{198}Au

(4) ^{220}Fr

29 Radioactive cobalt-60 is used in radiation therapy treatment. Cobalt-60 undergoes beta decay. This type of nuclear reaction is called

(1) natural transmutation

(2) artificial transmutation

(3) nuclear fusion

(4) nuclear fission

Note that question 30 has only three choices.

30 Given the balanced ionic equation:

$$2Al(s) + 3Cu^{2+}(aq) \rightarrow 2Al^{3+}(aq) + 3Cu(s)$$

Compared to the total charge of the reactants, the total charge of the products is

(1) less

(2) greater

(3) the same

Part B–1

Answer all questions in this part.

Directions (31–50): For *each* statement or question, write on the separate answer sheet the *number* of the word or expression that, of those given, best completes the statement or answers the question. Some questions may require the use of the *Reference Tables for Physical Setting/Chemistry*.

31 The percentage by mass of Br in the compound $AlBr_3$ is closest to

(1) 10.%   (3) 75%
(2) 25%   (4) 90.%

32 Which symbol represents a particle with a total of 10 electrons?

(1) N   (3) Al
(2) N^{3+} (4) Al^{3+}

33 Which electron configuration represents an atom of aluminum in an excited state?

(1) 2-7-4   (3) 2-8-3
(2) 2-7-7   (4) 2-8-6

34 At STP, an element that is a brittle solid and a poor conductor of heat and electricity could have an atomic number of

(1) 12   (3) 16
(2) 13   (4) 17

35 Based on Reference Table *S*, atoms of which of these elements have the strongest attraction for the electrons in a chemical bond?

(1) Al   (3) P
(2) Si   (4) S

36 A sample of a compound contains 65.4 grams of zinc, 12.0 grams of carbon, and 48.0 grams of oxygen. What is the mole ratio of zinc to carbon to oxygen in this compound?

(1) 1:1:2   (3) 1:4:6
(2) 1:1:3   (4) 5:1:4

37 Which process would most effectively separate two liquids with different molecular polarities?

(1) filtration   (3) distillation
(2) fermentation   (4) conductivity

38 Given the balanced equation:

$$AgNO_3(aq) + NaCl(aq) \rightarrow NaNO_3(aq) + AgCl(s)$$

This reaction is classified as

(1) synthesis
(2) decomposition
(3) single replacement
(4) double replacement

39 A solution contains 35 grams of KNO_3 dissolved in 100 grams of water at 40°C. How much *more* KNO_3 would have to be added to make it a saturated solution?

(1) 29 g   (3) 12 g
(2) 24 g   (4) 4 g

40 Which diagram best represents a gas in a closed container?

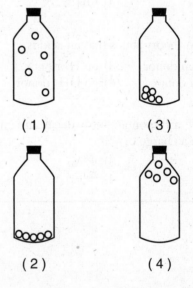

41 What is the total number of moles of NaCl(s) needed to make 3.0 liters of a 2.0 M NaCl solution?

(1) 1.0 mol   (3) 6.0 mol
(2) 0.70 mol   (4) 8.0 mol

42 Which Lewis electron-dot diagram is correct for a S^{2-} ion?

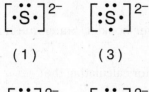

(1)   (3)

(2)   (4)

43 A student wants to prepare a 1.0-liter solution of a specific molarity. The student determines that the mass of the solute needs to be 30. grams. What is the proper procedure to follow?

(1) Add 30. g of solute to 1.0 L of solvent.
(2) Add 30. g of solute to 970. mL of solvent to make 1.0 L of solution.
(3) Add 1000. g of solvent to 30. g of solute.
(4) Add enough solvent to 30. g of solute to make 1.0 L of solution.

44 What is the total number of joules released when a 5.00-gram sample of water changes from liquid to solid at 0°C?

(1) 334 J   (3) 2260 J
(2) 1670 J   (4) 11 300 J

45 Which set of procedures and observations indicates a chemical change?

(1) Ethanol is added to an empty beaker and the ethanol eventually disappears.
(2) A solid is gently heated in a crucible and the solid slowly turns to liquid.
(3) Large crystals are crushed with a mortar and pestle and become powder.
(4) A cool, shiny metal is added to water in a beaker and rapid bubbling occurs.

46 At STP, a sample of which element has the highest entropy?

(1) Na(s)   (3) $Br_2(\ell)$
(2) Hg(ℓ)   (4) F_2(g)

47 Given the incomplete equation representing an organic addition reaction:

$$X(g) + Cl_2(g) \rightarrow XCl_2(g)$$

Which compound could be represented by X?

(1) CH_4 (3) C_3H_8
(2) C_2H_4 (4) C_4H_{10}

48 Given the incomplete equation:

$$4Fe + 3O_2 \rightarrow 2X$$

Which compound is represented by X?

(1) FeO   (3) Fe_3O_2
(2) Fe_2O_3 (4) Fe_3O_4

49 How are HNO_3(aq) and CH_3COOH(aq) similar?

(1) They are Arrhenius acids and they turn blue litmus red.
(2) They are Arrhenius acids and they turn red litmus blue.
(3) They are Arrhenius bases and they turn blue litmus red.
(4) They are Arrhenius bases and they turn red litmus blue.

50 The chart below shows the spontaneous nuclear decay of U-238 to Th-234 to Pa-234 to U-234.

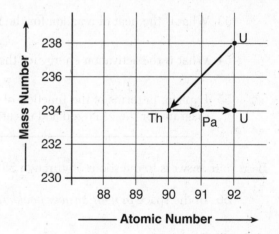

What is the correct order of nuclear decay modes for the change from U-238 to U-234?

(1) β^- decay, γ decay, β^- decay
(2) β^- decay, β^- decay, α decay
(3) α decay, α decay, β^- decay
(4) α decay, β^- decay, β^- decay

Part B–2

Answer all questions in this part.

Directions (51–67): Record your answers in the spaces provided in your answer booklet. Some questions may require the use of the *Reference Tables for Physical Setting/Chemistry.*

51 In the space *in your answer booklet,* show a correct numerical setup for calculating the formula mass of glucose, $C_6H_{12}O_6$. [1]

52 Write the empirical formula for the compound $C_6H_{12}O_6$. [1]

Base your answers to questions 53 through 55 on the potential energy diagram below.

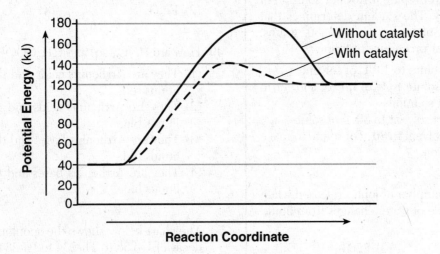

53 What is the heat of reaction for the forward reaction? [1]

54 What is the activation energy for the forward reaction with the catalyst? [1]

55 Explain, in terms of the function of a catalyst, why the curves on the potential energy diagram for the catalyzed and uncatalyzed reactions are different. [1]

Base your answers to questions 56 through 58 on the properties of propanone.

56 In the space *in your answer booklet,* draw the structural formula for propanone. [1]

57 Explain, in terms of molecular energy, why the vapor pressure of propanone increases when its temperature increases. [1]

58 A liquid's boiling point is the temperature at which its vapor pressure is equal to the atmospheric pressure. Using Reference Table *H,* what is the boiling point of propanone at an atmospheric pressure of 70 kPa? [1]

Base your answers to questions 59 through 61 on the information below.

Two isotopes of potassium are K-37 and K-42.

59 What is the total number of neutrons in the nucleus of a K-37 atom? [1]

60 How many valence electrons are in an atom of K-42 in the ground state? [1]

61 Explain, in terms of subatomic particles, why K-37 and K-42 are isotopes of potassium. [1]

---

62 A sample of oxygen gas in one container has a volume of 20.0 milliliters at 297 K and 101.3 kPa. The entire sample is transferred to another container where the temperature is 283 K and the pressure is 94.6 kPa. In the space *in your answer booklet,* show a correct numerical setup for calculating the new volume of this sample of oxygen gas. [1]

63 In the space *in your answer booklet,* draw a Lewis electron-dot diagram for a molecule of phosphorus trichloride, PCl_3. [1]

Base your answers to questions 64 through 67 on the table below.

First Ionization Energy of Selected Elements

Element	Atomic Number	First Ionization Energy (kJ/mol)
lithium	3	520
sodium	11	496
potassium	19	419
rubidium	37	403
cesium	55	376

64 On the grid *in your answer booklet,* mark an appropriate scale on the axis labeled "First Ionization Energy (kJ/mol)." An appropriate scale is one that allows a trend to be seen. [1]

65 On the same grid, plot the data from the table. Circle and connect the points. [1]

Example: ⊙—⊙—⊙

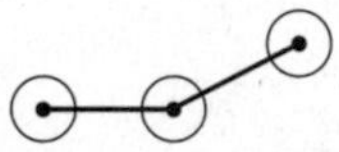

66 State the trend in first ionization energy for the elements in the table as the atomic number increases. [1]

67 Explain, in terms of atomic structure, why cesium has a *lower* first ionization energy than rubidium. [1]

Part C

Answer all questions in this part.

Directions (68–85): Record your answers in the spaces provided in your answer booklet. Some questions may require the use of the *Reference Tables for Physical Setting/Chemistry.*

Base your answers to questions 68 through 70 on the information below.

The decomposition of sodium azide, $NaN_3(s)$, is used to inflate airbags. On impact, the $NaN_3(s)$ is ignited by an electrical spark, producing $N_2(g)$ and $Na(s)$. The $N_2(g)$ inflates the airbag.

68 Balance the equation *in your answer booklet,* using the smallest whole-number coefficients. [1]

69 What is the total number of moles present in a 52.0-gram sample of $NaN_3(s)$ (gram-formula mass = 65.0 gram/mole)? [1]

70 An inflated airbag has a volume of 5.00×10^4 cm^3 at STP. The density of $N_2(g)$ at STP is 0.00125 g/cm^3. What is the total number of grams of $N_2(g)$ in the airbag? [1]

_____

Base your answers to questions 71 through 73 on the information below.

Element X is a solid metal that reacts with chlorine to form a water-soluble binary compound.

71 State *one* physical property of element X that makes it a good material for making pots and pans. [1]

72 Explain, in terms of particles, why an aqueous solution of the binary compound conducts an electric current. [1]

73 The binary compound consists of element X and chlorine in a 1:2 molar ratio. What is the oxidation number of element X in this compound? [1]

_____

Base your answers to questions 74 through 76 on the diagram and balanced equation below, which represent the electrolysis of molten NaCl.

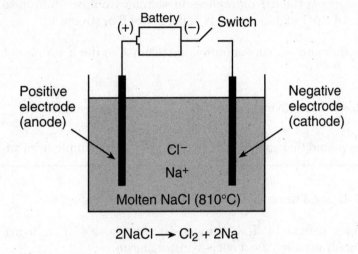

Positive electrode (anode)

Negative electrode (cathode)

Cl⁻

Na⁺

Molten NaCl (810°C)

$$2NaCl \longrightarrow Cl_2 + 2Na$$

74 When the switch is closed, which electrode will attract the sodium ions? [1]

75 What is the purpose of the battery in this electrolytic cell? [1]

76 Write the balanced half-reaction for the reduction that occurs in this electrolytic cell. [1]

Base your answers to questions 77 through 79 on the information below.

In a titration, 3.00 M NaOH(aq) was added to an Erlenmeyer flask containing 25.00 milliliters of HCl(aq) and three drops of phenolphthalein until one drop of the NaOH(aq) turned the solution a light-pink color. The following data were collected by a student performing this titration.

Initial NaOH(aq) buret reading: 14.45 milliliters

Final NaOH(aq) buret reading: 32.66 milliliters

77 What is the total volume of NaOH(aq) that was used in this titration? [1]

78 In the space *in your answer booklet,* show a correct numerical setup for calculating the molarity of the HCl(aq). [1]

79 Based on the data given, what is the correct number of significant figures that should be shown in the molarity of the HCl(aq)? [1]

Base your answers to questions 80 through 82 on the information below.

A student was studying the pH differences in samples from two Adirondack streams. The student measured a pH of 4 in stream A and a pH of 6 in stream B.

80 Compare the hydronium ion concentration in stream A to the hydronium ion concentration in stream B. [1]

81 What is the color of bromthymol blue in the sample from stream A? [1]

82 Identify *one* compound that could be used to neutralize the sample from stream A. [1]

Base your answers to questions 83 through 85 on the information below.

The radioisotopes carbon-14 and nitrogen-16 are present in a living organism. Carbon-14 is commonly used to date a once-living organism.

83 Complete the nuclear equation *in your answer booklet* for the decay of C-14. Include *both* the atomic number and the mass number of the missing particle. [1]

84 Explain why N-16 is a poor choice for radioactive dating of a bone. [1]

85 A sample of wood is found to contain $\frac{1}{8}$ as much C-14 as is present in the wood of a living tree. What is the approximate age, in years, of this sample of wood? [1]

Table A
Standard Temperature and Pressure

Name	Value	Unit
Standard Pressure	101.3 kPa 1 atm	kilopascal atmosphere
Standard Temperature	273 K 0°C	kelvin degree Celsius

Table B
Physical Constants for Water

Heat of Fusion	334 J/g
Heat of Vaporization	2260 J/g
Specific Heat Capacity of H_2O (ℓ)	4.18 J/g•°C

Table C
Selected Prefixes

Factor	Prefix	Symbol
10^3	kilo-	k
10^{-1}	deci-	d
10^{-2}	centi-	c
10^{-3}	milli-	m
10^{-6}	micro-	μ
10^{-9}	nano-	n
10^{-12}	pico-	p

Table D
Selected Units

Symbol	Name	Quantity
m	meter	length
g	gram	mass
Pa	pascal	pressure
K	kelvin	temperature
mol	mole	amount of substance
J	joule	energy, work, quantity of heat
s	second	time
L	liter	volume
ppm	part per million	concentration
M	molarity	solution concentration

Table E
Selected Polyatomic Ions

H_3O^+	hydronium		CrO_4^{2-}	chromate
Hg_2^{2+}	dimercury (I)		$Cr_2O_7^{2-}$	dichromate
NH_4^+	ammonium		MnO_4^-	permanganate
$C_2H_3O_2^-$ CH_3COO^-	acetate		NO_2^-	nitrite
			NO_3^-	nitrate
CN^-	cyanide		O_2^{2-}	peroxide
CO_3^{2-}	carbonate		OH^-	hydroxide
HCO_3^-	hydrogen carbonate		PO_4^{3-}	phosphate
$C_2O_4^{2-}$	oxalate		SCN^-	thiocyanate
ClO^-	hypochlorite		SO_3^{2-}	sulfite
ClO_2^-	chlorite		SO_4^{2-}	sulfate
ClO_3^-	chlorate		HSO_4^-	hydrogen sulfate
ClO_4^-	perchlorate		$S_2O_3^{2-}$	thiosulfate

Table F
Solubility Guidelines for Aqueous Solutions

Ions That Form *Soluble* Compounds	Exceptions
Group 1 ions (Li$^+$, Na$^+$, etc.)	
ammonium (NH$_4^+$)	
nitrate (NO$_3^-$)	
acetate (C$_2$H$_3$O$_2^-$ or CH$_3$COO$^-$)	
hydrogen carbonate (HCO$_3^-$)	
chlorate (ClO$_3^-$)	
perchlorate (ClO$_4^-$)	
halides (Cl$^-$, Br$^-$, I$^-$)	when combined with Ag$^+$, Pb^{2+}, and Hg$_2^{2+}$
sulfates (SO$_4^{2-}$)	when combined with Ag$^+$, Ca^{2+}, Sr^{2+}, Ba^{2+}, and Pb^{2+}

Ions That Form *Insoluble* Compounds	Exceptions
carbonate (CO$_3^{2-}$)	when combined with Group 1 ions or ammonium (NH$_4^+$)
chromate (CrO$_4^{2-}$)	when combined with Group 1 ions, Ca^{2+}, Mg^{2+}, or ammonium (NH$_4^+$)
phosphate (PO$_4^{3-}$)	when combined with Group 1 ions or ammonium (NH$_4^+$)
sulfide (S^{2-})	when combined with Group 1 ions or ammonium (NH$_4^+$)
hydroxide (OH$^-$)	when combined with Group 1 ions, Ca^{2+}, Ba^{2+}, Sr^{2+}, or ammonium (NH$_4^+$)

Table G   Solubility Curves

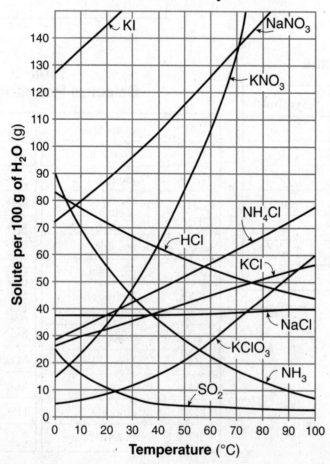

Table H
Vapor Pressure of Four Liquids

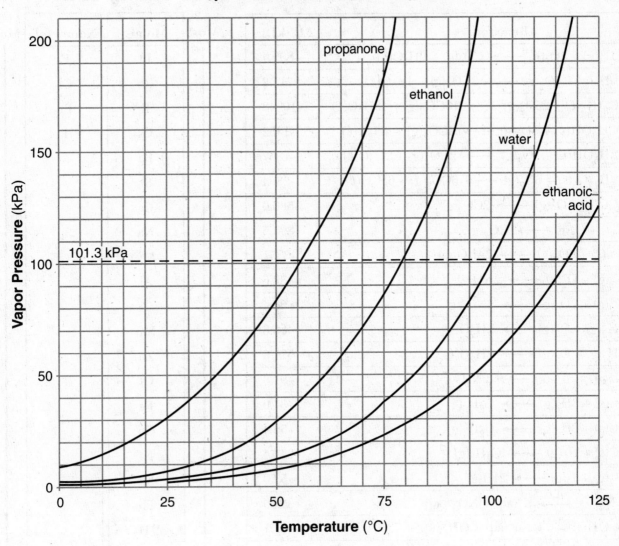

Table I
Heats of Reaction at 101.3 kPa and 298 K

Reaction	ΔH (kJ)*
$CH_4(g) + 2O_2(g) \longrightarrow CO_2(g) + 2H_2O(\ell)$	−890.4
$C_3H_8(g) + 5O_2(g) \longrightarrow 3CO_2(g) + 4H_2O(\ell)$	−2219.2
$2C_8H_{18}(\ell) + 25O_2(g) \longrightarrow 16CO_2(g) + 18H_2O(\ell)$	−10943
$2CH_3OH(\ell) + 3O_2(g) \longrightarrow 2CO_2(g) + 4H_2O(\ell)$	−1452
$C_2H_5OH(\ell) + 3O_2(g) \longrightarrow 2CO_2(g) + 3H_2O(\ell)$	−1367
$C_6H_{12}O_6(s) + 6O_2(g) \longrightarrow 6CO_2(g) + 6H_2O(\ell)$	−2804
$2CO(g) + O_2(g) \longrightarrow 2CO_2(g)$	−566.0
$C(s) + O_2(g) \longrightarrow CO_2(g)$	−393.5
$4Al(s) + 3O_2(g) \longrightarrow 2Al_2O_3(s)$	−3351
$N_2(g) + O_2(g) \longrightarrow 2NO(g)$	+182.6
$N_2(g) + 2O_2(g) \longrightarrow 2NO_2(g)$	+66.4
$2H_2(g) + O_2(g) \longrightarrow 2H_2O(g)$	−483.6
$2H_2(g) + O_2(g) \longrightarrow 2H_2O(\ell)$	−571.6
$N_2(g) + 3H_2(g) \longrightarrow 2NH_3(g)$	−91.8
$2C(s) + 3H_2(g) \longrightarrow C_2H_6(g)$	−84.0
$2C(s) + 2H_2(g) \longrightarrow C_2H_4(g)$	+52.4
$2C(s) + H_2(g) \longrightarrow C_2H_2(g)$	+227.4
$H_2(g) + I_2(g) \longrightarrow 2HI(g)$	+53.0
$KNO_3(s) \xrightarrow{H_2O} K^+(aq) + NO_3^-(aq)$	+34.89
$NaOH(s) \xrightarrow{H_2O} Na^+(aq) + OH^-(aq)$	−44.51
$NH_4Cl(s) \xrightarrow{H_2O} NH_4^+(aq) + Cl^-(aq)$	+14.78
$NH_4NO_3(s) \xrightarrow{H_2O} NH_4^+(aq) + NO_3^-(aq)$	+25.69
$NaCl(s) \xrightarrow{H_2O} Na^+(aq) + Cl^-(aq)$	+3.88
$LiBr(s) \xrightarrow{H_2O} Li^+(aq) + Br^-(aq)$	−48.83
$H^+(aq) + OH^-(aq) \longrightarrow H_2O(\ell)$	−55.8

*Minus sign indicates an exothermic reaction.

Table J
Activity Series**

Most	Metals	Nonmetals	Most
	Li	F_2	
	Rb	Cl_2	
	K	Br_2	
	Cs	I_2	
	Ba		
	Sr		
	Ca		
	Na		
	Mg		
	Al		
	Ti		
	Mn		
	Zn		
	Cr		
	Fe		
	Co		
	Ni		
	Sn		
	Pb		
	**H_2		
	Cu		
	Ag		
	Au		
Least			Least

**Activity Series based on hydrogen standard

Note: H_2 is *not* a metal

Table K
Common Acids

Formula	Name
HCl(aq)	hydrochloric acid
HNO$_3$(aq)	nitric acid
H$_2$SO$_4$(aq)	sulfuric acid
H$_3$PO$_4$(aq)	phosphoric acid
H$_2$CO$_3$(aq) or CO$_2$(aq)	carbonic acid
CH$_3$COOH(aq) or HC$_2$H$_3$O$_2$(aq)	ethanoic acid (acetic acid)

Table L
Common Bases

Formula	Name
NaOH(aq)	sodium hydroxide
KOH(aq)	potassium hydroxide
Ca(OH)$_2$(aq)	calcium hydroxide
NH$_3$(aq)	aqueous ammonia

Table M
Common Acid–Base Indicators

Indicator	Approximate pH Range for Color Change	Color Change
methyl orange	3.2–4.4	red to yellow
bromthymol blue	6.0–7.6	yellow to blue
phenolphthalein	8.2–10	colorless to pink
litmus	5.5–8.2	red to blue
bromcresol green	3.8–5.4	yellow to blue
thymol blue	8.0–9.6	yellow to blue

Table N
Selected Radioisotopes

Nuclide	Half-Life	Decay Mode	Nuclide Name
^{198}Au	2.69 d	β^-	gold-198
^{14}C	5730 y	β^-	carbon-14
^{37}Ca	175 ms	β^+	calcium-37
^{60}Co	5.26 y	β^-	cobalt-60
^{137}Cs	30.23 y	β^-	cesium-137
^{53}Fe	8.51 min	β^+	iron-53
^{220}Fr	27.5 s	α	francium-220
^{3}H	12.26 y	β^-	hydrogen-3
^{131}I	8.07 d	β^-	iodine-131
^{37}K	1.23 s	β^+	potassium-37
^{42}K	12.4 h	β^-	potassium-42
^{85}Kr	10.76 y	β^-	krypton-85
^{16}N	7.2 s	β^-	nitrogen-16
^{19}Ne	17.2 s	β^+	neon-19
^{32}P	14.3 d	β^-	phosphorus-32
^{239}Pu	2.44×10^4 y	α	plutonium-239
^{226}Ra	1600 y	α	radium-226
^{222}Rn	3.82 d	α	radon-222
^{90}Sr	28.1 y	β^-	strontium-90
^{99}Tc	2.13×10^5 y	β^-	technetium-99
^{232}Th	1.4×10^{10} y	α	thorium-232
^{233}U	1.62×10^5 y	α	uranium-233
^{235}U	7.1×10^8 y	α	uranium-235
^{238}U	4.51×10^9 y	α	uranium-238

ms = milliseconds; s = seconds; min = minutes; h = hours; d = days; y = years

Table O
Symbols Used in Nuclear Chemistry

Name	Notation	Symbol
alpha particle	^4_2He or $^4_2\alpha$	α
beta particle (electron)	$^{\ \ 0}_{-1}\text{e}$ or $^{\ \ 0}_{-1}\beta$	β^-
gamma radiation	$^0_0\gamma$	γ
neutron	^1_0n	n
proton	^1_1H or ^1_1p	p
positron	$^{\ \ 0}_{+1}\text{e}$ or $^{\ \ 0}_{+1}\beta$	β^+

Table P
Organic Prefixes

Prefix	Number of Carbon Atoms
meth-	1
eth-	2
prop-	3
but-	4
pent-	5
hex-	6
hept-	7
oct-	8
non-	9
dec-	10

Table Q
Homologous Series of Hydrocarbons

Name	General Formula	Examples Name	Examples Structural Formula
alkanes	C_nH_{2n+2}	ethane	H—C—C—H (ethane structure)
alkenes	C_nH_{2n}	ethene	C=C (ethene structure)
alkynes	C_nH_{2n-2}	ethyne	H—C≡C—H

n = number of carbon atoms

Table R
Organic Functional Groups

Class of Compound	Functional Group	General Formula	Example
halide (halocarbon)	—F (fluoro-) —Cl (chloro-) —Br (bromo-) —I (iodo-)	$R-X$ (X represents any halogen)	$CH_3CHClCH_3$ 2-chloropropane
alcohol	—OH	$R-OH$	$CH_3CH_2CH_2OH$ 1-propanol
ether	—O—	$R-O-R'$	$CH_3OCH_2CH_3$ methyl ethyl ether
aldehyde	$\overset{\displaystyle O}{\overset{\|}{-C}}-H$	$R-\overset{\displaystyle O}{\overset{\|}{C}}-H$	$CH_3CH_2\overset{\displaystyle O}{\overset{\|}{C}}-H$ propanal
ketone	$-\overset{\displaystyle O}{\overset{\|}{C}}-$	$R-\overset{\displaystyle O}{\overset{\|}{C}}-R'$	$CH_3\overset{\displaystyle O}{\overset{\|}{C}}CH_2CH_2CH_3$ 2-pentanone
organic acid	$-\overset{\displaystyle O}{\overset{\|}{C}}-OH$	$R-\overset{\displaystyle O}{\overset{\|}{C}}-OH$	$CH_3CH_2\overset{\displaystyle O}{\overset{\|}{C}}-OH$ propanoic acid
ester	$-\overset{\displaystyle O}{\overset{\|}{C}}-O-$	$R-\overset{\displaystyle O}{\overset{\|}{C}}-O-R'$	$CH_3CH_2\overset{\displaystyle O}{\overset{\|}{C}}OCH_3$ methyl propanoate
amine	$-\overset{\|}{N}-$	$R-\overset{R'}{\overset{\|}{N}}-R''$	$CH_3CH_2CH_2NH_2$ 1-propanamine
amide	$-\overset{\displaystyle O}{\overset{\|}{C}}-\overset{\|}{N}H$	$R-\overset{\displaystyle O}{\overset{\|}{C}}-\overset{R'}{\overset{\|}{N}}H$	$CH_3CH_2\overset{\displaystyle O}{\overset{\|}{C}}-NH_2$ propanamide

R represents a bonded atom or group of atoms.

Periodic Table

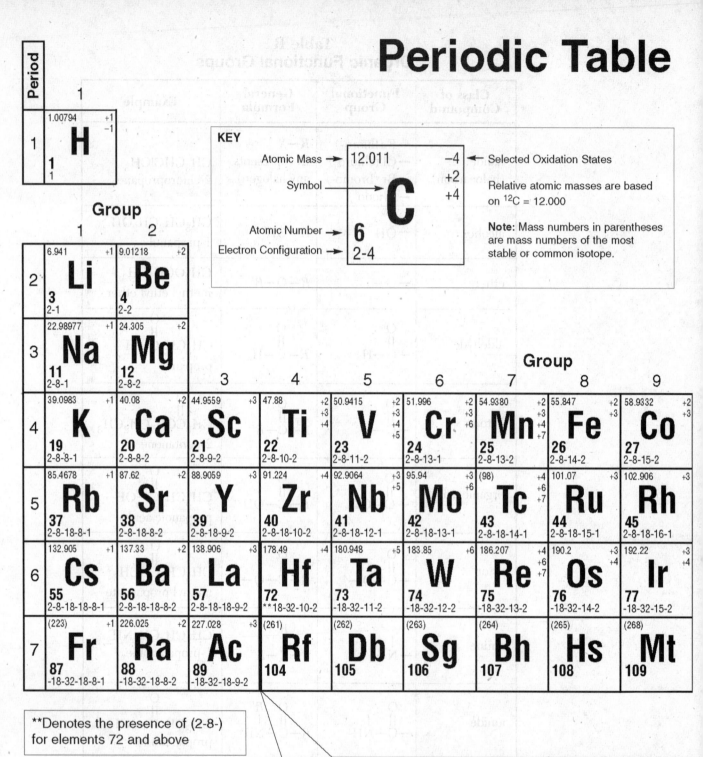

KEY

Atomic Mass → 12.011 — -4 ← Selected Oxidation States
Symbol → C, +2, +4
Atomic Number → 6
Electron Configuration → 2-4

Relative atomic masses are based on $^{12}C = 12.000$

Note: Mass numbers in parentheses are mass numbers of the most stable or common isotope.

**Denotes the presence of (2-8-) for elements 72 and above

of the Elements

18
4.00260 0
He
2 2

Group

13	14	15	16	17	18
10.81 +3 **B** 5 2-3	12.011 -4 +2 +4 **C** 6 2-4	14.0067 -3 -2 -1 +1 +2 +3 +4 +5 **N** 7 2-5	15.9994 -2 **O** 8 2-6	18.998403 -1 **F** 9 2-7	20.179 0 **Ne** 10 2-8
26.98154 +3 **Al** 13 2-8-3	28.0855 -4 +2 +4 **Si** 14 2-8-4	30.97376 -3 +3 +5 **P** 15 2-8-5	32.06 -2 +4 +6 **S** 16 2-8-6	35.453 -1 +1 +3 +5 +7 **Cl** 17 2-8-7	39.948 0 **Ar** 18 2-8-8

10	11	12

58.69 +2 +3 **Ni** 28 2-8-16-2	63.546 +1 +2 **Cu** 29 2-8-18-1	65.39 +2 **Zn** 30 2-8-18-2	69.72 +3 **Ga** 31 2-8-18-3	72.59 -4 +2 +4 **Ge** 32 2-8-18-4	74.9216 -3 +3 +5 **As** 33 2-8-18-5	78.96 -2 +4 +6 **Se** 34 2-8-18-6	79.904 -1 +1 +5 **Br** 35 2-8-18-7	83.80 0 +2 **Kr** 36 2-8-18-8
106.42 +2 +4 **Pd** 46 2-8-18-18	107.868 +1 **Ag** 47 2-8-18-18-1	112.41 +2 **Cd** 48 2-8-18-18-2	114.82 +3 **In** 49 2-8-18-18-3	118.71 +2 +4 **Sn** 50 2-8-18-18-4	121.75 -3 +3 +5 **Sb** 51 2-8-18-18-5	127.60 -2 +4 +6 **Te** 52 2-8-18-18-6	126.905 -1 +1 +5 +7 **I** 53 2-8-18-18-7	131.29 0 +2 +4 +6 **Xe** 54 2-8-18-18-8
195.08 +2 +4 **Pt** 78 -18-32-17-1	196.967 +1 +3 **Au** 79 -18-32-18-1	200.59 +1 +2 **Hg** 80 -18-32-18-2	204.383 +1 +3 **Tl** 81 -18-32-18-3	207.2 +2 +4 **Pb** 82 -18-32-18-4	208.980 +3 +5 **Bi** 83 -18-32-18-5	(209) +2 +4 **Po** 84 -18-32-18-6	(210) -1 +1 +5 +7 **At** 85 -18-32-18-7	(222) 0 **Rn** 86 -18-32-18-8
(269) **Uun** 111	(272) **Uuu** 111	(277) **Uub** 112		(285) **Uuq** 114				

*The systematic names and symbols for elements of atomic numbers above 109 will be used until the approval of trivial names by IUPAC.

151.96 +2 +3 **Eu** 63	157.25 +3 **Gd** 64	158.925 +3 **Tb** 65	162.50 +3 **Dy** 66	164.930 +3 **Ho** 67	167.26 +3 **Er** 68	168.934 +3 **Tm** 69	173.04 +2 +3 **Yb** 70	174.967 +3 **Lu** 71
(243) +3 +4 +5 +6 **Am** 95	(247) +3 **Cm** 96	(247) +3 +4 **Bk** 97	(251) +3 **Cf** 98	(252) **Es** 99	(257) **Fm** 100	(258) **Md** 101	(259) **No** 102	(260) **Lr** 103

Table S
Properties of Selected Elements

Atomic Number	Symbol	Name	First Ionization Energy (kJ/mol)	Electro-negativity	Melting Point (K)	Boiling* Point (K)	Density** (g/cm³)	Atomic Radius (pm)
1	H	hydrogen	1312	2.1	14	20	0.00009	37
2	He	helium	2372	—	1	4	0.000179	32
3	Li	lithium	520	1.0	454	1620	0.534	155
4	Be	beryllium	900	1.6	1551	3243	1.8477	112
5	B	boron	801	2.0	2573	3931	2.340	98
6	C	carbon	1086	2.6	3820	5100	3.513	91
7	N	nitrogen	1402	3.0	63	77	0.00125	92
8	O	oxygen	1314	3.5	55	90	0.001429	65
9	F	fluorine	1681	4.0	54	85	0.001696	57
10	Ne	neon	2081	—	24	27	0.0009	51
11	Na	sodium	496	0.9	371	1156	0.971	190
12	Mg	magnesium	736	1.3	922	1363	1.738	160
13	Al	aluminum	578	1.6	934	2740	2.698	143
14	Si	silicon	787	1.9	1683	2628	2.329	132
15	P	phosphorus	1012	2.2	317	553	1.820	128
16	S	sulfur	1000	2.6	386	718	2.070	127
17	Cl	chlorine	1251	3.2	172	239	0.003214	97
18	Ar	argon	1521	—	84	87	0.001783	88
19	K	potassium	419	0.8	337	1047	0.862	235
20	Ca	calcium	590	1.0	1112	1757	1.550	197
21	Sc	scandium	633	1.4	1814	3104	2.989	162
22	Ti	titanium	659	1.5	1933	3580	4.540	145
23	V	vanadium	651	1.6	2160	3650	6.100	134
24	Cr	chromium	653	1.7	2130	2945	7.190	130
25	Mn	manganese	717	1.6	1517	2235	7.440	135
26	Fe	iron	762	1.8	1808	3023	7.874	126
27	Co	cobalt	760	1.9	1768	3143	8.900	125
28	Ni	nickel	737	1.9	1726	3005	8.902	124
29	Cu	copper	745	1.9	1357	2840	8.960	128
30	Zn	zinc	906	1.7	693	1180	7.133	138
31	Ga	gallium	579	1.8	303	2676	5.907	141
32	Ge	germanium	762	2.0	1211	3103	5.323	137
33	As	arsenic	944	2.2	1090	889	5.780	139
34	Se	selenium	941	2.6	490	958	4.790	140
35	Br	bromine	1140	3.0	266	332	3.122	112
36	Kr	krypton	1351	—	117	121	0.00375	103
37	Rb	rubidium	403	0.8	312	961	1.532	248
38	Sr	strontium	549	1.0	1042	1657	2.540	215
39	Y	yttrium	600	1.2	1795	3611	4.469	178
40	Zr	zirconium	640	1.3	2125	4650	6.506	160

Atomic Number	Symbol	Name	First Ionization Energy (kJ/mol)	Electro-negativity	Melting Point (K)	Boiling* Point (K)	Density** (g/cm³)	Atomic Radius (pm)
41	Nb	niobium	652	1.6	2741	5015	8.570	146
42	Mo	molybdenum	684	2.2	2890	4885	10.220	139
43	Tc	technetium	702	1.9	2445	5150	11.500	136
44	Ru	ruthenium	710	2.2	2583	4173	12.370	134
45	Rh	rhodium	720	2.3	2239	4000	12.410	134
46	Pd	palladium	804	2.2	1825	3413	12.020	137
47	Ag	silver	731	1.9	1235	2485	10.500	144
48	Cd	cadmium	868	1.7	594	1038	8.650	171
49	In	indium	558	1.8	429	2353	7.310	166
50	Sn	tin	709	2.0	505	2543	7.310	162
51	Sb	antimony	831	2.1	904	1908	6.691	159
52	Te	tellurium	869	2.1	723	1263	6.240	142
53	I	iodine	1008	2.7	387	458	4.930	132
54	Xe	xenon	1170	2.6	161	166	0.0059	124
55	Cs	cesium	376	0.8	302	952	1.873	267
56	Ba	barium	503	0.9	1002	1910	3.594	222
57	La	lanthanum	538	1.1	1194	3730	6.145	138
Elements 58–71 have been omitted.								
72	Hf	hafnium	659	1.3	2503	5470	13.310	167
73	Ta	tantalum	728	1.5	3269	5698	16.654	149
74	W	tungsten	759	2.4	3680	5930	19.300	141
75	Re	rhenium	756	1.9	3453	5900	21.020	137
76	Os	osmium	814	2.2	3327	5300	22.590	135
77	Ir	iridium	865	2.2	2683	4403	22.560	136
78	Pt	platinum	864	2.3	2045	4100	21.450	139
79	Au	gold	890	2.5	1338	3080	19.320	146
80	Hg	mercury	1007	2.0	234	630	13.546	160
81	Tl	thallium	589	2.0	577	1730	11.850	171
82	Pb	lead	716	2.3	601	2013	11.350	175
83	Bi	bismuth	703	2.0	545	1833	9.747	170
84	Po	polonium	812	2.0	527	1235	9.320	167
85	At	astatine	—	2.2	575	610	—	145
86	Rn	radon	1037	—	202	211	0.00973	134
87	Fr	francium	393	0.7	300	950	—	270
88	Ra	radium	—	0.9	973	1413	5.000	233
89	Ac	actinium	499	1.1	1320	3470	10.060	—
Elements 90 and above have been omitted.								

*Boiling point at standard pressure
**Density at STP

Table T
Important Formulas and Equations

Density	$d = \dfrac{m}{V}$	d = density m = mass V = volume
Mole Calculations	number of moles = $\dfrac{\text{given mass (g)}}{\text{gram-formula mass}}$	
Percent Error	% error = $\dfrac{\text{measured value} - \text{accepted value}}{\text{accepted value}} \times 100$	
Percent Composition	% composition by mass = $\dfrac{\text{mass of part}}{\text{mass of whole}} \times 100$	
Concentration	parts per million = $\dfrac{\text{grams of solute}}{\text{grams of solution}} \times 1\,000\,000$	
	molarity = $\dfrac{\text{moles of solute}}{\text{liters of solution}}$	
Combined Gas Law	$\dfrac{P_1 V_1}{T_1} = \dfrac{P_2 V_2}{T_2}$	P = pressure V = volume T = temperature (K)
Titration	$M_A V_A = M_B V_B$	M_A = molarity of H^+ M_B = molarity of OH^- V_A = volume of acid V_B = volume of base
Heat	$q = mC\Delta T$ $q = mH_f$ $q = mH_v$	q = heat H_f = heat of fusion m = mass H_v = heat of vaporization C = specific heat capacity ΔT = change in temperature
Temperature	K = °C + 273	K = kelvin °C = degrees Celsius
Radioactive Decay	fraction remaining = $\left(\dfrac{1}{2}\right)^{\frac{t}{T}}$ number of half-life periods = $\dfrac{t}{T}$	t = total time elapsed T = half-life

DET 609 (8-03–350,000)
93-93703 93-041 CDC

A

accuracy: Refers to how close a measured value is to an accepted value.

acid-base indicator: A chemical dye whose color is affected by acidic and basic solutions.

activation energy: The minimum amount of energy required by reacting particles in order to form the activated complex and lead to a reaction.

addition reaction: An organic reaction that occurs when other atoms bond to each of two atoms bonded by double or triple covalent bonds.

alcohol: An organic compound in which a hydroxyl group replaces a hydrogen atom of a hydrocarbon; is used in medicinal products, foods, and beverages, and as a solvent and starting material in synthesis reactions.

aldehyde: An organic compound containing the structure in which a carbonyl group at the end of a carbon chain is bonded to a carbon atom on one side and a hydrogen atom on the other side.

alkali metals: Group 1A elements, except for hydrogen, that are on the left side of the modern periodic table.

alkaline earth metals: Group 2A elements in the modern periodic table.

alkane: A saturated hydrocarbon, such as methane (CH_4), with only single, nonpolar bonds between atoms.

alkene: An unsaturated hydrocarbon, such as ethene (C_2H_4), with one or more double covalent bonds between carbon atoms in a chain.

alkyl halide: An organic compound that contains one or more halogen atoms (F, Cl, Br, or I) covalently bonded to an aliphatic carbon atom.

alkyne: An unsaturated hydrocarbon, such as ethyne (C_2H_2), with one or more triple bonds between carbon atoms in a chain.

allotropes: Forms of an element with different structures and properties when they are in the same state—solid, liquid, or gas.

alpha particle: A particle with two protons and two neutrons, with a 2+ charge; is equivalent to a helium-4 nucleus, can be represented as α, and is emitted during radioactive decay.

amide: An organic compound in which the —OH group of a carboxylic acid is replaced by a nitrogen atom bonded to other atoms.

exactitud: Se refiere a la cercanía con que se encuentra un valor medido de un valor aceptado.

indicador ácido-base: Tinta química cuyo color es afectado por soluciones ácidas y básicas.

energía de activación: La cantidad mínima de energía requerida por partículas reaccionantes, para formar el complejo activado y conducir a una reacción.

reacción de adición: Reacción orgánica que ocurre cuando otros átomos se unen a cada uno de los dos átomos unidos por enlaces covalentes dobles o triples.

alcohol: Compuesto orgánico en que un grupo hidroxilo reemplaza un átomo de hidrógeno de un hidrocarburo; se utiliza en medicinas, alimentos y bebidas y como disolvente como material inicial en reacciones de síntesis.

aldehido: Compuesto orgánico en el cual un grupo carbonilo al final de una cadena de carbono está unido a un átomo de carbono por un lado y a un átomo de hidrógeno por el otro.

metales alcalinos: Elementos del Grupo 1A, exceptuando el hidrógeno, que se ubican en el lado izquierdo de la tabla periódica moderna.

metales alcalinotérreos: Elementos del Grupo 2A en la tabla periódica moderna.

alcano: Hidrocarburo saturado, como el metano (CH_4), con sólo enlaces sencillos y no polares entre los átomos.

alqueno: Un hidrocarburo insaturado, como el etileno (C_2H_4), con uno o más enlaces dobles entre átomos de carbono de una cadena.

alquilhaluro: Compuesto orgánico que contiene uno o más átomos de halógeno (F, Cl, Br o I) unidos covalentemente a un átomo de carbono alifático.

alquino: Hidrocarburo insaturado, como el acetileno (C_2H_2), con uno o más enlaces triples entre átomos de carbono en una cadena.

alótropos: Formas de un elemento con estructuras y propiedades diferentes cuando están en el mismo estado: sólido, líquido o gaseoso.

partícula alfa: Partícula con dos protones y dos neutrones, con una carga de 2+ que equivale a un núcleo de helio 4; se puede representar como α y se emite durante la descomposición radiactiva.

amida: Compuesto orgánico en que el grupo — OH de un ácido carboxílico es reemplazado por un átomo de nitrógeno unido con otros átomos.

amines: Organic compounds that contain nitrogen atoms bonded to carbon atoms in aliphatic chains or aromatic rings and have the general formula RNH_2.

anion: An ion that has a negative charge; forms when valence electrons are added to the outer energy level, giving the ion a stable electron configuration.

anode: In an electrochemical cell, the electrode where oxidation takes place.

aryl halide: An organic compound that contains a halogen atom bonded to a benzene ring or another aromatic group.

atom: The smallest particle of an element that retains all the properties of that element; is electrically neutral, spherically shaped, and composed of electrons, protons, and neutrons.

atomic mass: The weighted average mass of the isotopes of that element.

atomic mass unit (amu): One-twelfth the mass of a carbon-12 atom.

atomic number: The number of protons in an atom.

atomic orbital: A three-dimensional region around the nucleus of an atom that describes an electron's probable location.

aufbau principle: States that each electron occupies the lowest energy orbital available.

Avogadro's number: The number 6.0221367×10^{23}, which is the number of representative particles in a mole, and can be rounded to three significant digits: 6.02×10^{23}.

aminas: Compuestos orgánicos que contienen átomos de nitrógeno unidos a átomos de carbono en cadenas de alifáticas o anillos aromáticos y su fórmula general es RNH_2.

anión: Ion que tiene una carga negativa; se forma cuando los electrones de valencia se incorporan al nivel de energía externo, dando el ion una configuración electrónica estable.

ánodo: En una celda electroquímica, el electrodo donde se lleva a cabo la oxidación.

haluro de arilo: Compuesto orgánico que contiene un átomo de halógeno unido a un anillo de benceno u otro grupo aromático.

átomo: La partícula más pequeña de un elemento que retiene todas las propiedades de ese elemento; es eléctricamente neutro, de forma esférica y compuesto de electrones, protones y neutrones.

masa atómica: La masa promedio ponderada de los isótopos de ese elemento.

unidad de masa atómica (uma): Un doceavo de la masa de un átomo de carbono 12.

número atómico: El número de protones en un átomo.

orbital atómico: Región tridimensional alrededor del núcleo de un átomo que describe la ubicación probable del electrón.

principio de Aufbau: Establece que cada electrón ocupa el orbital de energía más bajo disponible.

número de Avogadro: El número 6.0221367×10^{23}, que es el número de partículas representativas en un mol, el cual se puede redondear a tres dígitos significativos: 6.02×10^{23}.

B

band of stability: The region on a graph within which all stable nuclei are found when plotting the number of neutrons versus the number of protons for all stable nuclei.

battery: One or more electrochemical cells in a single package that generates electrical current.

beta particle: A high-speed electron with a 1− charge that is emitted during radioactive decay.

boiling point: The temperature at which a liquid's vapor pressure is equal to the external or atmospheric pressure.

banda de la estabilidad: Región de la gráfica dentro de la cual se encuentran todos los núcleos estables cuando se grafica el número de neutrones contra el número de protones para todos los núcleos estables.

batería: Una o más celdas electroquímicas en un solo paquete que genera corriente eléctrica.

partícula de beta: Electrón de alta velocidad con una carga 1− que se emite durante la desintegración radiactiva.

punto de ebullición: Temperatura a la cual la presión de vapor de un líquido es igual a la presión externa o atmosférica.

C

carboxylic acid: An organic compound that contains a carboxyl group and is polar and reactive.

catalyst: A substance that increases the rate of a chemical reaction by lowering activation energies but is not itself consumed in the reaction.

cathode: In an electrochemical cell, the electrode where reduction takes place.

cation: An ion that has a positive charge; forms when valence electrons are removed, giving the ion a stable electron configuration.

chemical change: A process involving one or more substances changing into new substances; also called a chemical reaction.

chemical equilibrium: The state in which forward and reverse reactions balance each other because they occur at equal rates.

chemical property: The ability or inability of a substance to combine with or change into one or more new substances.

chromatography: A technique that is used to separate the components of a mixture based on the tendency of each component to travel or be drawn across the surface of another material.

coefficient: In a chemical equation, the number written in front of a reactant or product; tells the smallest number of particles of the substance involved in the reaction.

collision theory: States that atoms, ions, and molecules must collide in order to react.

combined gas law: A single law combining Boyle's, Charles's, and Gay-Lussac's laws that states the relationship among pressure, volume, and temperature of a fixed amount of gas.

combustion reaction: A chemical reaction that occurs when a substance reacts with oxygen, releasing energy in the form of heat and light.

compound: A chemical combination of two or more different elements; can be broken down into simpler substances by chemical means and has properties different from those of its component elements.

conclusion: A judgment based on the information obtained.

conjugate acid: The species produced when a base accepts a hydrogen ion from an acid.

ácido carboxílico: Compuesto orgánico que contiene un grupo carboxilo y el cual es polar y reactivo.

catalizador: Sustancia que aumenta la velocidad de reacción química disminuyendo las energías de activación pero él mismo no es consumido durante la reacción.

cátodo: En una celda de electroquímica, el electrodo donde se lleva a cabo la reducción.

catión: Ion que tiene una carga positiva; se forma cuando se descartan los electrones de valencia, dándole al ion una configuración electrónica estable.

cambio químico: Proceso que involucra una o más sustancias que se transforman en sustancias nuevas; también llamado reacción química.

equilibrio químico: El estado en que las reacciones directa e inversa se equilibran mutuamente debido a que ocurren a velocidades iguales.

propiedad química: La capacidad o incapacidad de una sustancia para combinarse o transformarse en uno o más sustancias nuevas.

cromatografía: Técnica usada para separar los componentes de una mezcla basada en la tendencia de cada componente para moverse o ser absorbido a través de la superficie de otra materia.

coeficiente: En una ecuación química, el número escrito delante de un reactante o producto; indica el número más pequeño de partículas de la sustancia involucrada en la reacción.

teoría de colisión: Establece que los átomos, iones y moléculas deben chocar para reaccionar.

ley combinada de los gases: Una sola ley que combina las leyes de Boyle, Charles y de Gay-Lussac, que indica la relación entre la presión, el volumen y la temperatura de una cantidad fija de gas.

reacción de combustión: Reacción química que ocurre cuando una sustancia reacciona con oxígeno, liberando energía en forma de calor y luz.

compuesto: Combinación química de dos o más elementos diferentes; puede separarse en sustancias más sencillas por medios químicos y exhibe propiedades diferentes de aquellas de sus elementos constituyentes.

conclusión: Juicio basado en la información obtenida.

ácido conjugado: Especie producida cuando una base acepta un ion hidrógeno de un ácido.

conjugate base: The species produced when an acid donates a hydrogen ion to a base.

control: In an experiment, the standard that is used for comparison.

covalent bond: A chemical bond that results from the sharing of valence electrons.

critical mass: The minimum mass of a sample of fissionable material necessary to sustain a nuclear chain reaction.

cyclic hydrocarbon: An organic compound that contains a hydrocarbon ring.

cycloalkane: A saturated hydrocarbon that can have rings with three, four, five, six, or more carbon atoms.

base conjugada: Especie producida cuando un ácido dona un ion hidrógeno a una base.

control: Estándar de comparación en un experimento.

enlace covalente: Enlace químico que resulta al compartir electrones de valencia.

masa crítica: La masa mínima de una muestra de material fisionable necesario para sostener una reacción nuclear en cadena.

hidrocarburo cíclico: Compuesto orgánico que contiene un hidrocarburo aromático (con un anillo).

cicloalcano: Hidrocarburo saturado que puede tener anillos con tres, cuatro, cinco, seis o más átomos de carbono.

D

Dalton's atomic theory: A theory proposed by John Dalton in 1808, based on numerous scientific experiments, that marked the beginning of the development of modern atomic theory.

decomposition reaction: A chemical reaction that occurs when a single compound breaks down into two or more elements or new compounds.

delocalized electrons: The electrons involved in metallic bonding that are free to move easily from one atom to the next throughout the metal and are not attached to a particular atom.

dependent variable: In an experiment, the variable whose value depends on the independent variable.

dipole–dipole forces: The attractions between oppositely charged regions of polar molecules.

distillation: A technique that can be used to physically separate most homogeneous mixtures based on the differences in the boiling points of the substances involved.

double-replacement reaction: A chemical reaction that involves the exchange of positive ions between two compounds and produces either a precipitate, a gas, or water.

teoría atómica de Dalton: Teoría propuesta por John Dalton en 1808, basada en numerosos experimentos científicos, que marcó el principio del desarrollo de la teoría atómica moderna.

reacción de descomposición: Reacción química que ocurre cuando un solo compuesto se divide en dos o más elementos o compuestos nuevos.

electrones deslocalizados: Los electrones implicados en el enlace metálico que están libres para moverse fácilmente de un átomo al próximo a través del metal y no están relacionados con cierto átomo en particular.

variable dependiente: En un experimento, la variable cuyo valor depende de la variable independientele.

fuerzas dipolo-dipolo: Las atracciones entre regiones opuestamente cargadas de moléculas polares.

destilación: Técnica que se puede emplear para separar físicamente la mayoría de las mezclas homogéneas, basándose en las diferencias en los puntos de ebullición de las sustancias implicadas.

reacción de doble desplazamiento: Reacción química que involucra el cambio de iones positivos entre dos compuestos y produce un precipitado o un gas o agua.

E

electrochemical cell: An apparatus that uses a redox reaction to produce electrical energy or uses electrical energy to cause a chemical reaction.

electrolysis: The process that uses electrical energy to bring about a chemical reaction.

electrolyte: An ionic compound whose aqueous solution conducts an electric current.

electrolytic cell: An electrochemical cell in which electrolysis occurs.

electromagnetic radiation: A form of energy exhibiting wavelike behavior as it travels through space; can be described by wavelength, frequency, amplitude, and speed and includes visible light, microwaves, X rays, and radio waves.

electromagnetic spectrum: Includes all forms of electromagnetic radiation, with the only differences in the types of radiation being their frequencies and wavelengths.

electron: A negatively charged, fast-moving particle with an extremely small mass that is found in all forms of matter and moves through the empty space surrounding an atom's nucleus.

electron configuration: The arrangement of electrons in an atom, which is prescribed by three rules—the aufbau principle, the Pauli exclusion principle, and Hund's rule.

electron-dot structure: Consists of an element's symbol, representing the atomic nucleus and inner-level electrons, that is surrounded by dots, representing the atom's valence electrons.

electron sea model: Proposes that all metal atoms in a metallic solid contribute their valence electrons to form a "sea" of electrons, and can explain properties of metallic solids such as malleability, conduction, and ductility.

electronegativity: Indicates the relative ability of an element's atoms to attract electrons in a chemical bond.

element: A pure substance that cannot be broken down into simpler substances by physical or chemical means.

empirical formula: A formula that shows the smallest whole-number mole ratio of the elements of a compound, and may or may not be the same as the actual molecular formula.

celda electroquímica: Aparato que usa una reacción redox para producir energía eléctrica o utiliza energía eléctrica para causar una reacción química.

electrólisis: Proceso que emplea energía eléctrica para producir una reacción química.

electrolito: Compuesto iónico cuya solución acuosa conduce una corriente eléctrica.

celda electrolítica: Celda electroquímica en la cual se lleva a cabo la electrólisis.

radiación electromagnética: Forma de energía que exhibe un comportamiento parecido al de una onda al viajar por el espacio; puede describirse por su longitud de onda, frecuencia, amplitud y velocidad e incluye a la luz visible, las microondas, los rayos X y las ondas radiales.

espectro electromagnético: Incluye toda forma de radiación electromagnética, en el cual las frecuencias y longitudes de onda son las únicas diferencias entre los tipos de radiación.

electrón: Partícula móvil rápida, cargada negativamente y con una masa muy pequeña, que se encuentra en todas las formas de materia y se mueve a través del espacio vacío que rodea el núcleo de un átomo.

configuración del electrón: El arreglo de electrones en un átomo, que está establecido por tres reglas: el principio de Aufbau, el principio de la exclusión de Pauli y la regla de Hund.

estructura punto electrón: Consiste en el símbolo de un elemento, que representa el núcleo atómico y los electrones de los niveles interiores, rodeado por puntos que representan los electrones de valencia del átomo.

modelo del mar de electrones: Propone que todos los átomos de metal en un sólido metálico contribuyen con sus electrones de valencia para formar un "mar" de electrones y esto puede explicar propiedades de sólidos metálicos como maleabilidad, conducción y ductilidad.

electronegatividad: Indica la capacidad relativa de los átomos de un elemento para atraer electrones en un enlace químico.

elemento: Sustancia pura que no se puede separar en sustancias más sencillas por medios físicos ni químicos.

fórmula empírica: Fórmula que muestra la proporción molar más pequeña en números enteros de los elementos de un compuesto y puede o no puede ser igual que la fórmula molecular real.

end point: The point at which the indicator that is used in a titration changes color.

enthalpy: The heat content of a system at constant pressure.

equilibrium constant: K_{eq}, which describes the ratio of product concentrations to reactant concentrations, with each raised to the power corresponding to its coefficient in the balanced equation.

equivalence point : The stoichiometric point of a titration.

ester: An organic compound with a carboxyl group in which the hydrogen of the hydroxyl group is replaced by an alkyl group; may be volatile and sweet-smelling and is polar.

ether: An organic compound that contains an oxygen atom bonded to two carbon atoms.

excess reactant: A reactant that remains after a chemical reaction stops.

experiment: A set of controlled observations that test the hypothesis.

punto final: Punto en el cual el indicador que se utiliza en la titulación cambia de color.

entalpía: El contenido de calor en un sistema a presión constante.

constante de equilibrio: K_{eq}, la cual describe la proporción de concentraciones de producto a concentraciones de reactante, con cada uno elevado a la potencia correspondiente a su coeficiente en la ecuación equilibrada.

punto de equivalencia: Punto estequiométrico de una titulación.

éster: Compuesto orgánico con un grupo carboxilo en que el hidrógeno del grupo de hidroxilo es reemplazado por un grupo alquilo; puede ser volátil y de olor dulce y es polar.

éter: Compuesto orgánico que contiene un átomo de oxígeno unido a dos átomos del carbono.

reactante en exceso: Reactante que queda después de que se detiene una reacción química.

experimento: Conjunto de las observaciones controladas para comprobar la hipótesis.

F

fermentation: The process in which glucose is broken down in the absence of oxygen, producing either ethanol, carbon dioxide, and energy (alcoholic fermentation) or lactic acid and energy (lactic acid fermentation).

filtration: A technique that uses a porous barrier to separate a solid from a liquid.

formula unit: The simplest ratio of ions represented in an ionic compound.

free energy: The energy that is available to do work—the difference between the change in enthalpy and the product of the entropy change and the absolute temperature.

freezing point: The temperature at which a liquid is converted into a crystalline solid.

frequency: The number of waves that pass a given point per second.

functional group: An atom or group of atoms that always react in a certain way in an organic molecule.

fermentación: Proceso en el que la glucosa se rompe en ausencia de oxígeno, produciendo ya sea etanol, dióxido de carbono y energía (fermentación alcohólica) o ácido láctico y energía (fermentación ácido láctica).

filtración: Técnica que utiliza una barrera porosa para separar un sólido de un líquido.

fórmula unitaria: La proporción más sencilla de iones representados en un compuesto iónico.

energía libre: Energía disponible para hacer trabajo: la diferencia entre el cambio en la entalpía y el producto del cambio de entropía y la temperatura absoluta.

punto de congelación: La temperatura a la cual un líquido se convierte en un sólido cristalino.

frecuencia: Número de ondas que pasan por un punto dado en un segundo.

grupo funcional: Átomo o grupo de átomos que siempre reaccionan de cierta manera en una molécula orgánica.

G

gamma rays: High-energy radiation that has no electrical charge and no mass, is not deflected by electric or magnetic fields, usually accompanies alpha and beta radiation, and accounts for most of the energy lost during radioactive decay.

gas: A form of matter that flows to conform to the shape of its container, fills the container's entire volume, and is easily compressed.

ground state: The lowest allowable energy state of an atom.

group: A vertical column of elements in the periodic table; also called a family.

rayos gamma: Radiación de alta energía que no tiene ni carga eléctrica ni masa, no es desviada por campos eléctricos ni magnéticos, acompaña generalmente a la radiación alfa y beta y representan la mayor parte de la energía perdida durante la desintegración radiactiva.

gas: Forma de la materia que fluye para adaptarse a la forma de su contenedor, llena el volumen entero del recipiente y se comprime fácilmente.

estado base: Estado de energía más bajo admisible de un átomo.

grupo: Columna vertical de elementos en la tabla periódica; llamado también familia.

H

half-cells: The two parts of an electrochemical cell in which the separate oxidation and reduction reactions occur.

half-life: The time required for one-half of a radioisotope's nuclei to decay into its products.

half-reaction: One of two parts of a redox reaction—the oxidation half, which shows the number of electrons lost when a species is oxidized, or the reduction half, which shows the number of electrons gained when a species is reduced.

halocarbon: Any organic compound containing a halogen substituent.

halogen: A highly reactive group 7A element.

Heisenberg uncertainty principle: States that it is not possible to know precisely both the velocity and the position of a particle at the same time.

Henry's law: States that at a given temperature, the solubility of a gas in a liquid is directly proportional to the pressure of the gas above the liquid.

Hess's law: States that if two or more thermochemical equations can be added to produce a final equation for a reaction, then the sum of the enthalpy changes for the individual reactions is the enthalpy change for the final reaction.

heterogeneous catalyst: A catalyst that exists in a different physical state than the reaction it catalyzes.

celdas medias: Las dos partes de una celda electroquímica en que se llevan a cabo las reacciones separadas de la oxidación y la reducción.

media vida: Tiempo requerido para que la mitad de los núcleos de un radioisótopo se desintegren en sus productos.

reacción media: Una de dos partes de una reacción redox: la parte de la oxidación, la cual muestra el número de electrones perdidos cuando una especie se oxida o la parte de la reducción, que muestra el número de electrones ganados cuando una especie se reduce.

halocarbono: Cualquier compuesto orgánico que contiene un sustituyente de halógeno.

halógeno: Elemento del grupo 7A, sumamente reactivo.

principio de incertidumbre de Heisenberg: Establece que no es posible saber precisamente la velocidad y la posición de una partícula al mismo tiempo.

ley de Henry: Establece que a una temperatura dada, la solubilidad de un gas en un líquido es directamente proporcional a la presión del gas por encima del líquido.

ley de Hess: Establece que si dos o más ecuaciones termoquímicas se pueden sumar para producir una ecuación final para una reacción, entonces la suma de los cambios de entalpía para las reacciones individuales es igual al cambio de entalpía para la reacción final.

catalizador heterogéneo: Catalizador que existe en un estado físico diferente al de la reacción que cataliza.

heterogeneous mixture: One that does not have a uniform composition and in which the individual substances remain distinct.

homogeneous catalyst: A catalyst that exists in the same physical state as the reaction it catalyzes.

homogeneous mixture: One that has a uniform composition throughout and always has a single phase; also called a solution.

Hund's rule: States that single electrons with the same spin must occupy each equal-energy orbital before additional electrons with opposite spins can occupy the same orbitals.

hydrocarbon: Simplest organic compound composed only of the elements carbon and hydrogen.

hydrogen bond: A strong dipole-dipole attraction between molecules that contain a hydrogen atom bonded to a small, highly electronegative atom with at least one lone electron pair.

hydroxyl group: An oxygen-hydrogen group covalently bonded to a carbon atom.

hypothesis: A tentative, testable statement or prediction about what has been observed.

mezcla heterogénea: Aquélla que no tiene una composición uniforme y en la que las sustancias individuales permanecen separadas.

catalizador homogéneo: Catalizador que existe en el mismo estado físico de la reacción que cataliza.

mezcla homogénea: Aquélla que tiene una composición uniforme a lo largo de todo su sistema y siempre tiene una sola fase; también llamada solución.

regla de Hund: Establece que electrones individuales con igual rotación deben ocupar cada orbital de igual energía antes de que electrones adicionales con rotaciones opuestas puedan ocupar los mismos orbitales.

hidrocarburo: Compuesto orgánico más simple compuesto sólo de los elementos carbono e hidrógeno.

puente de hidrógeno: Fuerte atracción bipolo- bipolo entre moléculas que contienen un átomo de hidrógeno unido a un átomo pequeño, sumamente electronegativo con por lo menos un par de electrones no combinados.

grupo hidroxilo: Un grupo hidrógeno-oxígeno unido covalentemente a un átomo de carbono.

hipótesis: Enunciado tentativo y sujeto a comprobación o predicción acerca de lo que se ha observado.

---

independent variable: In an experiment, the variable that the experimenter plans to change.

ion: An atom or bonded group of atoms with a positive or negative charge.

ionic bond: The electrostatic force that holds oppositely charged particles together in an ionic compound.

ionization energy: The energy required to remove an electron from a gaseous atom; generally increases in moving from left-to-right across a period and decreases in moving down a group.

ionizing radiation: Radiation that is energetic enough to ionize matter it collides with.

isomers: Two or more compounds that have the same molecular formula but have different molecular structures.

isotopes: Atoms of the same element with the same number of protons but different numbers of neutrons.

variable independiente: En un experimento, la variable que el experimentador piensa cambiar.

ion: Átomo o grupo de átomos unidos con carga positiva o negativa.

enlace iónico: Fuerza electrostática que mantiene unidas las partículas opuestamente cargadas en un compuesto iónico.

energía de ionización: Energía que se requiere para quitar un electrón de un átomo gaseoso; generalmente aumenta al moverse de izquierda a derecha a través de un período y disminuye al moverse un grupo hacia abajo.

radiación ionizante: Radiación que es suficientemente energética para ionizar la materia con la que choca.

isómeros: Dos o más compuestos que tienen la misma fórmula molecular pero poseen estructuras moleculares diferentes.

isótopos: Átomos del mismo elemento con el mismo número de protones, pero números diferentes de neutrones.

K

ketone: An organic compound in which the carbon of the carbonyl group is bonded to two other carbon atoms.

kilogram: The SI base unit for mass; about 2.2 pounds.

kinetic-molecular theory: Explains the properties of gases in terms of the energy, size, and motion of their particles.

cetona: Compuesto orgánico en que el carbono del grupo carbonilo está unido a otros dos átomos de carbono.

kilogramo: Unidad base SI para la masa; aproximadamente equivale a 2.2 libras.

teoría cinético-molecular: Explica las propiedades de gases en términos de energía, tamaño y movimiento de sus partículas.

L

law of conservation of energy: States that in any chemical or physical process, energy may change from one form to another but it is neither created nor destroyed.

Le Châtelier's principle: States that if a stress is applied to a system at equilibrium, the system shifts in the direction that relieves the stress.

Lewis structure: A model that uses electron-dot structures to show how electrons are arranged in molecules. Pairs of dots or lines represent bonding pairs.

limiting reactant: A reactant that is totally consumed during a chemical reaction, limits the extent of the reaction, and determines the amount of product.

liquid: A form of matter that flows, has constant volume, and takes the shape of its container.

liter: The metric unit for volume equal to one cubic decimeter.

ley de la conservación de energía: Establece que en un proceso químico o físico, la energía puede cambiar de una forma a otra pero ni se crea ni se destruye.

Principio de Le Châtelier: Establece que si se aplica un estrés a un sistema en el equilibrio, el sistema cambia en la dirección en que se disminuye el estrés.

estructura de Lewis: Modelo que utiliza las estructuras punto electrón para mostrar como están distribuidos los electrones en las moléculas. Los pares de puntos o líneas representan pares de unión.

reactante limitante: Reactante que se consume completamente durante una reacción química, limita el alcance de la reacción y determina la cantidad de producto.

líquido: Forma de materia que fluye, tiene volumen constante y toma la forma de su envase.

litro: Unidad métrica para el volumen igual a un decímetro cúbico.

M

mass: A measure of the amount of matter.

mass number: The number after an element's name, representing the sum of its protons and neutrons.

measurement: A comparison between an unknown quantity and a standard.

metal: An element that is solid at room temperature, a good conductor of heat and electricity, and generally is shiny; most metals are ductile and malleable.

metallic bond: The attraction of a metallic cation for delocalized electrons.

masa: Medida de la cantidad de materia.

número de masa: El número después del nombre de un elemento, la cual representa la suma de sus protones y neutrones.

medida: Una comparación entre una cantidad desconocida y una estándar.

metal: Elemento sólido a temperatura ambiente que es buen conductor de calor y electricidad y generalmente es brillante; la mayoría de los metales son dúctiles y maleables.

enlace metálico: Atracción de un catión metálico hacia electrones deslocalizados.

metalloid: An element, such as silicon or germanium, that has physical and chemical properties of both metals and nonmetals.

meter: The SI unit for length.

mixture: A physical blend of two or more pure substances in any proportion in which each substance retains its individual properties; can be separated by physical means.

molarity: The number of moles of solute dissolved per liter of solution; also known as molar concentration.

molar mass: The mass in grams of one mole of any pure substance.

mole: The SI base unit used to measure the amount of a substance, abbreviated mol; one mole is the amount of a pure substance that contains 6.02×10^{23} representative particles.

molecular formula: A formula that specifies the actual number of atoms of each element in one molecule or formula unit of the substance.

molecule: Forms when two or more atoms covalently bond and is lower in potential energy than its constituent atoms.

monomer: A molecule from which a polymer is made.

metaloide: Elemento, como el silicio o el germanio, que tiene las propiedades físicas y químicas tanto de metales como de no metales.

metro: Unidad base para longitud del SI.

mezcla: Combinación física de dos o más sustancias puras en cualquier proporción, en la cual cada sustancia retiene sus propiedades individuales; puede ser separada por medios físicos.

molaridad: Número de moles de soluto disueltos por litro de solución; también conocida como concentración molar.

masa molar: Masa en gramos de un mol de cierta sustancia pura.

mol: Unidad base del SI utilizada para medir la cantidad de una sustancia, abreviada mol; un mol es la cantidad de sustancia pura que contienen 6.02×10^{23} partículas representativas.

fórmula molecular: Fórmula que especifica el número real de átomos de cada elemento en una molécula o unidad de fórmula de la sustancia.

molécula: Se forma cuando dos o más átomos se unen covalentemente y la cual tiene menor energía potencial que sus átomos constituyentes.

monómero: Molécula a partir de la cual se forma un polímero.

net ionic equation: An ionic equation that includes only the particles that participate in the reaction.

neutralization reaction: A reaction in which an acid and a base react in aqueous solution to produce a salt and water.

neutron: A neutral subatomic particle in an atom's nucleus that has a mass nearly equal to that of a proton.

noble gas: An extremely unreactive group 8A element.

nonmetals: Elements that are generally gases or dull, brittle solids that are poor conductors of heat and electricity.

nuclear fission: The splitting of a nucleus into smaller, more stable fragments, accompanied by a large release of energy.

nuclear fusion: The process of binding smaller atomic nuclei into a single larger and more stable nucleus.

ecuación iónica neta: Ecuación iónica que incluye sólo las partículas que participan en la reacción.

reacción de neutralización: Reacción en que un ácido y una base reaccionan en una solución acuosa para producir una sal y agua.

neutrón: Partícula subatómica neutral en el núcleo de un átomo que tiene una masa casi igual a la de un protón.

gas noble: Elemento extremadamente poco reactivo del grupo 8A.

no metales: Elementos que generalmente son gases o sólidos quebradizos sin brillo y malos conductores de calor y electricidad.

fisión nuclear: Ruptura de un núcleo en fragmentos más pequeños y más estables, acompañado de una gran liberación de energía.

fusión nuclear: El proceso de unión de núcleos atómicos más pequeños en un sólo núcleo más grande y más estable.

nucleons: The positively charged protons and neutral neutrons contained in an atom's densely packed nucleus.

nucleus: The extremely small, positively charged, dense center of an atom that contains positively charged protons, neutral neutrons, and is surrounded by empty space through which one or more negatively charged electrons move.

nucleones: Protones positivamente cargados y neutrones neutros en el núcleo densamente poblado de un átomo.

núcleo: El diminuto centro de un átomo, denso y positivamente cargado, que contiene protones positivamente cargados, neutrones neutrales y está rodeado de un espacio vacío a través del cual se mueven uno o más electrones cargados negativamente.

O

octet rule: States that atoms lose, gain, or share electrons in order to acquire a full set of eight valence electrons (the stable electron configuration of a noble gas).

organic compounds: All compounds that contain carbon with the primary exceptions of carbon oxides, carbides, and carbonates, all of which are considered inorganic.

oxidation: The loss of electrons from the atoms of a substance; increases an atom's oxidation number.

oxidation-reduction reaction: Any chemical reaction in which electrons are transferred from one atom to another; also called a redox reaction.

oxyanion: A polyatomic ion composed of an element, usually a nonmetal, bonded to one or more oxygen atoms.

regla del octeto: Establece que átomos pierden, ganan o comparten electrones para adquirir un conjunto completo de ocho electrones de valencia (la configuración electrónica estable de un gas noble).

compuestos orgánicos: Todo compuesto que contiene carbono, con las excepciones primarias de óxidos de carbono, carburos y carbonatos, todos los cuales se consideran inorgánicos.

oxidación: Pérdida de electrones de los átomos de una sustancia; incrementa el número de oxidación de un átomo.

reacción de óxido-reducción: Cualquier reacción química en la cual se transfieren electrones de un átomo a otro; también llamada reacción redox.

oxianión: Ion poliatómico compuesto de un elemento, generalmente un no metal, unido a uno o a más átomos de oxígeno.

P

Pauli exclusion principle: States that a maximum of two electrons may occupy a single atomic orbital, but only if the electrons have opposite spins.

percent composition: The percent by mass of each element in a compound.

period: A horizontal row of elements in the modern periodic table.

periodic law: States that when the elements are arranged by increasing atomic number, there is a periodic repetition of their chemical and physical properties.

phase diagram: A graph of pressure versus temperature that shows which phase a substance exists in under different conditions of temperature and pressure.

principio de exclusión: de Pauli Establece que un máximo de dos electrones pueden ocupar un solo orbital atómico, pero sólo si los electrones tienen giros opuestos.

composición porcentual: Por ciento de masa de cada elemento en un compuesto.

período: Fila horizontal de elementos en la tabla periódica moderna.

ley periódica: Establece que cuando los elementos se ordenan por número atómico ascendente, existe una repetición periódica de sus propiedades físicas y químicas.

diagrama de fase: Gráfica de presión contra temperatura que muestra en qué fase se encuentra una sustancia bajo condiciones diferentes de temperatura y presión.

photoelectric effect: A phenomenon in which photoelectrons are emitted from a metal's surface when light of a certain frequency shines on the surface.

photon: A particle of electromagnetic radiation with no mass that carries a quantum of energy.

physical change: A type of change that alters the physical properties of a substance but does not change its composition.

physical property: A characteristic of matter that can be observed or measured without changing the sample's composition—for example, density, color, taste, hardness, and melting point.

Planck's constant: h, which has a value of 6.626×10^{-34} J•s, where J is the symbol for the joule.

polar covalent: A type of bond that forms when electrons are not shared equally.

polyatomic ion: An ion made up of two or more atoms bonded together that acts as a single unit with a net charge.

polymerization reaction: A reaction in which monomer units are bonded together to form a polymer.

polymers: Large molecules formed by combining many repeating structural units (monomers); are synthesized through addition or condensation reactions and include polyethylene, polyurethane, and nylon.

precipitate: A solid produced during a chemical reaction in a solution.

precision: Refers to how close a series of measurements are to one another; precise measurements show little variation over a series of trials but may not be accurate.

principal energy levels: The major energy levels of an atom.

proton: A subatomic particle in an atom's nucleus that has a positive charge of 1+.

efecto fotoeléctrico: Fenómeno en el cual se emiten fotoelectrones de la superficie de un metal cuando brilla en la superficie luz de cierta frecuencia.

fotón: Partícula de radiación electromagnética sin masa que lleva un cuanto de energía.

cambio físico: Tipo del cambio que altera las propiedades físicas de una sustancia pero no cambia su composición.

propiedad física: Característica de la materia que se puede observar o medir sin cambiar la composición de la muestra; por ejemplo, la densidad, el color, el sabor, la dureza y el punto de fusión.

constante de Planck: h, que tiene un valor de 6.626×10^{-34} J•s, donde J es el símbolo del julio.

covalente polar: Tipo de enlace que se forma cuando los electrones no se comparten igualmente.

ion poliatómico: Ion compuesto de dos o más átomos unidos que actúan como una sola unidad con una carga neta.

reacción de polimerización: Reacción en la cual las unidades monoméricas se unen para formar un polímero.

polímeros: Moléculas grandes formadas de la combinación de muchas unidades estructurales repetidas (monómeros); se sintetizan a través de reacciones de adición o de condensación e incluyen el polietileno, el poliuretano y el nilón.

precipitado: Sólido que se produce durante una reacción química en una solución.

precisión: Se refiere al grado de cercanía en que una serie de medidas están de unas de otras; las medidas precisas muestran poca variación durante una serie de pruebas, pero quiazás no sean exactas.

niveles de energía principal: Los niveles más importantes de energía de un átomo.

protón: Partícula subatómica en el núcleo de un átomo que tiene una carga positiva de 11.

Q

qualitative data: Information describing color, odor, shape, or some other physical characteristic.

quantitative data: Numerical information describing how much, how little, how big, how tall, how fast, etc.

quantum: The minimum amount of energy that can be gained or lost by an atom.

datos cualitativos: Información que describe el color, el olor, la forma o alguna otra característica física.

datos cuantitativos: Información numérica que describe cantidad (grande o pequeña), dimensión, altura, rapidez, etc.

cuanto: La cantidad mínima de energía que puede ganar o perder un átomo.

R

radiation: The rays and particles—alpha and beta particles and gamma rays—that are emitted by radioactive materials.

radioactive decay series: A series of nuclear reactions that starts with an unstable nucleus and results in the formation of a stable nucleus.

radioactivity: The process in which some substances spontaneously emit radiation.

radiochemical dating: The process that is used to determine the age of an object by measuring the amount of a certain radioisotope remaining in that object.

radioisotopes: Isotopes of atoms that have unstable nuclei and emit radiation to attain more stable atomic configurations.

radiotracer: An isotope that emits nonionizing radiation and is used to signal the presence of an element or specific substance; can be used to analyze complex chemical reactions mechanisms and to diagnose disease.

rate law: The mathematical relationship between the rate of a chemical reaction at a given temperature and the concentrations of reactants.

reaction order: For a reactant, describes how the rate is affected by the concentration of that reactant.

reaction rate: The change in concentration of a reactant or product per unit time, generally calculated and expressed in moles per liter per second.

redox reaction: An oxidation-reduction reaction.

reduction: The gain of electrons by the atoms of a substance; decreases an atom's oxidation number.

reversible reaction: A reaction that can take place in both the forward and reverse directions; leads to an equilibrium state where the forward and reverse reactions occur at equal rates and the concentrations of reactants and products remain constant.

radiación: Los rayos y partículas (partículas alfa y beta y rayos gamma) que emiten los materiales radiactivos.

serie de desintegración radiactiva: Serie de reacciones nucleares que empieza con un núcleo inestable y tiene como resultado la formación de un núcleo fijo.

radiactividad: El proceso en que algunas sustancias emiten radiación espontáneamente.

datación radioquímica: Proceso que se utiliza para determinar la edad de un objeto midiendo la cantidad de cierto radioisótopo remanente en ese objeto.

radioisótopos: Isótopos de átomos que tienen los núcleos inestables y emiten radiación para alcanzar configuraciones atómicas más estables.

radiolocalizador: Isótopo que emite radiación no ionizante y que se utiliza para señalar la presencia de un elemento o sustancia específica; puede usarse para analizar mecanismos de reacciones químicas complejas y para diagnosticar enfermedades.

ley de velocidad: Relación matemática entre la velocidad de una reacción química a una temperatura dada y las concentraciones de reactantes.

orden de reacción: Para un reactante, describe cómo la velocidad se ve afectada por la concentración del reactante.

velocidad de reacción: Cambio en la concentración de reactante o producto por unidad de tiempo, generalmente se calcula y expresa en moles por litro por segundo.

reacción redox: Una reacción de óxido–reducción.

reducción: Ganancia de electrones de átomos de una sustancia; disminuye el número de oxidación de un átomo.

reacción reversible: Reacción que puede ocurrir en dirección normal e inversa; conduce a un estado de equilibrio donde las reacciones normales e inversas ocurren a velocidades iguales y las concentraciones de reactantes y productos permanecen constantes.

S

safety symbol: A symbol that warns you about a danger that may exist from chemicals, electricity, heat, or experimental procedure.

salt: An ionic compound made up of a cation from a base and an anion from an acid.

salt bridge: A pathway constructed to allow positive and negative ions to move from one solution to another.

saponification: The hydrolysis of the ester bonds of a triglyceride using an aqueous solution of a strong base to form carboxylate salts and glycerol; is used to make soaps.

saturated hydrocarbon: A hydrocarbon that contains only single bonds.

scientific method: A systematic approach used in scientific study that typically includes observation, a hypothesis, experiments, data analysis, and a conclusion.

scientific notation: Expresses numbers as a multiple of two factors—a number between 1 and 10, and 10 raised to a power, or exponent; makes it easier to handle extremely large or small measurements.

significant digits: The number of all known digits reported in measurements plus one estimated digit.

single-replacement reaction: A chemical reaction that occurs when the atoms of one element replace the atoms of another element in a compound.

solid: A form of matter that has its own definite shape and volume, is incompressible, and expands only slightly when heated.

solute: A substance dissolved in a solution.

solution: A uniform mixture that may contain solids, liquids, or gases; also called a homogeneous mixture.

solvent: The substance that dissolves a solute to form a solution.

specific heat: The amount of heat required to raise the temperature of one gram of a given substance by one degree Celsius.

states of matter: The physical forms in which all matter naturally exists on Earth—most commonly as a solid, a liquid, or a gas.

símbolo de seguridad: Símbolo que te advierte acerca de algún peligro, ya sean sustancias químicas, la electricidad, el calor o las maniobras realizadas durante el procedimiento experimental

sal: Compuesto iónico constituido por un catión de una base y un anión de un ácido.

puente salino: Vía construida para permitir que los iones positivos y negativos se muevan de una solución a otra.

saponificación: Hidrólisis de los enlaces éster de un triglicérido usando una solución acuosa de una base fuerte para formar sales de carboxilato y glicerol; se usa en la elaboración de jabones.

hidrocarburo saturado: Hidrocarbón que contiene únicamente enlaces sencillos.

método científico: Enfoque sistemático utilizado en el estudio científico que incluye típicamente la observación, una hipótesis, los experimentos, los análisis de datos y una conclusión.

notación científica: Expresa los números como un múltiplo de dos factores: un número entre 1 y 10 y 10 elevado a una potencia o exponente; facilita el manejo de medidas extremadamente grandes o pequeñas.

cifras significativas: El número de dígitos conocidos reportados en medidas, más un dígito estimado.

reacción de reemplazo simple: Reacción química que ocurre cuando los átomos de un elemento reemplazan los átomos de otro elemento en un compuesto.

sólido: Forma de materia que tiene su propia forma y volumen, es incompresible y sólo se expande levemente cuando se calienta.

soluto: Sustancia disuelta en una solución.

solución: Mezcla uniforme que puede contener sólidos, líquidos o gases; llamada también mezcla homogénea.

disolvente: Sustancia que disuelve un soluto para formar una solución.

calor específico: Cantidad de calor requerida para elevar la temperatura de un gramo de una sustancia dada en un grado centígrado.

estados de la materia: Las formas físicas en que toda materia existe naturalmente en la Tierra, más comúnmente como un sólido, un líquido o un gas.

stoichiometry: The study of quantitative relationships between the amounts of reactants used and products formed by a chemical reaction; is based on the law of conservation of mass.

strong acid: An acid that ionizes completely in aqueous solution.

strong base: A base that dissociates entirely into metal ions and hydroxide ions in aqueous solution.

strong nuclear force: A force that acts only on subatomic particles that are extremely close together and overcomes the electrostatic repulsion between protons.

structural formula: A molecular model that uses symbols and bonds to show relative positions of atoms; can be predicted for many molecules by drawing the Lewis structure.

substance: A form of matter that has a uniform and unchanging composition; also known as a pure substance.

substitution reaction: A reaction of organic compounds in which one atom or group of atoms in a molecule is replaced by an atom or group of atoms.

synthesis reaction: A chemical reaction in which two or more substances react to yield a single product.

estequiometría: El estudio de las relaciones cuantitativas entre las cantidades de reactantes utilizados y los productos formados por una reacción química; se basa en la ley de la conservación de masa.

ácido fuerte: Ácido que se ioniza completamente en solución acuosa.

base fuerte: Base que disocia enteramente en iones metálicos e iones hidróxido en solución acuosa.

fuerza nuclear fuerte: Fuerza que actúa sólo en las partículas subatómicas que están extremadamente cercanas y vence la repulsión electrostática entre protones.

fórmula estructural: Modelo molecular que usa símbolos y enlaces para mostrar las posiciones relativas de los átomos; para muchas moléculas puede predecirse dibujando la estructura de Lewis.

sustancia: Forma de la materia que tiene una composición uniforme e inmutable; también conocida como sustancia pura.

reacción de la sustitución: Reacción de compuestos orgánicos en la cual un átomo o grupo de átomos en una molécula son reemplazados por un átomo o grupo de átomos.

reacción de la síntesis: Reacción química en que dos o más sustancias reaccionan para generar un solo producto.

T

theory: An explanation supported by many experiments; is still subject to new experimental data, can be modified, and is considered successful it if can be used to make predictions that are true.

titration: The process in which an acid-base neutralization reaction is used to determine the concentration of a solution of unknown concentration.

transition metal: A type of group B element that is contained in the d-block of the periodic table and, with some exceptions, is characterized by a filled outermost s orbital of energy level n, and filled or partially filled d orbitals of energy level $n - 1$.

transmutation: The conversion of an atom of one element to an atom of another element.

teoría: Explicación respaldada por muchos experimentos; está todavía sujeta a datos experimentales nuevos, puede modificarse y es considerada exitosa si se puede utilizar para hacer predicciones verdaderas.

titulación: Proceso en que una reacción de neutralización ácido-base se utiliza para determinar la concentración de una solución de concentración desconocida.

metal de transición: Tipo de elemento del grupo B contenido en el bloque D de la tabla periódica y que, con algunas excepciones, se caracteriza por un orbital exterior lleno con nivel de energía n, y orbitales d llenos o parcialmente llenos con niveles de energía $n - 1$.

trasmutación: Conversión de un átomo de un elemento a un átomo de otro elemento.

U

unsaturated hydrocarbon: A hydrocarbon that contains at least one darble or triple bard between carbon atoms.

hidrocarburo insaturado: Hidrocarburo que contiene por lo menos un enlace doble o triple entre átomos de carbono.

V

valence electrons: The electrons in an atom's outermost orbitals; determine the chemical properties of an element.

electrones de valencia: Los electrones en el orbital más externo de un átomo; determinan las propiedades químicas de un elemento.

voltaic cell: A type of electrochemical cell that converts chemical energy into electrical energy.

celda voltaica: Tipo de la celda electroquímica que convierte energía química en energía eléctrica.

W

wavelength: The shortest distance between equivalent points on a continuous wave; is usually expressed in meters, centimeters, or nanometers.

longitud de onda: La distancia más corta entre puntos equivalentes en una onda continua; se expresa generalmente en metros, en centímetros o en nanómetros.

weak acid: An acid that ionizes only partially in dilute aqueous solution.

ácido débil: Ácido que se ioniza sólo parcialmente en solución acuosa diluida.

weak base: A base that ionizes only partially in dilute aqueous solution to form the conjugate acid of the base and hydroxide ion.

base débil: Base que se ioniza sólo parcialmente en solución acuosa diluida para formar el ácido conjugado de la base y el ion hidróxido.

Index

Index

Index

Index

Art and Photo Credits

Photo Credits

Cover (bkgd)Ryan Mc Vay/Getty Images, (l to r)Steve Cole/Getty Images, Karl Weatherly/Getty Images, Marty Honig/Getty Images, (c)Andy Sotiriou/Getty Images

viii CORBIS;

2–3 Getty Images;

8 file photo;

25 StudiOhio;

37 file photo;

69 Matt Meadows;

79 Aaron Haupt;

92 Matt Meadows;

96 Matt Meadows;

113 Matt Meadows;

118 Matt Meadows;

158 (tl) Mark Steinmetz; (bl) Mark Steinmetz; (br) Rudi Von Briel;

167 (t)Aaron Haupt;(b) Geoff Butler.